Heal Yourself and

BOOKS BY BOB KLEIN

MAY I HAVE YOUR ATTENTION?

MOVEMENTS OF MAGIC – the Spirit of Tai-chi-Chuan

MOVEMENTS OF POWER – Ancient Secrets of Unleashing
Instinctual Vitality

HEAL YOURSELF AND THE WORLD WITH TAI-CHI

THE DOUBTING SNAKE (Novel)

ISBN 9781892198693

This book is not intended to diagnose, prescribe, or treat any ailment, nor is it intended in any way as a replacement for medical consultation when needed.

I gratefully acknowledge my wife, Jean, who has helped me every step of the way, both in writing this book and in life.

This book is dedicated to **Bill Elwell** - philosopher, transformer of lives, mystic, shaman and all-around good guy. (1941-2020)

HEAL YOURSELF AND THE WORLD WITH
TAI-CHI

How to Make Your Life Powerful and Become a Healer

Bob Klein

Tai-chi-Chuan School
www.movementsofmagic.com
info@movementsofmagic.com
(631) 744-5999

Table of Contents

Introduction

In 1957 herpetologist Karl P. Schmidt was bitten by a boomslang snake. He immediately began writing down his experiences of the effects of this snakebite and even refused medical treatment because that might interfere with those experiences. One day later he died from bleeding in his lungs, heart and brain. He was a dedicated scientist who wanted to take advantage of this situation by, as it turned out, describing his death.

I am chronicling the experience of coming to life in this book – how one goes through a traditional system of healing to restore the consciousness of the body and remember who you really are. I don't have the experience of dying of snakebite but the experiences I do have may prove more valuable to you.

I studied zoology at Cornell specializing in ecology and "ethology" (the evolution of animal behavior). Traveling through the jungles of Central America for my studies, I met with many local people who shared their ideas with me. For many years after, I continued studying with teachers of traditional healing from several cultures. My main study was Tai-chi-Chuan and my main teacher was Grandmaster William C. C. Chen. It is an ancient Chinese system of exercises and self-defense based on animal movements for the purposes of healing and re-alignment of one's life. Continuing to work in the field of zoology, I spent most of my time working directly with animals and considered them to also be my teachers. My Tai-chi-Chuan school opened in 1975 on Long Island, New York. The population of students ranged from athletes to seniors in nursing homes who are taught in

1

their wheelchairs. These experiences have allowed me to see life in a different way and in the time I have left on this earth I will chronicle how to perceive this way.

In 1957 the boomslang was not thought to be a deadly snake. That idea changed. We are also coming to realize that our way of life is also deadly. By looking at our world through ancient eyes, we can see our situation from different angles and find different solutions. When I teach self-defense, I tell the students that if you can't find an opening in the sparring partner, change the angle of your body and openings will become apparent that you couldn't see before.

This book allows you to see "us" through ancient eyes – specifically through the perspective of the philosophy of Taoism that gave rise to Tai-chi and other healing practices. All of the ancient ways of life I learned seemed to be saying the same things and offering the same solutions, though using different words and analogies, appropriate for their audience. It became my life's ambition to find out what, in fact, they were saying and how it might apply to our lives now.

As an ethologist I was used to taking apart behavior patterns, examining them in all their intricacy and understanding their origins and effects on the animal and the population of which it was part. I learned to distinguish population behaviors from the variations of behaviors in individuals. We were trained to understand each behavior in terms of the animal's ecological habitat.

In this book I am applying this same training plus my training from traditional healing teachers to find an approach to healing both you as an individual, and our culture as a whole - a method I call "Zookinesis". I will explain how each detail and principle in the training of Tai-chi-Chuan is designed to create specific healing effects physically, emotionally and spiritually. You may not practice these exercises or have no intention of ever practicing. Even so, the approach of this book reveals the internal mechanics of the body, thinking mind and spirit and how they interact to form the whole person. It helps you understand how everything works and where you can apply leverage points to make great changes in your life.

Tai-chi-Chuan consists of several types of exercises. "chi-gung" (or "Qi-gong") are simple exercises, repeated several times each, that bring mobility to the body, connect mind and body and promote the flow of energy through the body. "Forms" are series of movements.

2

There are slow forms, weapons forms and some based on specific animals. Many forms are slow but some are aerobic and acrobatic ("Wushu" forms). They teach the mechanics of flow of both the body and the attention. Push Hands is a two-person exercise in which each partner tries to push the other off balance. This teaches the principles of interaction with another person, and how to neutralize and transform force. Sparring is self-defense and includes punching, kicking, grappling, ground fighting, joint locks and pressure points. Defending yourself is, of course, the goal, but this practice challenges fragilities in your emotional state and helps you to attain emotional balance. It strengthens the natural intelligence of the body. There are other practices as well, but the aforementioned are what we will concentrate in this book. We will learn how each aspect of each exercise was designed to create specific healing effects. What appears as simple physical exercises hides a much deeper, ancient training that reveals our full power as human beings.

Readers of my previous books, "Movements of Magic" and "Movements of Power" wrote many letters to me, all saying basically the same thing. They already understood the ideas in the book but had no language to describe what they felt. By giving them this language, they felt they were freed from isolation and could proceed to heal themselves.

We are very language oriented and to a large extent, cannot experience something unless we can name it. That traps us within the dynamics of our language. Let's now use language to escape that trap.

Tai-chi not only allows us to experience more of our world internally and externally but also allows us to know the "experiencer", our true creative nature. It gives us the tools to repair ourselves on every level – physically, spiritually, emotionally, mentally and to restore senses that have been lost in modern times. We will travel "upriver" to the small springs of body awareness that combine to form our river of consciousness.

As our culture becomes more machine-oriented and our lives and minds try to conform, we need balance by remembering what it is to be human and to be part of the flow of life that constitutes the living, spherical creature we live on.

While you do not need to do Tai-chi to benefit from this book, a series of seven instructional DVDs with almost fourteen hours of instruction have been produced to teach the sixty movement Yang short form. (This form was named for its creator, Yang, Lu-Chan). This series is designed to be used with this book, should you become interested in learning this approach to Tai-chi. More information about the DVDs is provided on the last pages.

Chapter 1
Healing Mind and Body

When we are born, we are all attention. We soon learn to divide our attention into "self" and "other". "Self" is what we can control most. "Other" is what we can control least. This is the most basic division, on which the rest of our consciousness is structured.

A great problem arises when we place our body in the category of "other". If we are not involved in exercise that trains us to have a connection to our body, the body seems to be just a "vehicle" that carries around our head – where we "really live".

One important principle of Tai-chi (as well as other healing systems) is that "attention" should be evenly distributed throughout the body, so that you feel you are as much your feet as you are your head. A traditional Tai-chi practitioner experiences energy such as momentum, gravity, the vitality of the body and even consciousness itself as clearly and substantially as we feel the physicality of the world. Tai-chi can be defined as the study of the interaction of these and other energies with the physical world, such as your body.

Small children in our society usually draw people as big heads with tiny arms and legs sticking out of the heads. I wonder if they are just seeing the distribution of attention in a person, and drawing their pictures accurately from that perspective. At their age they see the distribution and quality of energies such as attention as much as they see the physicality of the world. As they grow, they lose the ability to see energy due to conditioning and so their drawings become more "accurate". By re-connecting our consciousness to our body, we heal the original split of "self" and "other" that divides us from ourselves.

The students soon realize that they tend to bring their energy and attention up because their eyes are at the top of their bodies. They feel their force needs to emanate out from where they're looking. In practicing forms this results in the head leading the movement instead of the center of the body leading the movement. This tendency for the senses such as the eyes to rob our attention from the rest of our body has led to the Zen saying that our senses are the "five thieves".

A beginning student of Push Hands pushes from the shoulders and is disconnected from the ground. He has to learn that the push emanates from the ground up. We have many ridiculous habits formed during childhood, which make no mechanical sense. Or, the habits make sense only for limited uses but become permanent and are used all the time.

As a teacher, I am amazed by the habits my students discover as they practice Tai-chi. By cleaning out those habits we release tremendous amounts of trapped energy and can feel much more relaxed and happy. We also can avoid the subconscious habits building into even more destructive habits such as drug abuse.

As children we learn about time – which is a line from past to future. We seem disconnected from both past and future and the present is very fleeting. This disconnects us from the world around us. Controlling what is taught about the past and the possibilities for the future, controls our present. When we explore the past more fully on our own, we can better understand what has happened to us and to our world and can live more powerfully.

We can see how the dynamics of world and national history create the pressures we have to grow through in our individual lives. We can then choose a path that extricates ourselves from the distortions in our lives caused by those pressures so that we can live more fully in the present.

The practice of meditation returns us to our natural state. Our culture and our own minds have weaved many tales of who we are, where we came from and how we must conduct our lives. Yet within us, there is a direct experience of our biological nature and our connection to the rest of nature. These direct experiences are

Heal Yourself and the World with Tai-chi
overshadowed, in modern times, by the stories we have been told about who we are.

The direct, natural experiences are like a small child who constantly tugs at his parent's clothes to get attention. The adults keep talking to each other and ignore the child.

Meditation is the act of yielding to the tug of your biological nature. It is like water sinking into the earth. As it sinks, the water enlivens the earth, allowing life to flourish. As your attention sinks back into your body, and then into your connection to the rest of nature, the body, mind, emotions and all the other parts of a human being become enlivened. You realize that you are not just your thinking process. You are not just your opinions. You are not just your job title. You are the experience of life itself. This experience is often lost in the hustle and bustle of everyday living. Tai-chi is moving meditation.

To a baby sights, sounds, thoughts, emotions and other experiences are equally part of its identity. We teach it to differentiate the world it experiences into parts and assign values to each part. In this way we control its behavior, its experience of the world and thereby the course of its life.

Unless that programming is challenged, the course of that person's life is set. Many things can challenge the programming – traumatic experiences, emersion in a new culture, etc. A Tai-chi teacher's primary job is to reveal to the student how his programming controls his life and even his perceptions.

It starts with revealing how a student tenses unnecessarily and how her thoughts and emotions that are connected to that tension interfere with the smoothness of her movements. The student learns how her tensions and fearful emotional states limit her breathing to only a small part of the volume of her lungs.

It could be said that the entire purpose of Tai-chi training is to end the internal battles that damage consciousness itself. When you stop battling yourself you don't need to battle the world.

Our consciousness has been reshaped especially after the industrial revolution, when bosses viewed workers as parts of the machinery of the factory. Creative, alive people would have a hard time working in a factory. Now in our computer age, we are entering another narrowing and limiting of the full function of consciousness, even while we have more access to information. Many people know the world only through their cell phones.

The cell phone acts as a border checkpoint between the individual's consciousness and the biological world. Every year the border wall is built higher. Is it any wonder that many Americans long for border walls to keep out the "undesirables" from the south, when their cell phones keep out their connection to the real world?

To many people, their own body is a foreigner. They live in their heads and try to keep out the "undesirable" physicality "down south". Changes in the state of consciousness have real-life effects. The battle to keep the body consciousness subdued is projected onto national politics. You can see this if you watch how some politicians hold themselves and move. Use the perspective of Tai-chi to analyze the internal condition of our politicians.

The Tai-chi teacher is a subversive, fighting to bring students back to an experience of Tao – the original, undifferentiated consciousness. In this way the student can see which aspects of his programming are useful and which should be tossed away. If he can let go of tension in his shoulder, he may be able to let go of the rigidity of the mind. It is really the rigidity of the mind that caused the tense shoulder. Mind (thinking mind) is just the divided, programmed Tao.

The development of civilization was an attempt to limit the dangers of nature to the individual so he would have the time to develop himself. But if you are absolutely safe, you may feel that you don't need to develop yourself in any way. This is why sudden wealth can be dangerous. You can become lazy. In our culture we demand safety so much that we sue anyone who causes us any inconvenience. Without external incentive to learn and grow, you would need internal incentive – the joy of learning and growing. That seems to be in short supply.

I can site some simple examples that may make this change clearer. When you walk in the woods, your hips have to shift and tilt to accommodate the uneven ground and all of your other joints have to accommodate the shifting and tilting in order to keep you balanced. You become aware of the random unevenness of the ground. In this way the body's movements flow with the pattern of the ground. All the trees and plants must tune their growth to this same pattern (and their roots may cause some of the bumps). The animals' behaviors are tuned into the growth pattern of the trees and plants. In a more complex way, all the behavior of all life in the forest is connected. When you walk on the uneven ground, you participate in a basic pattern of that forest, which is part of all the other patterns of the forest. You become part of the forest. We say that the feet are the "gateway to consciousness".

We now walk on flat floors. You could sue someone if you trip on an uneven floor. How dare their floor be the slightest bit natural! Many people are injured by tripping on tiny irregularities in the floor. I'm reminded of the "Princess and the Pea" story.

The forest floor is not only uneven; it varies in its solidity. If you step on a soft spot your foot goes right through. "Forest walking" is very different from "floor walking". In floor walking, the hip rotates up during the step, tightening the low back. You step with your full weight with jammed back and tight hips, knees and ankles. This would be a disaster in the forest.

Forest walking is really cat walking. The cat gently places its paw on the ground, testing it and then gradually shifts its weight forward. With Tai-chi walking the hip rotates downward before the step and the hip and low back are relaxed. Then you let your leg swing forward with no weight. When the foot lands you gradually shift your weight forward.

With floor walking you land with all your weight while your joints are tight. This injures them. Imagine all the back pain, spinal injuries and hip and knee replacements that could be avoided if we used forest walking. You can still use this safe form of walking on flat floors. Ask any Kung-fu practitioner.

There is a "benefit" in floor walking. You don't have to pay attention to the ground. This frees your mind to pay attention to other things, mainly your mind itself. How much of your attention is used in mulling over thoughts in your mind? The "great achievement" of our civilization is that it frees the attention to live in the mind and not in nature.

Our world is largely dead to us. When we watch people on television, we are watching an electronic box. Even if we watch nature, it is often filtered through the thinking mind.

9

Among the living, the dynamics of attention permeate to the core and connect all life. Even though the scene in a forest may seem still, attention (as opposed to thinking) is in dynamic action and someone who lives there can perceive this. His behavior largely emanates from this interaction. The attention of one living thing plays with all others in the area. The individual animals and plants in an area work together ecologically, as the parts of our own body should.

It is a joy to be such an integrated community of independent awareness (which I call "attention") within our body, living in a similar community of attention as that of plants and animals in a forest. The joy is that attention itself can move along the dimension of the spirit.

I use the term "spirit" to describe this interaction of consciousness in the natural world. Attention is not constricted into three dimensions (or four if you include time). The vibrancy and agility of the interaction of attention within a habitat is experienced as its own dimension.

It is a mistake to associate awareness only with thinking and with the five senses because that gives us the feeling that we are completely separate objects interacting with other separate objects. When you are living in a natural area and the attention of all its inhabitants are interconnected, you don't feel like a separate object anymore.

Each part of the body is not only aware of itself; it is aware of all the other parts of the body. This awareness of its neighbors comes from the connection of each part to the root. When each part sinks into the earth (this is called, "sung" in Chinese), they are all connected through the earth. Their connection to the earth allows them to be aware of each other. When the earth is flat concrete, with no relationship to the natural surroundings, it is hard for the body parts to be aware of each other, let alone to the rest of the living things in the area.

Each part of the body, each joint, muscle and bone, must relax so that it sinks towards the earth, without interfering with the sinking of the other joints, muscles and bones. The sinking, or rooting process, is very alive and aware.

The goal of Tai-chi practice is to allow each part of the body to pay attention to itself, in coordination with all the other joints and muscles. This requires that our thinking mind delegate authority to the body.

Yet the thinking mind thinks it is the only thing that can perceive and react to things. It can barely conceive that the body is intelligent.

The Gnostics tell a story of Sofia (representing the seeking for wisdom) trying to find God. During her journey she gave birth to the demiurge (lesser God) and then continued on her way. The demiurge looked around and thought he was the only one there and so he must be God.

If our attention is isolated in our heads, as if in a box, then all perception is related to the head. We feel isolated in that box and perceive other people as being boxes. Each of us wants to be a bigger box, or a more powerful, or smarter or braver box. Our identity is related to our isolation.

With decentralized attention, our identity is related to our connections – to other people, to nature, of the mind and the body, etc. We don't feel opposed to others but connected to them, part of them.

Imagine if everyone in the world was like this. Their very identity would depend on their connection to everyone else and every other living thing. How would the world be different? When a Tai-chi teacher teaches, he or she not only tries to improve their students' health, but also is laying the groundwork for a more peaceful world.

The body requires an even distribution of attention in order to maintain its health. When attention is locked up in the head, the body is starved of the energy of attention. Notice how you feel after finishing a Tai-chi class. Your body feels empowered and connected, relieved of stress. You feel more open to other people and to nature. You are helping to heal the world every time you take a Tai-chi class or spend time practicing.

The thinking mind can be defined as that which blocks the flow of attention and chi. The mind fights for its dominance to make the form happen, thinking about doing this movement and then the next movement – and you can see the result in someone's form. Once you say to yourself, "Oh, stop it already" and let the form happen, a great change takes place inside of you. You notice another type of "knowing" besides thinking. You notice another type of flowing besides shoving the body around.

And then you notice how much the calculating mind has created your relationship to the world around you and deprived you from experiencing the world directly. The mind has acted as an agent, negotiating your relationship to the world. You are not allowed at the meetings between the agent and the world. And you are not sure what secret deals your agent put in your contract. Tai-chi training encourages you to read the contract.

If the agent acts without your consent or knowledge, then he becomes you. This again is the Gnostic demiurge; it takes the place of your creative spirit. Moving in flows of momentum and then allowing attention to flow in the same way, drains the demiurge of its power and restores your original creative identity. That identity, that spirit, functions by connection. It is what connects you to the world around you in a direct way.

The dynamics of how the attention can heal the body is a vital part of all ancient healing systems. But just what are those dynamics? I have spent most of my life studying this subject, apprenticing with traditional healers of several cultures and reading ancient manuscripts of others. As a writer, my job is to distill that information and to express it in a way that is appropriate and understandable to modern readers.

Firstly, I need to further explain the concept of "attention". It is important to understand that attention does not mean thinking. Pure attention (called, "True Yin" in Taoist Alchemy) is the state of awareness when thinking stops. You are perfectly capable of functioning, but your intentions come from a deeper part of you than thoughts.

When you surf the web, you are using "Yang attention". When you watch a sunset, you are using "Yin attention". Yang attention tightens your focus to a point while Yin attention is released and finds its own way. We seek a balance of Yin and Yang attention.

Our society is becoming more Yang, tighter, more wound up. I think no one would disagree with that! I describe this as becoming "more frozen". In this state, the thinking mind separates from the body and you live more and more in your mind. It is even hard to imagine your attention living equally in the body as in the mind. It is my job as a teacher of Tai-chi and Zookinesis to allow students to experience a state of consciousness in which your attention is evenly distributed throughout your body and not just in your head. In this state you realize that consciousness is an inherent force in all things and not just

12

the end result of your brain nerves at work. I remember a story from childhood which explains all of this very well. It was in a "Weird Tales" comic book and struck me, even then, as a very clear and spiritual story. It goes something like this:

A man heard that a guru in the Himalayan Mountains was the wisest guru in the world and lived to eight hundred years old. The man sold all his possessions and spent weeks traveling to Tibet to visit the guru. When he finally reached the town where the old man lived, the people were impressed that he had given up everything to meet the guru and they brought him to the cave where he lived.

The guru, sitting on a large stone in the cave, was equally impressed and agreed to give the visitor his secrets. Standing up, he bade the visitor to sit down on the stone. He explained that he had been sitting on that stone for eight hundred years and that, as long as he didn't get up, he would live forever. But if he were to get up off that stone, he would die, unless he could find someone to take his place. Now the man who had traveled up to this high mountain to seek wisdom had saved the guru from an eternity of misery. The guru laughed and left.

The visitor was left to contemplate his fate. Would he really die if he left the stone? Had he given up everything to be trapped in this cave forever? And that's how the story ends. I would ask you, which part of you does the stone represent? Do you think you will die if your consciousness leaves it and rejoins the rest of the world? What have you given up to spend the rest of your life in that cave?

The man in the story is frozen by his fear of death. And all he wanted was just to find out the meaning of the universe from someone who he thought had all the answers.

I hope that in this story, you will discover how you are frozen and what you need to do to melt the mind and body together, so they can regain their natural fluidity. In the fluid state your consciousness is connected to your body and to all of nature. Your thinking process is grounded in reality. You feel the vibrancy of nature as her energies flow through you.

While you may not live to be eight hundred years old, your life is fulfilling at every moment, even at times of stress. You feel that you are part of the natural world and supported by it. You feel nature's consciousness and realize that your sense of that consciousness dies as long as you are trapped in that cave.

Your relationship with other people is a reflection of the relationship of your thinking mind and Body-Mind. If you can respect that another person can be intelligent and yet disagree with you then you can more easily accept that the body can have an intelligence that is different in its nature than the thinking mind but equally as valid. You might also be willing to accept that the body can be more intelligent than the thinking mind.

Many aboriginal cultures want to maintain their way of life, with perhaps, just a few well-chosen modern advances. If there are "resources" beneath their land (oil, coal and gas for example), it seems to us unreasonable that they don't allow another culture to come in and tear apart their land to acquire those resources. But perhaps their perspective makes more sense in the long run. Our own ideas may not lead to our long-term survival. Body consciousness is like an aboriginal village. An unbalanced thinking mind is like the conquerors who want to rip the land apart to steal its resources.

To the extent that our behavior comes from fixed patterns – we are dead. To the extent that it comes from awareness – we are alive. This is the meaning of spirituality. Spirituality is awareness. Awareness is the interaction of attention and creativity. Attention is Yin –the substance of life. Creativity is Yang – the activity of life. I use the term, "creative attention", to differentiate this from simply seeing something. Some people think that if you see something, you are aware of it. I use the term "awareness" very differently.

I also differentiate awareness from thinking. Thinking is a fixed creative art. It is a manipulation of attention according to certain rules. It is a form, just as the "Yang Form" in Tai-chi is a form. It is a game like Push Hands that can be used to train your awareness.

Just as most of the people who play Push Hands do not use it to develop awareness, most people who think also do not use thinking to develop awareness.

I believe that to develop awareness you should start by developing the awareness of each part of the body. Then there will be many independent yet interrelated "awarenesses" within you and you will never become deadened.

Heal Yourself and the World with Tai-chi

It is common for my students to say, "I didn't know I had a back" (or some other body part). Of course, they knew it intellectually. They could even see it in a mirror. But this is not the same as awareness. Now, their back itself is aware. It is aware of itself and that is a different type of knowing. It is the difference between "knowing someone" because you met them vs. "knowing someone" because you lived with them.

I have explained to my students that I see objects in multiples. Each object appears to me as many objects, though I can't tell how many.

This is because my awareness is decentralized and even though I am looking with only two eyes, I am looking with many angles of awareness. I am aware of each independent awareness reacting to the images from the brain, each in its own way.

Yet there is no confusion. The multiplicity of attentions in a vibrant, creative community within me is very cohesive and fulfilling. Likewise, the multiplicity of their perception of my visual world is a joy – not a hindrance.

It is hard for me to believe that other people only see a single object. Each of my little Body-Minds lives within the physical world. The physical world has a depth that is beyond length, width and height; it is a depth of awareness. The dimension that allows this depth of awareness I call the "spirit world". It is the usual world all of us know but with full awareness. The spiritual quest is the quest for this dimension of life.

It is a unique perspective of Tai-chi and Zookinesis that to achieve this depth of dimension, you must give independent awareness to each part of your body – each cell of the body. The more each part of the body becomes aware of itself, the greater the dimension of the spirit world.

There is no point in fighting against the mental chatter that interferes with your practice because you are then just creating a battle. By teaching the body to move and to be mindful of that movement, you are re-joining mind and body.

Our lives are becoming more disconnected. We interact through our cell phones and computers and less through face-to-face interaction. We don't see our food being grown but purchase prepared, chemically enhanced, nutrient poor food, and just warm it up. We need body skills less and less, except for our thumbs for texting and so we live in our minds.

Tai-chi works by first connecting our minds and bodies. We become aware of how every muscle and joint works in an intricate and beautiful harmony. When we step, or breathe or smile, it is with full awareness and full participation of every part of us, connected and alive. When we speak with another person, we learn how to really listen, rather than just argue. The Push Hands exercise teaches us to be completely aware of what is going on inside of another person so that we understand their behavior. This allows us to be comfortable with them and appreciate their individual spirit.

When you practice Push Hands, you accept the push of the partner as force added to the dynamics of the interaction and not as an attack. You and your partner are experienced as one dynamic.

In our school we keep our eyes closed during Push Hands because the sense of sight so stimulates our thinking mind and habits that it overshadows the internal process of body intelligence. When people ask me why I keep my eyes closed during Push Hands, I say it is "so I can see". I want to see the inner dance because that is the real performance of this exercise. I learn from the way the muscles and joints respond. They teach me about this level of intelligence so that the thinking mind can deepen in its wisdom.

The goal of the game seems to be to push the partner over, but really, it is to release the flow of energy inside of you into the partner. When a very strong partner pushes you, the game might be to release *his* pressures through your legs into your root in the ground. It is all about receiving and releasing. The "pushing over" part of the game is just the method of teaching these internal principles. Once you think of Push Hands as a battle, you forgo the chance to learn internal principles.

Rather than your body and thinking mind battling each other, you experience integration because the mind takes its place as a subset of attention. This affects your relationship with other people resulting in a less combative feeling. In this way any practice of meditation can lessen the conflicts between members of a society resulting in less animosity and a more enjoyable way of life. At the same time, each person is more of an individual. Rather than tying your identity to the stories of the society, you identify with the experience of your own individual nature. The stories are then seen as creative expressions of deeper truths rather than as shallow facts.

Wisdom comes from Body-Mind and its connection to nature. Allow that wisdom to bubble up to the thinking mind so that it can be expressed in words, but don't forget the source of the wisdom. The thinking mind can toss ideas around like juggling balls, but only the Body-Mind, connected to the rest of nature, is creative. Body-Mind is like the inventor who comes up with a new idea and the thinking mind is like the technician who designs the product. Both are intelligent in a sense, but it is the inventor who creates the new idea. If you try to invent from the thinking mind, your source of inspiration will soon dry up. Rather – live and experience to churn up the Body-Mind.

When the mind and body are frozen, they begin to die quickly. You lose the feeling in your body and even in your emotions, and life become less fulfilling.

To allow the Body-Mind to have equal sway in one's life as the thinking mind is like courtship. You want the other to be part of you but you don't really know who she or he is at first. Is she intelligent or does she just parrot what she has heard? Is she kind? Will she treat you well? You look for signs within your interactions that will answer these questions. Yet somehow you know that she is part of you and you cannot grow as a human being without her. You look for ways of working together in harmony.

When mind is willing to give up absolute power, you no longer "shove" the body from move to move but yield to an inner knowing of the form. It is no longer a master/slave relationship. You find the Body-Mind wants to do the form differently than the ideas in your head, and you yield to that.

Yielding is respecting. It takes a lot of self-assurance and inner power to yield. Yielding is not a sign of weakness. When the thinking and the Body-Minds are balanced, each respects the other. They no longer battle each other.

When you allow the inner relationship to change, you are more comfortable being affected by the qualities of the consciousness of others. The two lovers grow mentally and emotionally from knowing each other. The thinking mind and Body-Mind each grow from having to interact with each other.

Respect, and yielding, allow growth. Without growth we deteriorate physically, emotionally and spiritually. We would engage in battles both within and outside of ourselves.

What is the degree of respect and yielding in our culture today? Are we becoming more rigid or relaxed and fluid? Where are we headed?

In the course of evolution, single celled animals have evolved into multi-cellular animals. As single cells, an animal had to perform all functions. As single cells within a multi-cellular animal, each cell gave up some of its functions. Yet all the cells are affected by the external environment and so their functions have to adapt to the changes in their environment. It is not just the mind, making its decisions to deal with these changes that allows the body to remain healthy; there is also a more direct connection of the body to the environment, which I have called the spirit.

Push Hands may be the first time you have had to allow each part of your body to pay attention to each part of someone else's body. Each of your muscles have to respond to each change within the partner's body.

Push Hands cannot be done with the thinking mind. There is too much going on. While thinking is necessary to learn any activity, it must be abandoned at some point. There is a Zen saying that to cross a river, we use a boat. But when we get to the other side, we must leave the boat behind. Thinking ultimately traps us if we don't let it go. We have been taught to think by freezing our bodies. Our school experience is sitting rigidly while memorizing facts. So, we are used to preparing to think by freezing the body. Yet the body is the home of the spirit, which has evolved to connect the body to the world around us in a fluid way.

When the spirit and the mind work together, a person is at peace and healthy. When they are in conflict the person is weakened. Push Hands teaches you to develop this spirit just as school taught you to develop your thinking ability. The Push Hands partner represents the changing environment. You can't think your way through Push Hands; you have to feel your way through it, in the same way you feel your way through riding a bicycle.

When we do Push Hands, we are constantly choosing whether our intent emanates from our self-image (to be powerful and respected) or from our natural spirit. The self-image, if not playful, maintains the

18

battle between us and others and the natural spirit is what seeks balance and connection.

Acting requires a willingness to allow the image of another person to take the place of our own. This "playfulness" with our self-image can only be done when you feel very secure. It is the playfulness itself that results in feeling secure. When you can act as an imperfect character and can laugh at the nature of the imperfections, that allows you to use your own imperfections as a path to greater awareness and skill. See how the thinking mind comes up with clever tricks to "defeat" the "enemy" in Push Hands and how that attitude traps you from really flowing with your partner.

The self-image is like a fulcrum. If the goal of your activities is to enhance that image then it determines what can be "moved" in your life. Let Body-Mind lead the body to change the leverage for the purpose of regaining your health.

The fulcrum, or "seat of attention" should be in every part of the body. When you receive a push, every seat rebalances in relation to the other seats. This means that your job is to keep your attention even throughout the body and the interaction, not to come up with a trick. Tricks are the tools of the mind.

A Tai-chi teacher cannot teach anyone tricks. He can only teach Tai-chi, which is the absence of tricks. The thinking mind is a product of our culture. The Body-Mind is the evolutionary result of billions of years of evolution. It contains within it the whole of that evolution and the connection to all living things. The thinking mind does not contain that.

When the thinking mind is divided from the Body-Mind it becomes dominant and repressive. That violence towards Body-Mind then affects how you see the world around you. The thinking mind cares only about thoughts. The more repressive it becomes towards Body-Mind, the sicker the person gets. It sees Body-Mind as a threat to its dominance and may even seek to destroy it and the physical world of which it is part.

When it experiences moments of Body-Mind taking over, such as when someone falls in love, it may react against "losing itself" in that flowing connection by building walls. A battle is set up with the natural part of yourself yearning to connect and flow, and the mind setting up barriers. This can deteriorate a relationship.

Push Hands heals that battle by allowing an "interpenetration" of mind and Body-Mind. Some people say that you have to learn to love yourself first before you can love someone else. I say that you have to become whole before your relationship with others can be whole. Mind and Body-Mind learn to work together and form a cooperative relationship, which teaches you lessons about working together with other people. It teaches you how to connect, yield, remain rooted, keep your attention undisturbed and not be the slave of detrimental habits. Learning about how mind and Body-Mind interpenetrate and learn to work together reveals how to heal yourself and our culture.

What a teacher must do is to get the student to appreciate the beauty and fulfillment of his body moving properly and his attention becoming more creative. As a simple example, you may feel gravity as a force pulling you down. Yet if you yield to gravity, allowing all joints and muscles of the body to relax a little, your body becomes properly aligned and your movements become easier. If you relax both your chest and your upper back at the same time, you will notice that your head pops into its proper place because of this alignment. Gravity becomes a force that relaxes and aligns you and because of this, actually energizes you. You no longer battle against gravity but use it to energize and heal you.

You can think of gravity as a masseur, massaging you. Your muscles can fight against the pressure of the masseur's palms or fingers or you can yield to them, allowing the muscle to relax. Many people are uncomfortable about massage precisely because it is designed to eliminate the rigid body tensions that a person identifies with. But the result is that your identity itself is cleansed. You now identify yourself with the healing process of your body, with your awareness of life around you and with your creative attention.

Consciousness is experienced as a natural force, permeating all things in nature. The consciousness of each living thing is connected to all others. In this way, the earth is a conscious being and the state of health of one part of it is vital to the state of health of all other parts. An attack on one part of the earth is an attack on the whole. The natural flow of consciousness through all living things is vital for the health of any one of them. We now live in a culture that fosters blocking ourselves off from that flow of consciousness and so it fosters the deadening of the body.

We watch football rather than play football. We text our friends rather than talk to our friends. If anyone is interested in making a lot of money, I have a great idea. Imagine a cell phone that you can talk into and it creates text, so that you don't have to press on the letter keys. That would be convenient, wouldn't it? Now imagine a cell phone that receives that text and translates it into voice, so you don't have to look down at the phone (for example, when you're driving). That would be convenient, wouldn't it? But I think that technology may have already been invented. It is called, "Calling someone on the phone".

There are several types of healing besides massage that are connected with Tai-chi practice such as acupuncture, herbal medicine and more. This type of healing is based on the idea that the body is an ecological community of many types of cells and organs that work best when kept in balance. There is a biological energy that flows through the body called "chi". When chi flows evenly through every cell and organ of the body, the body is in the best health.

The healing principle "The inside and outside reflect each other" means that we are part of the ecology of the planet. When we heal ourselves, we are healing part of the planet. Since each part of the planet is connected to each other part, healing our self really helps to heal the whole living planet.

There is a Taoist saying (from the Tao-Te-Ching), "That which can be named is not eternal." Eternal, in this sense, does not necessarily mean lasting forever. It means something that is really there. If we see a rose, we say, "That is a rose." The rose is really there. The word, "rose" is used to refer to the rose itself. Something that is eternal is a thing (or an experience) directly perceived. The Gnostics of the ancient Middle East said that the fragrance of God comes not through the ears but through the nose. (This is one of my favorite sayings).

When we are children we ask, "What is this?" We want to know the names of everything. When we are grown there is the tendency to believe that the purpose of perception is to name things. Once we have named something, we "know It". Knowing means knowing the name, not necessarily really being sensitive to and aware of the experience itself.

When a student feels a tingling in the hands, he asks, "Is this internal energy?" If you say, "Yes," he feels good about himself.

I would answer that it is what it is. Your job is to be aware of the part of you that is experiencing it. Develop that part of yourself so you can experience more things. Don't think your responsibilities as a student are over when you have named it.

Your job is to discover parts of yourself that are capable of perception, to develop those parts and use them to more accurately perceive the world around you.

The big issue is not the tingle in the hand. It is opening up your ability to perceive. The purpose of perception is not to name things; it is to join with the rest of life. One student may feel the tingle, name it as "internal energy" and say, "Boy I am good! I've got internal energy!" Another student would say, "Aha! Look what I found. I wonder what else is there."

When we do Push Hands, we have to be able to feel the state of readiness of every muscle and joint in the partner and his ever-changing pattern of attention from moment to moment. The only way we can be this aware is by keeping our own attention completely calm and even, even though we are being pushed and shoved around. We then use this awareness to easily take advantage of the partner's inefficiencies.

You are extending your attention into your partner, merging your attention with each point in his body. We try not to be forceful with our attention but allow our attention to "ride piggyback" on the partner's attention of that part of his body. In this way, many parts of our attention are each, individually, following the dynamics of attention of each part of our partner's body.

In Homer's Odyssey, a ship of Greeks under the leadership of Odysseus landed on the island of the one-eyed Cyclops. When they entered the Cyclops's cave, he trapped the Greeks and started to eat them. Each day the Cyclops sent out his flock of sheep, which slept in the cave at night. The way the Greeks escaped was by spearing the Cyclops's one eye and then hiding underneath the sheep. When the Cyclops sent out his flock the next day, he felt the top of each sheep to make sure the Greeks didn't try to ride out on them, but neglected to feel underneath the sheep. In this way, the Greeks escaped.

I tell this story because we must "ride" beneath the attention of the Push Hands partner. He is probably "blinded" in the sense that he can only sense external pressure and not the dynamics of attention. So, when he tries to sense what you are doing, he doesn't realize your attention is hiding "beneath the sheep". That attention can turn into physical force at any moment.

When Cyclops asked Odysseus his name, Odysseus replied "Nobody". So, when the Cyclops yelled for his friends to help him, after the Greeks speared his eye, his friends asked, "Who did this?" The Cyclops replied, "Nobody" because he thought that was Odysseus' name. His friends walked away saying, "Then don't bother us". We want to be "nobody" within the Push Hands partner - to be unseen and unknown.

If our partner is not skilled in Push Hands, then he has very little independent movement of each part of the body. His attention is dull. It is then easy to ride piggyback (energetically) on his body parts without being noticed. As his attention focuses on you, your attention (now inside his body), watches him watching you. You can see what he is looking at inside of you and you know his intent.

If you are skilled, you can also nudge the dynamics of his attention to look at a part of you, so that you can "set him up." He will think it is his idea. You try to "grab the reigns" of his attention so you can steer him to do what you want.

When you sneak up behind your Push Hands partner's body awareness, you hide in "spaces" where his awareness is dead. You hide in his death. He tries not to have any such dead spaces. If he has only live spaces (spaces he is aware of and lives in), there is nowhere for you to hide.

When we are born, we are aware. Then we are presented with forms (practices) to develop our awareness further. Most of us just learn to deal with these forms on a basic level – bare survival – and don't use it to develop awareness. The body is a form; living your life is a form; earning a living is a form; Push Hands is a form of developing awareness.

The dynamics take place with that interconnection of attention that permeates each other's bodies as water permeates earth. This allows you to understand the mechanics of the relationship of consciousness to the physical body. This understanding allows you to become more alive.

Through the trickery of Push Hands, you teach your partner to develop greater awareness so that you won't be able to "sneak up" behind his attention. By trying to control him, you teach his spirit to regain control of his own body and mind.

The goal is to enliven and wake up the awareness of each part of his body so he can become a completely aware person. It is as if you are breathing life into the body of your partner so he can become aware of his deeper self. The universe was created physically and yet consciousness was borne from it.

Both creativity and proper mechanics are part of this universe. Our culture has divided these two parts of the universe so that the mechanics are what can be known and the spontaneity, the awareness itself, is considered mysterious and religious. There is little awareness of the interaction of these two factors of nature. Push Hands shows you the interaction of proper body mechanics and proper attention mechanics ("The Dynamics of Attention"). As our lives have been created, so we can participate in creating life within ourselves, bringing to conscious life, each part of ourselves.

When you are pushed by your partner, all of your many parts receive part of that push individually. The pusher's force is divided and "conquered". Part of the force is received by the ligaments and tendons that stretch as they receive it. The partner's force energizes you because each part of you is connected to the ground and you receive the force by storing it. Then each part of the body springs back out of the earth, sending the pusher's own energy back to him.

When you step, the weight of your own body loads each body part towards the earth. When you begin to step with the next leg, the load releases, sending that next leg forward. All the organs in your body stretch with each step.

When you re-connect with your root, the force of the body's movements moves in and out of the root. Walking energizes and massages the body. In this way the ground can act as your Push Hands partner. You don't feel that the ground and the gravity that pulls you

24

into it are a competitor that needs to be conquered. They are part of you and they enliven you. This is the same attitude you should have with your Push Hands partner.

Our culture teaches us to conquer. The history we teach our children is of one group conquering another. There are cultures not based on conquering but they are so far removed from ours that it is hard to imagine how one would live in such a culture. I hope this book makes that easier to imagine.

In this two-person game of "pushing" each other off balance, using tension by just shoving with the arms puts you at a disadvantage. Force is generated from the legs up with a sequential expansion of each joint, creating a wave of force. This wave can then be sent out through the arms. The arms provide a channel through which the wave of force is directed but the arms themselves do not generate the force.

The Tai-chi forms teach us to generate all movements from the center of the body, and then, like a wave, allow each joint and muscle to flow out. The initiation of that wave is a relaxation – just like a pebble dropped into still water creates circular waves.

So, if I want to turn right, I relax my left hip, breathing out, and then allow a wave of motion to move up my spine, breathing in (in the movement, "Ward off Left"). This results in a spiraling turn from the bottom of the left foot through the spine, called "silk reeling energy".

It is very difficult to bring the student to the natural state of attention centered at the center of the body, but it is the basis of healing in this system. As long as the attention is "trapped" in the head and thinking process, all the drugs and surgeries in the world, will not bring him to great health. The centering of attention is the first process that leads you to the experience of "chi" which is the sense that reveals how every part of the body is interconnected. The term "chi" is also used to describe the energy that allows for that connection.

I remember an episode of "Truth or Consequences", which was a game show in which you were asked to answer a question, and if you didn't answer correctly, you paid the consequences. The consequences were in the form of zany activities. In one show, several cups were hung from a clothesline by clothespins. The contestant had to open the clothespins, one by one, allowing each cup to drop. He then had to quickly (with the same hand), catch each cup with a large strainer. He approached the line of hanging cups and then opened one clothespin, allowing the cup to crash to the floor, making no attempt to catch it. He then was able to let each of the other cups drop but this time, he caught each one. When asked why he let the first one drop, he said that he just wanted to get the feel of how the cup would drop so he would know how to respond correctly.

I bring up this story because you need to get the feel of how to let the attention drop into the body. You need to know how to open the "clothespin" that traps the attention and catch the attention "cup" with the center of the body. Attention then radiates throughout the body. You will find out how to do this as you read this book.

At a deeper level the artificial structures of the thinking mind cause deeper physical problems. At the cellular level, trillions of interactions take place every second and for the most part, everything works well according to the biological blueprint inherent in our make-up. This activity, and the ability of each cell to organize its activity in relation to all the others, is all thanks to a biological communications system. Part of that system is the nervous and endocrine systems. But the substrate of that communications system is "chi" – the energy that connects, sustains and progresses a person through his stages of development. It is the living blueprint of our biological and spiritual nature.

A programmed mind can impose its own structure on the body, impeding the body's natural functioning even down to the cellular level. It jams up the system of chi. When the meridians (channels) of chi are opened such as with acupuncture and acupressure, that frees the body and frees Tao (your original, creative nature).

The experience of chi (connection) is what dissolves the illusion of separateness, the illusion that one's soul is a product on a shelf within your head. Just as chi is distributed throughout your body, you come to remember that consciousness is distributed throughout the body. That happens when the consciousness of each part of the body is so strong (through Tai-chi training), that the thinking mind is no longer able to subdue it. Just as chi is distributed throughout the living world, you remember that your consciousness is part of the entire living world, as soon as the war of the thinking mind against the body consciousness comes to an end.

Heal Yourself and the World with Tai-chi

Returning to this awareness is the most powerful political tool and the teachers of this awareness can play a powerful role to return our society to sanity. It saddens me that much of modern Tai-chi training has become just memorizing forms or memorizing philosophical clichés. Push hands has become what ten-year-olds do in a shoving match. The programming of the mind has turned the cure for the programming into just another program. Learning a form or chi-gung set becomes an "acquisition". When people tell me how many forms they have learned, I ask, "But have you learned Tai-chi yet?"

As you move smoothly in your form, habits and thoughts pull you away from your smoothness. If you concentrate on the smoothness you can feel how those habits and thoughts grab and yank your physical body. This reveals your internal state that stays with you 24 hours a day, even during sleep. Grabbing and yanking are not useful and take a great deal of energy. When they are cleared from your form and your life you ask yourself, "Why did I do that?" For some people, the grabbing and yanking constitute the whole of their lives. When you are clear, you are ready to feel experiences that you never felt before because they were blocked.

Students sometimes make the mistake of trying to duplicate an experience they had before, which they think is the "correct" experience. This disrupts them from the flow of life, which changes. Instead, they must learn to perceive whatever they are experiencing now and trust the ever-changing collage of experiences.

The sense of chi is really an internal technology. When you are not locked into seeing the world as a collection of objects, as a projection of your internal rigidity, then you can see other possibilities. It is not that the world itself has changed. It is that your perceptions are no longer controlled by your rigidity.

Be aware of everything happening in the body at the same time in practicing form. This is done by "sinking down" the attention into the body as you practice. Just as you would drop some ink into swirling water to "see" the water, you "drop" your attention into your body to see the body's internal activities.

To achieve this, you first allow the momentum caused by your moving body to affect each joint as it moves through that joint. At first the joints resist and are stuck. The student attempts to "let go" of the

27

resistance (which she, herself is causing) so the momentum can flow through.

This reveals how the student is resisting the flow of momentum through the body. What are the emotional and physical reasons for the resistance? How does the resistance feel? How does it feel when you let go of the resistance? So, you learn about the role of resistance, tension and "holding". Generally, this role is to use the body to express emotional states and to hold onto those states. Letting go means not holding onto those states anymore.

The momentum then "interpenetrates" the resistance. It connects with the emotional state, giving it a path to change. This is why it is so important to "release" momentum in the form at the end of the in-breath and out-breath. That allows the tense emotional state to be released. Once released, you can feel the role the resistance played in your life. Perhaps it made you feel safe for some reason. You will find that the reasons for the resistance don't really make any logical sense. They don't really help you. They are more like a security blanket.

When momentum can flow easily through the body, your attention can more easily flow, and it then releases into the body. Attention and the body interpenetrate as water moistens earth. The form requires a pathway and pattern of momentum through the body for each movement. It is not just a question of moving the body from here to there smoothly. For example, when shifting from leg to leg, you are not just trying to cover distance on the floor. You are moving from the rear hip and sinking into the front hip. Then you expand up from the front hip and from your center (lower belly). It is more of an internal movement.

Once that pathway is established, the attention flows along the same path. Each movement requires a different pathway through the body. You can experiment with different pathways for each movement as long as it results in proper alignment and makes sense for self-defense purposes.

Each pathway requires a different set of cooperative compensations of all the joints and muscles of the body. One of the reasons you practice different pathways is to see how your joints and muscles respond to each. You learn that they sense the pathway and intelligently adjust to it in a way your thinking mind cannot do.

You watch these adjustments to "see" the behavior of each part of the body; how it responds to different influences. But you "see" this without interfering with it. The ability to "not interfere" as your attention moves through your body and the body responds, strengthens Body-Mind, which now feels more secure that the thinking mind respects it. If mind respects Body-Mind (which is the "you" that is nature itself), that teaches you about respect itself. With mutual respect, interpenetration is possible so that mind and Body-Mind can work together.

Your mind can imagine an animal, for example, and the body will duplicate the quality of that animal insofar as you know it. You can imagine the movement of clouds, water or anything else and the body will duplicate it.

The image you use to influence the body should be passive – like hitting a gong and then letting the sound do the work of reaching everyone's ear. If the gong signals dinner, this would create a response in everyone's body to walk to the dining room. Once you hit the gong, you don't need to then run over to everyone and push them toward the dining room.

At the beginning of your practice the consciousness of the body may not respond well because it is deadened in most of us. Some of the dinner guests may be hard of hearing and not hear the gong. Some may not know where the dining room is. In a similar way, the consciousness of some parts of the body might not respond as well as other parts to the mind's image, but give them time

You can also feel and visualize the internal state of your Push Hands partner through your arm connections, and the body will assume an alignment that is secure and allows force to move from the earth into the partner. This is different than "using a technique".

We first work with momentum flowing through the body in the form and eliminate any tensions that block that flow. At a certain point, we feel a flow through the body even while we are still and we experience that flow in a finer and finer way. This is part of what we call "chi". If we are still enough, the attention itself begins to flow. We can practice standing chi-gung (Qigong), using the state of the "passive observer" to notice the dynamics of these flows. This is a state of just observing without internal comment. You don't direct your attention in any way but just allow it to flow wherever it may.

At the beginning we cannot maintain this state of non-interference with attention for long as the slightest distraction contracts the attention, locking it up. We practice allowing the flow of attention to last longer. When we practice a form, we "long for" the flow of attention and chi. The attention "knows" the form. Each muscle and joint "knows" the form. And we discover that even chi "knows" the form. The only one interfering with the form is the calculating mind.

The form is no longer a series of postures where you move from one posture to another. It is a series of circular flows of momentum within the body, created by the movement of each part of the body. These momentums interact with each other causing patterns. The student's creative ability is to move the parts of the body so they create interesting and useful patterns of momentum. At the same time each such dynamic must have martial applications and the body mechanics have to be sound to be considered a legitimate Tai-chi form.

It's difficult to teach a martial arts student to stop freezing. He feels the effects of his freezing when he gets hit by a student of an internal martial art, such as Tai-chi-Chuan. The effect of freezing on the average person depletes your power just as much, but it is much harder to understand this in everyday life. I have taught Tai-chi and Zookinesis to thousands of people, and each discipline requires fluidity in mind and body. I am constantly amazed at how frozen people are, and how little they realize they are frozen. Compare the state you are in when you are surfing the web to when you are watching a sunset. In both cases your attention moves out. It moves out to the computer screen or to the sunset. But in the latter case the movement comes about because of relaxation. In the former case it moves out because of the tightening of your attention, and usually, the tightening of the body. Tai-chi teaches you how to focus without tightening.

I used to spend a few months at a time in the jungles of Central America, hunting for unusual reptiles. They were used for research programs to study how to develop captive breeding colonies in case the species became extinct in the wild. When you first walk through a jungle you don't see the animals. They are camouflaged. It takes a while to recognize them. Once you are used to seeing them, you realize the jungle is filled with animals.

Heal Yourself and the World with Tai-chi

There is a similar problem in working with your attention. When you practice Tai-chi and Zookinesis, attention is perceived as a force which energizes the body and connects it to all living things. The development and refinement of attention is a large part of the practice. But we usually associate attention with the head and eyes. To most people attention just means which direction your head is aimed.

To detect the camouflaged force of attention, the Tai-chi forms require that the head remain in an aligned position with the rest of the body. This means that you cannot look from side to side or look down to see where your feet are going. Yet you must pay attention to your stepping so the foot will land up in the correct position. To do this, you pay attention to the flow of momentum going into the leg, to the feeling of weight in the leg and to the way in which the step affects the joints of the body so the body stays aligned.

In this way you break free from the attention being disguised as the head and eyes. You now experience it as a force mediating all the actions of the body and the breathing and connecting you to your environment.

You practice strengthening the attention. You practice making the attention agile so that it can actively mediate all the parts of your body to keep you properly aligned. Attention becomes a living force.

Your attention becomes so strong that it cannot be controlled by outside influences that are vying to control you. These influences may be other people, advertisers, politicians, religions and philosophies. You remain free and independent.

You also start to perceive how these various groups are in a battle to control your attention and you begin to understand how people can be made to do things they would normally not do.

Simply by requiring you to keep your head aligned and to keep your eyes looking forward, Tai-chi starts you on a path that eventually leads to your ability to see dynamics at play in our society, which you never noticed or understood before.

The head also must participate in the flow of momentum so that the circles of movement, which begin at the hips, permeate throughout the body and the head. The result is that the head and neck are not locked but move in a circle about one inch in diameter.

There are many subtle aspects to this training that yield big results. It is important for the student to understand these underlying principles. It is even more important for the teacher to understand them. If you do not understand then you are learning and you are teaching blindly. This is where the thinking mind is useful.

Once you can detect the patterns and qualities of attention of other people, you can understand them better. You see how their patterns, which are usually habitual and not free and spontaneous, control their behavior. You can say to yourself, "That pattern is them. It is not I." You can avoid playing into their habitual patterns of behavior.

The Tai-chi and Zookinesis teacher consciously teaches with these principles in mind in order to lead the student to freedom and to personal power.

Imagine you are walking through a carnival. The carnival barkers (the people running the games) call out to you to put a dollar down to throw a ball to knock down some bottles or to throw a dart to puncture balloons. As you walk, each barker shouts at you loudly to get your dollar.

Life is like this. The story our culture tells you is that your choice in life is to decide which game to play – which barker to yield to. You may yield to the barker of buying the latest fashions or the newest cars. The barker's job is to convince you that you can only be a good person; you can only be satisfied, if you yield to him. That barker may also be selling a religion or a political party.

When you experience your biological nature, the barkers no longer have any hold on you. They are merely people yelling at you. When an advertiser tries to keep you on the phone after you told him you're not interested, you can easily hang up.

Those students who practice chi-gung by pushing energy around their bodies in particular ways, generally wind up moving even more attention to their thinking minds. This is because they have the attitude that this character, "I", is pushing and shoving around energy in "correct" paths. This approach is still a way of "I" ordering the body around. My teachers taught a gentle approach. Strengthen what is weak and calm what is too intense – the basis of Oriental medicine. In this approach you balance internal energy ("chi") and consciousness so that they evenly fill the whole body and your surroundings. But you may ask, "If there is no real 'I', then who is doing the balancing"?

32

As you do your practice, you will find that the body's consciousness strengthens just as plants grow in the spring. There is no one who goes around ordering the seeds to sprout.

One of my students is an actor. If he has just finished one role and must now begin working on a completely different role, there must be a time in between where he sheds the first role before taking on the second role. At this time, he has to be neutral – not one role or another role.

We try to remain in this "neutral state" throughout the form. The form is not a movement from one attitude to another but must be free of attitude throughout. In this way the body and mind are always open and ready for anything new. The mind does not cling to any frozen state or feeling of "I". It is a state of non-attachment.

My students often express their frustrations that they are not progressing as fast as they would like. When frustrations build to a head, the students are usually ready for a breakthrough. They are ready to let go of the conflict of mind and emotions. Their frustration is an expression of the last gasp of that conflict.

We even learn this lesson in Tai-chi-Chuan (the fighting training of this art). At the beginning we may see sparring as two opponents each trying to win. But the result of proper training in this martial art is to flow with the "opponent" so that there is only one flow. While there is action, your goal is to take control of the interaction so there is no opposition. You are always in a position of power but with no anger. This allows you to feel confident, yet not aggressive, not only in sparring, but in any interaction in everyday life. You are no longer battling your way through life as if you were always on the outside of it. Creativity takes the place of battling.

We say that we cannot take control of the sparring partner's body – only his mind. If your mind is free and creative, as it is through Tai-chi training, it can never be trapped. As an example, if someone is grabbed, they usually tense up. This just makes it easier for the grabber to control his victim. But if you are loose you can easily slip out of the grab. And so, sparring teaches you how to avoid getting trapped in any situation.

While most people do not learn the martial aspect of Tai-chi training, each part of the training teaches all the principles. You can learn slow forms (movements), aerobic and acrobatic forms (Wushu), chi-gung (simple exercises), Push Hands, healing – just learning as much as you like. There is something for everyone in this system of exercise and healing.

You can practice a Tai-chi form with your eyes closed because you are paying attention to feeling instead of to seeing. When you begin to step you cannot focus your attention on the sight of the foot moving to the floor since your eyes are closed. This requires you to focus on how the momentum flows through the body and how all the muscles and joints of the body participate in sending out the leg. Each movement of the Tai-chi form requires this same whole-body attention.

The forms also require a certain type of breathing. You generally breathe in as you move forward and expand and you breathe out as you shift your weight back and sink into the ground (in my lineage of training). The timing of the breath must be paced exactly with the timing of the movements. Your attention must be on the relationship of all the muscles and joints of the body as well as on the breathing. Some teachers tell their students to "just breathe naturally". If you could breathe naturally you wouldn't need to do Tai-chi. Our bodies are very far from being able to do anything naturally because we are so controlled by habits and tension. Telling someone to "breathe naturally" really means letting breathing be controlled by those habits and tensions.

When the momentum sinks into the legs, it moves down past the feet into the ground. The release of the compression in the legs then "pulls" new energy back up when you rise (and breathe in). The momentum then flows up and out through the head and arms. Your attention follows the momentum as it moves out of the body and then the body's sinking creates a new flow downward.

You don't pull the same energy back down into the body as was released. The release must be complete. If each muscle and joint yields to gravity after the release upward, the body will gradually sink down, drawing in new energy.

There is an internal sense of balance that allows all your parts to work together efficiently. This natural sense is called, "The Elixir of Immortality" or "Golden Elixir". It is the elixir that cures the deadness of the body and even allows the thinking mind to become more connected to reality. When you feel your body and are intimately aware of the world around you, your thoughts are more grounded. You feel more comfortable in your body and therefore more sensuous.

"Mixing" the elixir really means doing your practice. Each time you do your exercise, the elixir (sense of energy balance) strengthens each muscle, nerve, bone, etc. Gradually the awareness of the interconnectedness of all your parts and your connection to nature and to other people becomes the central character in your life, rather than "I" being the central character. It is a more relaxed and vibrant way of life and certainly more fulfilling. While the student can legitimately ask about the techniques of his practice, it is important to point out that techniques should not be used to prop up the "I" feeling and order the body around.

If a student transitions from an "external" (tension-oriented) martial art to an "internal" martial art, the most difficult habit to break is freezing the body and mind. Most martial arts students are used to tightening the body and mind at the end of a strike. This is supposed to give you added power. In the internal martial arts, you remain fluid, mentally and physically, at all times. At the end of a strike, it immediately bounces back, and the bounce-back becomes the beginning of the next movement. All strikes emanate from the center of your body (the "Tan-tien") and the bounce-back returns to the center. Your body rotates around the center so that turning to a new direction is very quick and easy. Freezing at the end of a strike makes it awkward to turn to a new direction. It also prevents your full energy from leaving your body and moving into the opponent. A lot of your energy is used in freezing rather than in striking. At the moment you freeze, your attention is caught up in freezing rather than in what is going on around you. This gives your opponent a chance to come in. The more you freeze, the less you perceive. The more you freeze, the more time you spend away from being centered. The more you freeze, the more you cut off the flow of energy through your body, which connects you to your surroundings.

In Zookinesis, there is the concept of a thrust-block. This is basically what you push off of to move. If you were to jump up, the thrust block would be the ground. If you saw someone who was a bad example because of their behavior and you made sure not to act that way yourself, the bad example would be your thrust-block. You used that example to change yourself.

For many people the names of things are the thrust-block. It is words that cause them to act. They are not acting from anything eternal. They can be easily manipulated by people knowledgeable about words and images.

The student must not have words and images as his thrust-block. Perception is a better thrust-block.

Some may point out that perception can be illusory – a mirage in the desert for example. I say that perception cannot be illusory. You actually do perceive that mirage. What that perception is really made of is a separate question.

The Zookinesis student should then go one step further and try to experience thought itself – not to name it. This means that when the initial jolt of a thought comes to him, he resists the temptation to translate that thought into words in his own mind. There is the initial thought, then your mind needs to explain it in words. But the student should sacrifice the words and concentrate instead on the actual experience of the thought.

He discovers that thought and words are two separate things. Thought is a pattern of relationships among things. Words are a way to convey that to someone else. The explanation is not the experience. The Zookinesis student remembers what original thinking really is. It is not the same thing as talking to yourself. Once the student knows what thought is, he cannot be manipulated by words. The actual experience of thought then motivates you, not just the label of that experience.

The concept of thrust-block is also important in martial arts. The floor would always be your thrust-block. It is your grounding, your root. Yet when someone grabs you, there is a tendency to make their force your thrust block. You fight against their force. In Tai-chi-Chuan you connect their force to the ground in a spot outside their base of support. Their support base is the area between their feet. If you connect their power to a spot on the ground outside that base, they will have no power over you. This connection is made by manipulating the alignment of your body and pressing against their body at specific spots. The point is that everything you do in response to their force should be in relationship to the ground.

Heal Yourself and the World with Tai-chi

When politicians speak about defining their party's issues and not letting the other party define the debate, they are talking about the thrust-block. How you define the debate decides, to a great extent, who will win it.

If you ask, "When did you stop stealing?" you are defining my response to the question. I might respond, "Yesterday". Or I could challenge the basis of the question by saying, "I never steal". In the latter case, you would be maintaining control of the thrust-block.

The movements of Tai-chi encode lessons of how to bring power back into the body. Each principle of movement is like the chapter of a book, explaining how to keep the body young and the mind creative. A teacher must explain how to read this movement book so the student can discover its secrets. The most striking feature of Tai-chi forms is the smoothness of movement - an unbroken, even current, ebbing and flowing.

In order to achieve this movement, the attention must also flow smoothly, rather than jump from one point to another. In this way attention, rather than being at one point at one time, must expand, filling up the whole space within and surrounding the body.

Your thinking mind can interfere with this smoothness by acting as a thrust-block. When you "order" a body part to move, you are "pushing" that part from the mind, which you perceive to be in the head. In this way the form arises from the relationship of the mind, that maintains a rigid stance, and the body that moves. The only thing that should be solid is the real floor. Just as we mistook the force of our grappling opponent for the floor, we can also mistake the thinking mind for the floor. Your mechanics then become upside-down. The thrust-block should be beneath you not on top of you.

Tai-chi has a powerful effect on the way our minds work. We are used to using our minds linearly, as you would when reading words in a book, one word after the other.

So, when we practice Tai-chi it is very difficult to allow all our joints and muscles to move at the same time. We can only concentrate on one thing, then the next, etc. You may see Tai-chi forms in which the body is held stiffly but the arms and legs move gracefully. This shows the limitation of how many things the student can pay attention to at once.

The thinking mind should not be the King. Each part of the body is a center of intelligence. It is the seeking of consciousness within each part of the body as well as each part of nature – and yielding to that consciousness - that really constitutes our practice. Tai-chi allows us to achieve this decentralized attention so that we can be better coordinated, healthier and have better relationships with other people.

For some, direct experience feels too personal. They are used to having an intermediary identity to deal with the world. They are not comfortable with direct connection. They don't want the responsibility of dealing with their lives directly and honestly so they play little games with people to give them a little "space" or wiggle room. That wiggle room of games is their agent (their created personality) that intercedes with life on their behalf.

They aren't sure of their competence to deal with their lives directly. If the games have become their identity, then that's all they have as far as they know. They have become the demiurge.

Tai-chi solves the last problem by giving them the experience of their Body-Mind, a more primordial level of consciousness that lies underneath the thinking mind. It provides them with activities that require the Body-Mind to be competent. When they gain this competence, they are more confident to deal with their lives directly and honestly. As they gain confidence in handling their lives, they no longer fear the responsibility of their own choices but look forward to applying the Tai-chi principles to everyday life.

We originally made sense of the world by placing our experiences into convenient categories, like file folders, so any new experience could be dealt with by reviewing information from the files. This solidified our lives and also our view of the world. It removed the aliveness from the world, the three-dimensionality, so that it could fit into the files.

Tai-chi students are comfortable with, knowledgeable about and competent with fluidity in their attention and in the world around them. They are competent with the connection of their aliveness to the aliveness of the world. That connection is chi. It is the substitute for the file cabinet and the agent. It is experienced when you are familiar with its dynamics and when you yield your attention and identity to it. You don't really lose anything. You re-gain your original creative spirit – your true identity. You understand that you are the creator not the created. You are no longer impressed with deadness or strive to attain it. When you experience the fluid aliveness of the world around you, you know what your true identity must be and you can relax.

When I ask people in class to tense up a muscle, they can do that with ease. But it is very difficult for them to relax a muscle. Tensing involves sending a signal through the nervous system to the muscle. When you relax you just stop sending the signal. It would seem that it is easier to stop doing something than to do it. In Tai-chi this is called, "not doing". It really means "not doing anything you don't need to be doing". As people learn a Tai-chi form or Zookinesis exercise, the movements are quite simple. Yet they struggle to learn them.

The process of learning involves more of "not doing" extra, unnecessary things than it is to learn the actual movements. You learn to do each movement in its simplest, easiest form with no excess movement or intention. The result is an effortless flow as if you were a cloud drifting in the sky.

And yet people feel they need to whip their bodies into doing the movement "right". They use excess movement and tension and their thinking minds are buzzing with worry about how they look and what others might think about them. Their minds and bodies are in a great battle. Yet when they finally learn the movements properly, it feels as if they are not even doing them because the body and mind are so light and effortless.

In this state the body is constantly re-energized yet relaxed. The attention is calm yet very alert and responsive because it is rooted in Body-Mind rather than in habit and programming. The thinking mind that keeps track of time is in a resting state. So, after doing a form, you might not even remember if you did it or not. You were in a different state while moving and now that you've returned to your more programmed state, you don't have the time landmarks to remember. Practicing your form is so much a part of you that it is not in the "time folder" anymore.

As a teacher I am most excited by teaching people who want to become teachers. I can get them involved in much more advanced training. People ask me, "How do you have the patience to teach beginners?" Teaching beginning classes involves going over the same basic training again and again. Yet teaching beginners gives me a great insight into the most basic causes of illness and the most basic problems in coaxing people into a better state of health. I can clearly see the resistance people have to letting go of their lifetime of destructive habits. They feel those habits as being who they are. If I suggest that they change the habits they feel that I am challenging their identity.

Identity is a fundamental problem to heal on a cultural level. After all isn't much of the cause of war that this guy feels he belongs to one group and has to oppose the other guy who is a member of another group? We may fear belonging to the wrong group because we may not get to heaven. The groups fight with each other about who has the only right philosophy or which group is using up all the resources.

On an individual level we may identify with our thought patterns, tension patterns and emotional patterns. Patterns are fixed and not creative, not adaptive. It is the rare individual who identifies with his or her creativity.

When we identify with fixed, rigid patterns, our bodies become rigid. When we go to a Tai-chi or Zookinesis class and are taught to relax and let our bodies move fluidly, this may seem like a challenge to all the fixed, rigid patterns of our lives which are our identity. This is what makes learning these arts so difficult. We resist healing ourselves because that may undermine our habits of injuring ourselves, habits we have identified with.

We all know that drug habits and eating disorders are destructive but there are more fundamental levels of behavior that we are only dimly aware of. One of my students recently realized that an old behavior as a child permanently shaped how he uses his attention. He has a "lazy eye" and had to concentrate in a certain way in order to make the in his eyes, while reading, merge into one image. This extreme focusing of attention became permanent and required a great deal of energy. As an adult he forgot about what he had done because it just became part of who he is. The behavior threw the mechanics of his body way off. He has learned to see clearly without distorting his attention. I told him about my way of perceiving multiple images and that allowed him to relax his "eye attention" and still see perfectly well.

Heal Yourself and the World with Tai-chi

When new Tai-chi students practice Push Hands, they tighten up their bodies and raise their centers of gravity, the exact opposite of what is required. Push Hands requires a loose body and low center of gravity so that you can't be pushed and so that your own push emanates from the ground and shoots out like a whip.

There can be habits of movement, of thinking and of emotion. The habits become an image of us, rather than our true, free, creative selves. We tend to solidify our habits and defend them because we feel we are defending ourselves. Even the groups we belong to such as political parties may be a reflection of our ingrained habits.

This sanctifies patterns of behavior that were created during childhood, when we really didn't understand much. The result can be a whole society based on patterns of behavior created during childhood and institutionally maintained.

The greatest political power any individual can have is, as the Beatles said, "Free your mind instead". Examine the fundamental habits of your life and allow your creative spirit to heal you. Tai-chi and Zookinesis practice was specifically designed for this purpose.

Why do people prefer texting? I think it is because they don't have to actually talk to anyone. Texting provides a separation between people, just as an addiction to thinking provides a separation from your own body. But thinking that emanates from the combined consciousness of the whole body and its connection to the entire world of life, is truly creative. It is the balance of thinking and creativity that allows the body to constantly heal itself. To heal is to be creative and to experience the creativity of others. Art, in whatever form, is healing. Comedy is healing. Allow your attention to expand, relax and play, and you will stay younger and more vibrant. Spend more time in nature and feel how you are connected to it. This will help you to become more connected to yourself. *Play* ball and talk to people face to face, like in "the old days". Feel how watching the rising or setting sun can heal the body. As the Tai-chi saying goes, "Relax (to allow attention to expand), smile (be playful) and breathe (feel your connection to nature)".

The thinking mind has been filled with attitudes and behaviors from outside influences, with their own agendas. What we take to be our identity is to a large extent, pushed into us. It is as if we were forced to wear a suicide vest as we go through life. When we practice Push Hands we have to let go of these attitudes and programmed behaviors, because that is what our Push Hands partner uses to push us off balance. Instead, we have to resort to our creativity and sharpness of attention. We learn that many of our patterns of tension just set us up to get pushed and so we learn to let them go. Letting go is a large part of the training. We even let go of fear itself by examining what fear feels like and understanding that it is just a pattern of tension.

What would the world be like if everyone could let go of self-destructive behaviors? What if our identity was no longer based on our intellectual differences and fears but on realizing that the consciousness that flows inside of me is the same as that which flows inside of you?

Groups of men, dressed in funny outfits, tell us what God has to say. As a result, millions of people die in wars. When one religion argues with another about who is right, the concept of God (rather than the experience of God) is the thrust-block.

The experience of God should be the thrust-block and that experience is individualistic. To experience God is the spiritual journey. To argue about what he says, is the journey of people whose thrust-block is not eternal – not real.

When you experience anything real, you are on a spiritual journey. You have learned that the name of something isn't the thing itself. To experience without naming is the skill of taking a spiritual journey. Religious Jews are not allowed to speak the name of God. To think without talking to yourself is the path to God. "Be still and know that I am God." When you experience without naming you understand God's name "I am that I am" (in Judaism).

A rose does not need its name to provide fragrance. A thought doesn't need words to be valuable.

The power of a word is very clear when someone says they cannot do something because they are afraid. That person is saying he *is* that fear. He identifies with the fear. In fact, he is just experiencing some body sensations that he names as fear. At the same time, he experiences something else that he says is making him afraid. So, he experiences body sensations and something else. He tells himself that he must not experience those body sensations he calls fear and so he must stop experiencing the cause of the fear. His whole thrust is to not experience things. This is his story.

Another story may be, "Hey here are these interesting body sensations and they seem to come up whenever I experience this other thing. Let me experience both so I know what they are about".

The second story is that you are the experiencer and your job is to experience things. The first story is that you are a delicate little flower and must avoid tarnishing it with strong experiences.

The first story robs you of power. The second story leads you to power. If fear can stop you from doing things (assuming they are not really life threatening) then fear is powerful. If the story of who you are is someone searching for the power to live an effective life, then you would jump for the opportunity to learn about something powerful.

Love is also very powerful and fear and love often go together. You fear being controlled or hurt because of your love. Fear can keep you from love. It is *that* powerful. It is really the idea of fear that controls you and the battle you set up to get rid of the feeling of fear, can hurt you.

You can turn fear into power by getting to know it rather than avoiding it. How does it feel in each part of your body? Turn the vague idea of fear into concrete physical experience.

You will soon discover your own personal history, not just the events of your life but of how you learned to craft the story of your life, the story of who you are. Crafting that story skillfully propels you to a happier and more fulfilling life than being chased by fear.

We see many groups trying to control the story of God and this is to control the behavior of people. Whether God is somehow real or just a story almost doesn't matter. What matters is the story we tell *about* God, and how that propels people to act. Does that story cause us to feel fear about another group of people and to try to destroy them to stop experiencing fear?

The stories we tell about ourselves as individuals reflect the stories we tell about ourselves as a people and vice versa. The approach of training such as Tai-chi and Zookinesis is to examine the former, the story about who we are as an individual.

As a nation rallies its people to defend itself by instilling national pride, most people rally to defend their individual identities. When someone tells you about what he did you rush to say what *you* would do in that situation. If he tells you the baseball team he likes, you rush to tell him how much you like a different team. In each case you are solidifying your identity. The story of who we are as individuals can control our behavior as we fight to display our identities to the world. The idea that the identity battle must be fought is so ingrained that few question it. And so, we create an elaborate story about who we are that controls every aspect of our behavior.

We get to a certain point in our training where we must choose to defend that story or to understand it *as* a story – not as our real selves – and choose to become masters of the story. This requires a less combative attitude and leads to a more relaxed way of life.

When two people practice Push Hands and each tries to push the partner over, whoever controls the story controls the Push Hands. For example, when I press my palm into your chest, your story may be that I am applying force to your chest. Yet it is actually your resistance to the movement of my palm that creates the force. If you simply moved out of the way, there wouldn't be any force. In that case the story would be that I am moving my hand, not that I am applying force.

If you think in terms of force and resistance the result is very different than if you think of what is really going on. It is true that I am moving my hand. That we can both agree on. But I feel that your resistance is the cause of the force while you feel that the movement of my palm is the cause. We each have a different story.

When both Push Hands partners are skilled there is very little force used. Each partner tries to float out of the way of the movement of the other. The story is then about how well each partner was able to respond to and connect to the other. The story is one of connection rather than of resistance.

Stories about God, about the people and about ourselves can always change and should be based on common sense and practicality. When we become rigid and feel we have to maintain our story at all costs, that's when trouble follows.

Know people by their stories and by how much they are in creative control of their stories. Then examine the stories you have come to believe and how they affect your behavior. Imagine the story you

44

would like to become and the story you would like the world to become. Then believe in that story.

Belief in a story leads you in a new direction. You know it is a fiction and yet part of you knows it could be true someday. And every day you think to yourself, "What do I need to do today to bring me closer to that story?"

Many years ago, a missionary visited a Southwestern Indian tribe. He spent the evening telling them about his religion and the Bible. They thanked him and told him they loved to hear what he had to say. Then they began telling him about the Great Spirit. The missionary was angry. He said, "I just spent three hours telling you about the truth and now you are talking about these superstitious tales."

The chief of the tribe answered, "You obviously know a great deal about the Bible but you don't know about the rules of politeness. We believed your stories and now you refuse to believe ours."

If our bodies are smoothly flowing and cannot be jerked about by our own patterns of thoughts and tension, then surely our attention cannot be jerked around by the forces around us. As your attention learns to move smoothly it becomes more connected to your creative nature and you remember how the dreams and hopes of childhood gave you enthusiasm for life. That enthusiasm still lives inside and can return home. When you forget your dreams, you lose your power. They tug at you when you sleep, fighting their way up through the layers of conflict that have pressed them down.

When conflict no longer tears you apart, when your dreams become part of your life, then you physically experience your connection to the biological aliveness and consciousness of the world you live in. The shell that seemed to contain you dissolves and permeates into the world around you. You have come home to that world, you are well known in that world, and you are loved by that world. This does not result in laziness. You can still fight for justice for example, but you do so in a way that doesn't add more conflict to the world.

Before writing, Tai-chi was handed down teacher to student. There were no books. The first book in China was the Emperor's treatise on medicine, written 4500 years ago. Until then an early version of a Tai-chi form or a chi-gung series was like a book. Each movement was a chapter. The content of the chapter was the principles that led you to

Tao. The same is true of Push Hands and sparring, later additions to Tai-chi training. Just learning the movements without the deeper principles is like just reading the chapter heading and not the chapter itself.

The great thing about Tai-chi training is that you don't need to tell the students all of this. You are just teaching them to relax or to be more aligned, or to defend themselves. But there has always been the secret agenda of leading the student to the experience of his original identity.

The problem is that few such students complete their training and they then go on to teach without an understanding of the purpose of the teaching. This is especially true when the Chinese government is opposed to any such underlying, traditional goal of the training and they are the de-facto authority on Tai-chi.

There are even organizations now that will give you a Tai-chi teaching certification after two days of training. The same is true of Pilates and Yoga, and perhaps soon, brain surgery.

At this time in our history we need traditional Tai-chi more than ever. Fewer teachers now hold the key to the training and it is becoming no more than the packaging – another product on the shelf. When a student says, "Why should I pay you this much for classes when the next guy charges only half as much", what can you say besides, "That sounds like a bargain. Go there".

It makes you want to sell packaging, which seems to be far more lucrative. But this is a plea to Tai-chi teachers to provide the content, not just the packaging; to provide the chapter, not just the chapter heading. These teachings have been handed down to us to use in times of need, and this is a time of great need.

The modern version of chi-gung (pushing the internal energy around in various orbits within the body) does not start your training at the root.

For us to push energy through our bodies would be like trying to push water along a stream. Wouldn't it be easier to just remove the obstructions? Water flows because of space (the stream bed) and root (gravity). Take care of your spaces and your root and the energy will flow.

This difference in approach to chi-gung is similar to different approaches to life. You can push yourself through life or you can remove obstacles.

When practicing chi-gung you can get caught up in ordering the energy around but it is the inherent intelligence of that energy that should be the boss. Yin and Yang must both be strong. Yin is the inherent intelligence and Yang is its creative movement. Allow the interaction of Yin and Yang within your spaces so that energy will flow properly. If you just concentrate on ideas about the proper flow of energy you might try to use the thinking mind to shove that energy around. To do chi-gung properly we need to remember the internal process that truly creates this flow and that is certainly not our manipulation. The process in this case is not the clever mind but the natural forces of attention (Yin) and creativity (Yang) which reside within Body-mind.

The effective method is to remove obstacles to the flow of energy and then experience the result. For example, relax one muscle and see how that feels. Notice if the tension in that muscle was related to any emotional stress. Experiment how a physical relaxation can result in an emotional release. Do this throughout the body, one tense muscle at a time.

Trust that if the energy is not flowing properly, there is yet another obstacle to dissolve. The obstacles are the way your thinking mind tries to hold the energy in place so it can examine it. It tries to freeze your experience of the world to examine and comment on it. Rather, learn to release attention so that you can see what is going on as you live your life.

In sparring, some students come in with a flurry of action and then stop to see what happened – if they hit anything. While coming in they are blind, so there is this sequence of blindness and then contemplation about the result of blindness.

Tai-chi students have to learn to develop the clarity of their attention as the sparring is happening so they can adapt their movements second by second and be more effective. They can act and evaluate at the same time. Part of this training is to not "shove" our bodies around in clever ways by using "techniques" but to make our bodies alive and conscious so the way to respond is obvious. We remove the obstacles that cause our blindness. Those obstacles are usually our cleverness and fear. We don't need to adapt the attitude of battle, even when we are defending ourselves. We understand that it is the inability of our attention to function in real time that causes our physical weakness.

The modern understanding of why we get sick is that we are attacked by bacteria and viruses. While these organisms constitute a vast majority of the cells in our bodies and most are beneficial, some do cause disease. The bacteria in our gut is a large part of our immune system and a disturbance to that bacterial community compromises that system. While the prescription drugs we take allow us to live longer and more fulfilling lives, many attack the gut bacteria. We need to replenish that community with probiotics such as fermented foods.

To a large extent our medical system is based on our military system. We are attacked and we fight back with "weapons". Maintaining our health on a day-to-day basis is an individual responsibility. The medical system is only for emergencies.

Tai-chi and Zookinesis can be considered a medical system for the purpose of maintaining our health. It concentrates on keeping the communities within our bodies healthy. The body is understood as an ecological system with many energetic cycles just as we have the water cycle, weather, evolutionary succession, the daily cycle, etc. in the "external" world. The internal and external world are not seen as separate and what happens with one affects the other.

It seems to me that the political antagonism and the violence we are experiencing in our country is a natural result of the widening of the original split of the internal and external. Training such as Tai chi, which specifically heals that split can be very helpful. So can gardening, working with animals and anything else that reminds us that all life on this earth is one inter-connected living being.

As much as we strive to be individuals and achieve greatness, we also need to deepen our roots into the living earth. When a tree's branches grow wider, the roots also grow wider and deeper to balance the weight above. Let us not, as a society, be a tree with thick, wide branches and shallow roots.

I used to teach physical therapy students. The workshop that I gave every year gave the students a different perspective of how to bring a patient's body back to a healthy state. While a physical therapist only works on the physical level, they have to deal with all the emotions of their patients as well. Sometimes that is the greatest challenge.

My ending point in that workshop is that in order to be effective in dealing with the patients, the therapist has to be comfortable in his or her own body. If your mind, body and emotions are not connected, balanced and centered, then your patients will certainly not feel comfortable with you and you will not be able to connect with them. Learning something like Tai-chi or Zookinesis can be a very valuable aid in working with physical therapy patients.

We also discuss how the way be breathe, walk and do other everyday activities can either help our physical condition or deteriorate our bodies. By understanding Tai-chi principles, you can make suggestions to improve these everyday activities to strengthen the patient in general. In this way you will not only be helping the particular condition they came in with but help to prevent other problems in the future.

Unfortunately, most physical therapy practices only give ten or fifteen minutes to each patient, certainly not really as much time as they need. But due to economic considerations, many practices just try to get as many people through the door each day as possible.

A good physical therapist would suggest that a patient get involved in a more thorough practice of exercise once their physical therapy sessions are over. This is why some schools of physical therapy expose their students to several exercise modalities so they can make intelligent suggestions to their patients once the students open their own practice.

The physical therapist may not directly address all the dynamics of a patient's condition because they are only licensed to correct a specific physical problem in a physical way. But in a Tai-chi class (or Yoga or Pilates or Zookinesis class), it is more informal. You can work on many levels at the same time and explain how a human being works on all these levels in an integrated way. Tai-chi practice is not limited by law to only fixing a physical problem in a physical way.

I believe that our modern-day culture makes us a foreigner to our own bodies and disrupts the integration of body, mind and emotions. It makes sense that we fix the fundamental problem with our health and not just patch up the symptoms as they pop up as in the "whack a mole" game. Many people get involved in Tai-chi practice because of health problems. They know that Tai-chi can improve general health and put them back on a path of general recovery.

At a certain point, any healing teacher looks back over all the clients he has healed and asks, "What are the main problems causing poor health among all these people?" Is there a fundamental change in our lives that can heal all people at once?

In my experience as a teacher of Tai-chi, Zookinesis and Tai-chi massage, I have been astounded by how disconnected people are from their bodies. Their understanding of proper body mechanics is way off and the result is that they are constantly injuring their bodies.

This is actually very understandable. In ancient cultures a student would learn from his teacher in an apprenticeship position. He would be practicing his craft while the teacher taught him – learning and moving at the same time. Action was coordinated with using the mind. In our culture we learn to freeze our bodies by sitting in a still position while we learn to think. Then when we go to a gym class there is little thinking and only action. We have learned to separate the movement of the body from the movement of attention in the process of thinking. So when we are about to think, we automatically prepare ourselves by freezing our bodies.

When the dynamics of the body and the dynamics of attention are separated, it is as if a large knife cut you in half. Attention normally energizes the body. The body's dynamics ground the attention. The attention/body split de-energizes the body and the attention as well.

We are left with a very different type of thinking – that of imagining that we are split into two people and one person is talking to the other. This is the constant mental chatter that all of us are too familiar with. Many cultures teach sitting meditation to clear the mental chatter. When Bodhidharma, a Buddhist monk, first came to China, he found the monks there sitting all day in meditation. Their health was very poor because they didn't exercise. He taught them to exercise and from these basic exercises the martial art of Shaolin was born.

When I was 60 years old my doctor told me that it was unusual for a 60-year-old man not to be on prescription drugs. That shocked me. Apparently, most people that age take several drugs on a regular basis. Does this mean that we are an advanced society because we have invented so many drugs or a very sick society that we need so many drugs?

I recall a monkey I knew in the jungles of Panama. He was the head of his tribe but was badly battered from territorial fights or perhaps from encounters with predators. Three fingers were missing from one hand, two from the other and he had only one eye. Yet he still was the alpha male of his monkey troop. I asked a primate researcher who studied this group how he could be the alpha male with all his injuries. The researcher said one word, "attitude"!

One day a potential Tai-chi student walked into my studio with a severe affliction. He was only able to walk by leaning over and holding his knee with his hands, inching his way forward. As soon as he made it into the studio he sat down, exhausted from the fifty-foot walk. I thought to tell him that he would never be able to learn Tai-chi but I would never discourage anyone who was willing to try. At first, he did the Tai-chi Yang form while holding onto two chairs, which I re-adjusted for him with each movement. He could only last for two or three minutes at a time and then had to sit down. To make a long story short, he learned the entire sixty-movement form without holding onto chairs, and the tiger form and the staff form, which are very vigorous. He also learned Push Hands and was quite good.

After a few years he told me that he was very discouraged. He practiced the forms for forty-five minutes a day, then did Yoga for fifteen minutes, worked out with weights for forty-five minutes and then practiced chi-gung for another fifteen minutes. So what was the problem? He told me that after all this he was so tired he had to stop and sit down. I reminded him that he used to be tired after two or three minutes and could barely stand up without holding onto something. He had gotten so used to being healthy that I guess now he expected that he could leap over tall buildings at a single bound.

To some degree we can determine whether we slide down the slope of increasing sickness or lift ourselves up to greater health. It largely depends on whether we focus on our ailments or our potential. This is not to so say that we don't all have some legitimate medical problems. While modern medicine makes our lives better with great advances, it can also make us lazy. We reach for the pill or the operation rather than trying exercise first.

Healing Mind and Body

Many doctors will try to encourage their patients to try exercise to alleviate their problems before trying drugs but unfortunately many people don't want to be bothered with the exercises. It is easier to pop a pill down their throats. But remember that each drug has side effects and you may start taking drugs to alleviate the side effects and then more drugs to alleviate the side effects of that drug and so on.

If your doctor suggests exercise rather than drugs then you probably have a caring and knowledgeable doctor. While the television ads push you to ask your doctor for drugs, I suggest you ask him or her for exercise alternatives. A healthy diet wouldn't hurt either.

Your body and mind are powerful when they work together cooperatively. Even if you do take drugs, exercise itself can help to alleviate the negative side effects.

Tai-chi strengthens each cell of the body. The movements promote the movement of intercellular fluid and lymph, which brings oxygen and nutrients to the cells and removes their waste. Without the type of intricate movement you get with Tai-chi, the cells receive little nutrients and oxygen, food is stored as fat and cellular waste is not removed. The cells metabolize poorly and degenerate quickly, which leads to early aging. Tai-chi prevents these problems.

Tai-chi keeps the connective tissue flexible. This tissue surrounds all the organs, muscles, body cavities, and bones and forms ligaments and tendons. It tends to shrink and lose elasticity with age, which condenses the body. It is as if each part of the body is slowly being crushed. Tai-chi movements keep you young by keeping you flexible and maintaining full range of motion of the joints. You are also able to breathe more easily.

The National Institutes of Health lists many research papers showing that Tai-chi helps with arthritis, Parkinson's disease, heart disease and other conditions as well as improving balance. If we can be healthier as a society, then we will need less medical intervention and the cost of health care will be less. Our productivity will increase because we will be more energized and spend less time being sick.

The Tai-chi student learns that the conflicts we see or read about in the world around us, superimpose themselves inside of us, so that our minds are filled with conflict. The thinking mind and body seem to be in conflict as the mind tries to make the body do what it wants (and usually fails). Our relationships and everyday lives seem to consist of

52

one conflict after another. At a certain point in our training it becomes obvious that we have adopted the mode of conflict we see around us into the very essence of who we are. But what would it be like if conflict was not the basis of every level of our lives?

It would be like the Tai-chi form. This form is a movement code for a harmonious mind and body, a harmonious human being living a natural way of life. Indeed, if the form were done with conflict, with tension, with jerkiness, it would not really be Tai-chi. So the smoothness of the form tells us to look at nature for flowing harmony and let that driver control your bus.

Just as our attention flows into the earth and sky with our breath, you can also control whether your attention moves to conflict or to harmony. In this way you learn to drive your own bus. You learn to become the harmony that others can learn from. By expanding your attention so that it fills your whole body and surroundings, you learn that your surroundings are really part of you.

Your sense of identity moves from a set of opinions and a pattern of emotions to a whole living body and vibrant, creative awareness. From there, it expands to your natural environment, your community and to all life. At that point, conflict is hardly possible. You had to be convinced that you are completely separate from nature and from other people in order to be trained into a life of conflict. When you cast that illusion aside your life regains its natural power.

TEACHING TAI-CHI

Every student asks me, "Am I the worst student you ever had?" I tend not to constantly shout out, "Great job! You're doing great," as you would hear in gym classes. Maybe that's what students are used to. I do tell the students when they are doing the movements properly, which is quite often.

It is hard to pay attention to all the mechanics and principles as you practice. I suggest that you concentrate on one as you do the form for example. The next time concentrate on another. When you feel more confident, pay attention to two principles at the same time, then three. Eventually you will not need to "pay attention to" the principles because they will become how the body works. The body consciousness will no longer be "on a leash" but will run free. As you do your form, the creativity of each part of the body will play and interact with the others and develop skills in cooperating with each other.

My students get frustrated that I continue to correct their postures in the Tai-chi form. They feel their postures should be perfect by now. I explain that, while they know how to achieve perfect postures, there is an issue that is interfering with their form.

I correct their postures to get them to achieve an "emotionless state". This means ending the battle of the mind and emotions in which the natural, relaxed state of body feeling is disturbed by the worries and fears of the thinking mind. This battle then gets represented in the postures of the body. This also disturbs that internal community of human cells and organs as well as bacteria and viruses and so disturbs the internal cycles that community depends on.

In the "emotionless state" you are still feeling things such as your connection to the world around you, your energy and enthusiasm, etc. But your body is not being used to express internal battles.

If most of a student's energy is in his head for example, his posture will be too high and too forward. By correcting the posture, you help drain the head of excess energy and return it to the body. This helps to eliminate the battle of the head stealing energy from the body.

When students try to remember the proper stance in a particular part of the form, they try to remember the feeling associated with that stance and duplicate the feeling, hoping that will make the body assume the proper shape. But they are also dragging along all sorts of other emotional expressions. It is difficult to remember the proper "stance feeling" cleanly without other emotional expressions hanging on.

Instead, they need to "clean house" by freeing every joint and muscle of the body from emotional control and letting each part of the body "sit" comfortably and yet be fluid enough to move in any direction at every moment. It is a "suspended" state in which the body is open to anything – to any sort of response. It is that openness, that relaxed and suspended state, that they need to use as a reference.

This state allows the internal battles to stand out more starkly, their ridiculous nature to become obvious and thereby easier to let go. Your emotional state is no longer a reflection of battles but of your creative, healing nature growing within you, blossoming into view.

The students already know the right way to hold their bodies for a particular stance in the form. But they need to be free of conflict in that stance.

When I correct a posture in a Tai-chi form I have to take into account all the emotional expressions that control the body. Each part of the body is in an emotional relationship with all the other parts and as a whole, the body expresses very complex emotions.

If I were to correct only one part of the body the student would feel very awkward because he is used to a particular configuration of expression and now, one element of that expression is in the "wrong" position. So at the beginning, the student doesn't appreciate the corrections because he is still judging his posture by how well it expresses his emotions. I have to correct as much of the emotional control of the body as possible to give the student an appreciation of how beautifully the body is designed and how good it feels to be in the natural, "neutral" postural position.

If we tend to lean forward and the teacher straightens our stance, it feels as if we are leaning backward to the same degree we leaned forward before. Our attention is usually unbalanced as well, concentrated in the head and depleted in the body. The attention is usually heavily weighted forward because that is what we can see. It is weighted in sight itself and that is why we, as a culture, do not experience chi just as we cannot see the stars when the sun is shining.

If we can balance attention, we can more easily align the body properly. A student can understand how he may be leaning forward or how his head is forward just by looking in the mirror. But it is harder to experience an imbalance in attention. I teach the students practicing a form to soften their eyes and don't focus on anything in the room. Just keep their head and neck in line with their back, facing the same direction as their body. Yet they can't help but look towards where they will move next as if they don't want to knock into anything. This action creates misalignments.

Each student comes to the class with his or her load of tensions, misalignments, emotional fears and mental programming (or "meshugas" in Yiddish). Tai-chi has to be taught to each individual differently, considering what they come in with.

When you are teaching a group class and are correcting postures, for example, you have to remember what approach you are taking with each student as you move from one to the other. It is like playing multiple games of chess.

You can't make too many corrections at one time because the student will become frustrated and won't remember what you did anyway. You have to stick with a theme of correction (e.g. "relax the hips") throughout the class, for that student.

You realize that the real benefit of Tai-chi training is not memorizing a form or chi-gung set, but the student working through all of his or her issues, whether physical, mental or emotional and coming out as a truly free and powerful individual. That is what the teacher should be going for, not just to teach people to memorize yet another thing.

The teacher must know how each principle of Tai-chi achieves that. While all the students will arrive at that same free, powerful state, they are each taking different paths through Tai-chi training. If you force them to take only the path you yourself learned, then they will never really learn.

You not only have to learn chi-gung, forms, Push Hands, fighting and healing to be a teacher; you also have to learn how to teach. You have to leave the limited path of your own journey to see the whole landscape and appreciate the many ways students can travel through it. In doing this, you gain a greater insight into the magnitude of the training itself and of the genius of the thousands of teachers who contributed to it.

Tai-chi teachers who actually expect their students to learn Tai-chi fear that they will lose students. Tai-chi is a very exacting practice and requires awareness of each muscle and joint of the body, restoring full function. While many people would love to learn Tai-chi, few are ready to do the work.

So the teacher must decide how much he or she asks of the students. The less he asks, the more students he has. The more he asks, the higher quality of students he has. Sometimes the decision rests on how many bills he has to pay each month, unless he has a "real job".

Heal Yourself and the World with Tai-chi

To the degree that the decision is based just on paying the bills, the students get a "make-believe" version of Tai-chi and that version is passed down, as that teacher's students themselves become teachers, believing that they are really practicing Tai-chi. The original teacher may defend himself by saying, "If I didn't dilute Tai-chi, these students wouldn't come to class. At least they are moving. That has to help them a little".

These are the issues in the back of each teacher's mind. I have been hearing the same issue raised in the field of Pilates exercise. Some Pilates teachers say that they don't mind if a teacher changes the training as long as they don't call it Pilates.

My choice is to require that my students learn Tai-chi. They sometimes complain that I keep teaching new principles and they can't keep up with the pace of learning. Yet I am teaching the same thing all the time even though I may explain it differently. They may ask, "Why didn't you ever say that before" even though I say it all the time.

I recently gave a Zoom class online to a student. She told me to wait a moment because she wanted to write down a correction. She picked up a piece of paper near her computer to write the correction and realized she had written the same correction down on the paper in the previous week's class.

When you are presenting the deeper aspects of Tai-chi training, the body of the student has to learn. The brain may feel that it is not "getting it", but the brain doesn't have to get it. The body learns and the student has to become comfortable with and learn to perceive that level of learning. Yet the brain always feels that if it hasn't learned something then it hasn't been learned.

When you really teach Tai-chi you bring the student through a transformation in the learning process. The student learns about his body and attention (how they work), and then learns *from* the body and attention and then body, attention and the world around him all become connected.

Make-believe Tai-chi, of course, is just memorizing as many forms as you can and learning to say spiritual clichés. This may seem like a cynical attitude but the schools that emphasize this approach really irk sincere teachers. While the students of these schools certainly enjoy their classes, the downside is that the reputation of Tai-chi as transforming peoples' lives just comes down to parroting phrases and movements.

Is there a danger that Tai-chi will become a cartoon of itself? If this is happening to other disciplines as well, are we all simply slipping into cartoon lives?

I have heard the argument that during most times in history, only a few people really practiced each art and the rest practiced a shallower version and yet these arts survive. These times are no different from any other.

You are attracted to this training in order to acquire a more powerful identity but you learn to let your identity be fluid.

You grab each piece of knowledge to become clever but you learn to feel.

You want to separate yourself from all others in order to "know yourself" but you discover how to let go and connect.

You want to be more powerful than your opponent in fighting but you learn how to make his actions irrelevant.

You want to learn skills of healing but learn how to stop hurting yourself.

You want to learn how to control others but learn how not to be controlled *by* others.

You want others to think well of you but learn how to see the beauty in others.

You want to develop magical skills but learn how to live simply.

You grasp for techniques yet billions of years of the evolution of life are already within you.

You grasp for secrets yet no one is hiding your inner natural skills.

In many cultures the circle is a symbol of power. The circle can represent seniors giving their lifetime of knowledge, wisdom and skills, back to the next generation. In our culture, the emphasis is on "progress" and the knowledge and skills of the past are not as valued as they used to be.

The circle also represents the constant renewal of the life-giving properties of nature. The ceremonies of many cultures welcome each new season and celebrate the cooperation of humans and nature. Imagine spending time welcoming each new day and each new season, rather than plunging headlong towards each year's vacation or towards retirement. Celebration of the cycles of nature becomes an important part of the culture, as important as inventing faster computers and new cell phones are in *our* society.

I think we have all noticed that in one generation, people have become faster, louder, more frantic and less fulfilled. While we are told that fulfillment depends mainly on improving the economy and inventing even faster and more powerful equipment, we can also examine how repairing the cycles in our lives plays a part in our psychological and physical health.

One of the purposes of the Tai-chi forms is to allow the body to move in smooth, unbroken circles. This heals the "rush, rush, rush" modern attitude, and allows us to feel comfortable and relaxed in our bodies

The smooth, flowing Tai-chi form also heals the attitude that life consists of always rushing to finish the next project. We have to run faster and faster, to get more and more done, so we can be happy at some unknown time in the future. The form gives us a few minutes each day to just be relaxed, happy and content in the beautiful feelings of the body, mind and emotions flowing with the cycles of nature.

The form, or the Zookinesis exercises (or whatever similar practice you are involved in) becomes the daily ceremony reminding you that everything is all right because you are always part of nature. It reminds you that the ancient wisdom of our connection to nature is still relevant and in fact, is vital to our physical and psychological survival. By keeping you healthy in many ways, these exercises keep the circle unbroken. They remind us that it is often the simplest things in life that are the most fulfilling.

These ancient training systems were developed before modern technology. They were based on the idea that what we can see and know in the world is only as good as our ability to perceive the world around us. Their technology was to improve our sensing abilities. This required that every part of the body and mind be alert, sensitive, functional and adaptable at every moment. This resulted not only in greater perception but also in greater health. Their technology of perception was as advanced in its own way as our technology is today.

There was a Zen teacher who would come up to a student, while holding up a stick. The teacher would suddenly say, "Tell me what this is. If you say it is a stick, I will hit you with it. If you say it is something else, I will hit you with it. If you say nothing, I will hit you with it." What else could you do but take that stick away from the teacher?

We need to take the sticks away from the programming of battles that has snuck into our identities. We don't need to be beaten into submission by ourselves – there are plenty of other people more than willing to do that for us. If we stop beating ourselves, maybe we will stop beating other people too.

There is a belief in these teachings that the way we treat ourselves is reflected in how we treat other people. The relationship between our minds and bodies serves as the basis of relationships with other people.

This relationship serves as a sort of base. Since it is a relationship, it is dynamic and growing. Growth, learning and creativity serve as the base in Tai-chi and Zookinesis. When we practice sparring, we constantly make up our techniques each moment, rather than coming in with robotic, pre-planned techniques. A dynamic relationship is a good base for one's life because it prevents you from becoming stagnant.

Rigid belief systems can sometimes destroy one's life. I think we all can see the silliness of the many forms of religion that differ from each other on fine points of doctrine. Did the founder mean this or that?

Wars are fought because we feel we are on the side of one fine point of doctrine or another. Of course, most of the people don't even know what those points are. Their leaders manipulate them to fight with each other. Then they create more fights to revenge the previous fight.

The goal of the leaders is their own power. All we can do is look inside ourselves for how we may have fallen for these rouses. The more we are locked, the more we hurt ourselves and the less we can really see what is being done to us by someone else.

Tai-chi and Zookinesis have far reaching implications for living a better life and developing better communities. If each of us can live in harmony with ourselves, we can certainly live that way with other people and with the earth.

Chapter 2
Continuum of Consciousness

Much of my training has been with traditional teachers of healing from pre-industrial cultures. This training leads me to feel and experience rather than to memorize and deduct. On the other hand, my degree from Cornell is in zoology and so I have an appreciation for a modern Western approach to studying a subject as well.

I found that it was important for me to step back and find the simplest point of view by which to understand seemingly contradictory philosophies. In this regard I understand the subject of attention (consciousness) in this way.

In the modern world we feel that physical matter and the energy that affects it, are the foundations of the world we experience. Consciousness is a by-product of matter and energy in that it is the electrical and chemical activity of the nerves of the brain.

In the ancient cultures I worked with, attention itself was in an equal relationship with matter and other energy. In some, attention creates matter, in that the way we are trained to interpret sensory data has a lot to do with how we actually experience it.

The result of these two approaches to attention is that in the modern world, our attention exists as a point, moving from one thing to another. We pay attention to this and then to that. When attention is as primary as matter, attention interpenetrates matter. It is three-dimensional. We are within matter rather than feeling apart from it and watching it.

For most of us, attention resides in the head because our eyes are in the head. From the head, we "place" our attention on various items of interest, whether an object, thought or physical feeling. For a Tai-chi person, our attention resides in all that we see and experience. The foot pays attention to the action in front of us as much as do the eyes, since attention connects all the parts of us together.

It is the one-dimensionality of our attention and its location in the eyes that forms the world around us in the way we are used to experiencing it. We have a one-dimensional attention trying to function in a three-dimensional world. It isn't very effective. And the effort required to condense our attention into a point robs our bodies of energy.

In order to move from one point to another, we freeze (condense) most of our attention and then move from there, using the frozen attention as a "thrust-block". It is like an inchworm, anchoring its rear on a leaf, moving its front forward and then bringing up the rear again.

In the Gnostic "Gospel of Mary" (Magdalene), she explains it well. She says basically that your attention (soul) is captured by the things you experience. She uses the example of emotions. Your attention is so well captured that you think it is part of what you are paying attention to. And so, you lose your experience of your own attention. She says that the emotion wears your attention like a cloak. Once you recognize the difference between your attention (soul) and what you are paying attention to, you are free. She says this is basically what Jesus was trying to teach. Advertising agencies are well aware of this principle and use it every day.

Each culture explains this concept in its own way. Once you know your attention, you are in control of your life. As long as you don't know it, others are in control. The key, in Tai-chi training, is to develop a three-dimensional attention. The path to achieving that is to understand the difference between Yin and Yang attention.

To understand this, it is important to understand the dynamics of our attention (our consciousness) according to Tai-chi principles. There are two types of attention – Yin and Yang. And there is a biological energy called "chi" that energizes all living things. You can think of chi as a glass of water. You can swirl the water with a spoon but you cannot really see the water move. Think of Yang attention as a small jar of ink. The jar restricts the ink to a certain shape. If you hold the jar in the water you still cannot see the movement of the water. Yin attention is attention that is released. If you pour the little jar of ink into the swirling water you will see the ink swirled about. By inference you can see how the water moves. When you allow beautiful music to "move you", your attention is Yin. When you are reading a book, you concentrate your attention from word to word. That is Yang attention.

Most of us are in the Yang attention mode almost all the time. We can move our attention around and manipulate it. We can be clever with concepts. But we don't really feel as much as we could because our attention doesn't seep into the world around us and make the energy (chi) in our world visible to us.

The student may feel "light headed" when his attention is more balanced because his head is relaxed – not pressurized with attention. That is why I tell students practicing forms to feel the eyes as the edge of a waterfall in which the water is flowing into the eyes and down to the Tan-tien. The eyes should not feel as if there are two arms sticking out of them, grabbing onto what they see. If the eyes let go of the world, they can see that world better.

Grabbing is holding what you see in place. It is like grabbing a bird. You have it and know where to look but you can't see it because your fingers are around it. Even if you pry a finger or two open, all you would see is a frightened, frozen bird. This is called, "Yang attention". Yin attention is when you let the bird go. You can't control where it goes, but you can see it and how it behaves.

The term, "golden elixir" refers to the best balance of Yang and Yin attention at each moment, preferably the least Yang attention and the most Yin attention. Yin attention goes where it wants and feeds you information and Yang attention directs your attention but you don't get much information from it. Yin attention is like watercolor ink painted onto wet rice paper – it gets absorbed. You learn about the world by its effect on your Yin attention.

Using Yin attention implies trust. You trust where it will go and what it will tell you. When I used to do fire-walking the teacher gave us a chant: "Release the mind, see what you find, and bring it on home to the people."

It is not that Yang attention is bad and Yin attention good. It is just that there needs to be a balance. When Yin and Yang attention are balanced, your true nature ("individual Tao") comes through. You remember that you created a personality to function in this world and you remember who created that personality.

That creator is creativity itself – playfulness. This creator (your true nature) plays with attention and creates the world you experience. You are not the personality it created (except as play).

"See yourself, be yourself, appreciate yourself" (a Zookinesis saying). This means remember who you are. Remember that you are most powerful when you are just being yourself. Appreciate all the struggles you have gone through to bring yourself this far in life. The personality has fought for you. But now it's your turn to take over and allow your original spirit to come back into your life.

This is why the issue of attention is so important. It is the central issue of whether you will be happy and effective in life. If you think you are your created personality you can never be happy because you are making decisions to please a fantasy.

In some mythologies letting go of the created personality and just being you is likened to jumping off a cliff. In Christianity it is Christ's sacrifice. In the Tarot card it is the Tower card (a burning, crumbling tower with people jumping off the top).

In pagan cultures there is a trust in the benevolence of nature. That culture is based on the joy of living in nature and the joy of sharing consciousness with people. It is not a fear-based culture. And so, it is easier to trust in the future even with the vicissitudes of the weather and other factors of life.

Changing from a "watching your back" culture to a "trust" culture can be very difficult. It can drastically change the nature of your attention. You have to let those castle towers crumble.

Several of my students over the years have worked with autistic children and have had great success in applying Tai-chi and Zookinesis principles. Our discussions of their experiences have led me to an understanding of autism that I believe can benefit everybody. I view autism and the so-called "normal" state as two extremes of human consciousness.

I believe the autistic child's attention is almost all Yin. His behavior is controlled by his connection to the world around him and to the experiences of his body but he has trouble focusing his attention to a specific goal. When you focus your attention, you cut off its Yin quality because you are containing and manipulating it rather than letting it go to flow as it pleases. This flowing Yin quality is very fulfilling but doesn't allow you to be goal oriented.

The accepted approach to dealing with autistic children who are at one extreme of the quality of attention is to force them into the opposite extreme which *we* are most comfortable with. My students take a different approach. They have spent many years learning how to blend Yin and Yang attention in balance so they can feel and be aware and yet can direct their activities. They are not at the extremes of the qualities of attention anymore but are somewhere in the middle. They "meet" the child from this centered, balanced quality of attention and in a non-verbal way, ask the child to meet them there. They can change the mixture in the golden elixir to suit the situation. By understanding the situation of the child's attention, they can participate in that quality to begin with and then gradually move him towards the center, just as I do with my Tai-chi students.

The students tell me that sometimes parents of an autistic child have gone through three or four counselors over several years but with no success. The Tai-chi trained counselor can meet the child and have a great deal of success even the first day. When the parents ask the counselor how he could affect such a change in such a short time, my students cannot really explain themselves because the parents don't understand Tai-chi principles. The students themselves understand the process very well but their methodology is not the "accepted" methodology so they have to just say nothing.

By understanding the extremes of the qualities of attention it is easier to understand the middle. Both Yin and Yang attention are important and need to be blended in the right proportions. Tai-chi and Zookinesis training is based on that principle.

We must trust our bodies by allowing Yin attention to permeate it. Attention is like water and the body is like earth. If the earth is moist with water the plants will grow. If all the water is in a container and the earth is dry, plants will not grow. At first the dry earth finds it hard to receive the water. If a heavy rain came the water would wash away and there would be a flood. But if it rained lightly first, so the earth became a little moist, the earth could then absorb the heavy rain.

We train to always keep our earth slightly moist. The golden elixir is also the right mixture of water and earth so that our creativity can grow. Absorbing the Push Hands partner's force into our connective tissue is like absorbing a little water. The body becomes enlivened by absorbing the force.

Trusting the body doesn't make it immediately competent. It still needs training. While the body is still awkward, the student has to resist the response of the mind to jump in and take over. "I'll show you how it's done. Do it this way!" says the mind. You must let your body be awkward. The feeling of awkwardness in a group class causes many people to quit. They don't want others to see how incompetent they are, even though everyone is a beginner in a beginner class.

How different is this from the king ordering the body around? Your Push Hands will no longer be the mind pulling techniques from its bag of tricks. The consciousness of the body will play with the forces of the partner as people "play" with waves rolling in on the beach. The stiff, calculating person will be hurt by the wave and the relaxed person will become the wave.

To become the wave means to allow the qualities of the wave, rather than the king, to inform your body's consciousness. The "culture" of nature replaces the king. That culture is born within you.

Native American religion describes each of us as being born with an animal spirit. We acquire additional animal spirits as we live our lives. Their culture is not about conservative vs. liberal but directs you to look for your source of enlivening your consciousness and body, in nature. It is not about the battle but experiencing the natural world as a wet rice paper and you as the ink when painting in watercolor. Life is about being absorbed into nature.

If we are cells of nature, then healing ourselves is the most important way to heal nature. When there is decompression on an airplane you are instructed to put the oxygen mask on yourself first and then help others. You can't help others if you are unconscious. Most of us in modern culture are unconscious. We know only of the mind's battles but little of the world around us. Push Hands is a first step to deeply connecting to another person. Love, of course, is a deeper step. The issues you find in Push Hands tell you a lot about your relationships with other people. Are you wet rice paper or are you dry earth? Do you resist the partner because you don't trust the body's competence? Are you uncomfortable with someone in your space?

What is attention and creativity? The relationship between creativity and attention and how both relate to the physical body, lies at the heart of the study of Zookinesis. Zookinesis explains that attention is an energy that is universally present. It flows through us as it flows through animals, plants and rocks. It is not created by our brains or any other part of us. Creativity is the part of us that manipulates the energy of attention and uses it for many things. Creativity uses attention for moving the body, for example and for thinking. This means that thinking is not attention. It is a manipulation of attention by creativity.

Then, what is creativity? When light flows through a prism, the prism bends it. When water flows through a stream it is diverted by the rocks in the stream, which causes it to move in many patterns. Each of us has different bodies. We have different emotions and memories. Attention flows through each of us differently. If we had no creativity we would just function robotically as a result of the way the energy of attention flows through us.

We would be like a rock, through which attention also flows, but there is no variability in that flow. In fact, many people are so controlled by their patterns of behaviors that they are in essence, an animated rock. Yet some people have a lot of variability in the way they act so that we may be surprised by what they say. We would call those people, "creative". They can look at a situation in new ways and find new solutions. They are able to let go of old patterns of behavior and patterns of perception. They seek new experiences and new ideas so that their lives are vibrant.

The difference between "rock people" and "creative people" is that creative people are not afraid of change, even if they are not sure what the change will mean for their lives. Fear keeps us holding onto our comfortable patterns of behavior and thinking. Thinking itself can be a constant repetition of familiar patterns or it can be creative. But thinking is not attention.

Creativity is the part of us that plays and play is a natural part of many species' behavior. Culture is human play that has become institutionalized. The idea that a piece of paper with the number 100 is more valuable than the same piece of paper with the number 1, as in paper money, is a type of cultural play. A culture that is flexible and can adjust to changing times can survive. A culture that resists change at all costs may cause a great deal of suffering and eventually collapse.

If we can balance the growth and vitality of play with the security and simplicity of culture, we can live comfortable, safe lives and adjust to changes.

If we believe that patterns of ideas and behaviors are sacred and must never change, then culture serves to deaden the human spirit. For many cultures the meaning of the word "sacred" is the understanding that when we speak of God, we speak of the creativity within us and the awareness of how we are all connected by the energy of attention. We are all strumming on the strings of attention and are participants in a great universal orchestra. Those who can hear the music are conscious.

Play is a natural behavior of many animals. Puppies and kittens understand that they aren't really trying to kill each other. They understand make-believe. They also understand reality as when a large animal runs after them, growling loudly. Play is not to be taken literally but is good practice for reality. Play teaches you to perceive clearly and for your body to react quickly. It develops a lively connection of attention to the body.

Our civilization uses this understanding to train us to replace the body as the arena of action, with ideas. We live in the world of ideas. This changes the role of the body, and by extension, the whole physical world in our creative process. Media has always made their profit by packaging and selling your attention and social media has perfected this art. Is your creative spirit using media or is that media using you? When you watch children play video games, to what is their attention connected? It is hardly connected to the body or even to ideas. It is connected to computer screen images.

This slow progression heads in one direction – to disconnect attention from the body and the physical world and to connect it to factors than can be manipulated by other people. It is hard to manipulate someone's body. It is easier to manipulate their ideas. But if their attention is connected to "machinery", you can control the programming even more easily.

The advertiser's job is to move people's attention in the direction of more manipulation. The teacher's job is to move the attention back to creative ideas and to the physical world.

When you manipulate symbols – a national flag for example – you are trying to control peoples' behavior. In most cases this manipulation is not for the benefit of that person. It is for the benefit of the manipulator.

There are many human histories. There is the history of wars and politics. There is the history of the condition of the average person. There are labor and social movements. Histories of religion, philosophy, arts and science fill university curriculums. But really, they are all the history of the attempted manipulation of attention to control behavior.

It is the history of storytelling – the story of who we are, where we came from and why we are here.

Zookinesis principles teach us how our attention becomes controlled by the stories we are told. It teaches us to understand the dynamics of attention itself so that we can notice when and how it is being controlled and to regain that control.

The job of a parent or teacher is to balance the forces of environmental influence and creativity in the child or student. The point of balance between these two forces is called "the gate" in Zookinesis. The goal of the training is to become "the gatekeeper", that is, to be fully aware of and control the balance of environmental influences and playful creativity on the flow of attention.

The role of a teaching, such as Zookinesis or Tai-chi, is to provide the student with the skills to maintain that balance. To what degree do you allow yourself to be molded by the influences around you and to what degree do you step outside of those influences and "create your own story"?

At the advanced level of any teaching, the student begins to perceive "who" it is that is learning, controlling this balance and creating the story. Religious people would call this "union with God", meaning that you perceive the source of your own creativity. The created sees the creator. You understand your uniqueness and yet your complete connection to all other people and forms of life.

You cannot do this by handing over your attention to any particular dogma, whether a philosophy, religion or any teaching. You can use these vehicles to develop the balance of external influences and creative influences on the attention flowing through you, but you do not allow them to fully mold your perspective. There are many vehicles on the road but in the end, you need to step out of the vehicle and get to your destination.

Ancient religions and other teachings were based on "the elements". This was an early form of psychology. You became aware of the influences of your body, your thinking mind, your will and your emotions and the balance of these factors in each moment of your life. Your goal was to keep the "elements" in balance. The result was that you became aware of the fifth element – "spirit".

Spirit was the force that connected all life together, or what we would call "chi" in Taoist philosophy – a sort of biological internet. When you achieved the balance of the first four elements it would be as if you were standing in the middle of a spiral staircase and could look all the way up and down the stairs. Spirit is all the activity that you see going on. Each level is a level of life or consciousness. Your next goal in these teachings was to explore all the floors. The final step of training was to be aware of all the levels of consciousness at the same time so that you are a fully conscious being and that universal spirit can blossom into your life in its own, creative way.

This is the basis of Zookinesis training. You first become aware of the dynamics of your physical body. In order to do this, you have to allow your attention to connect to all parts of your body. This requires working on the flow of attention as your body flows through its movements, and letting go of any blockage to that attention. You gradually become aware of that part of you that directs the flow of attention (creativity). Now when you practice the exercises, you are not just shoving your body parts around. You are lightly manipulating the flow of attention in your body and that, in turn, affects the movements. Your efforts and movements become lighter and lighter and yet more effective and powerful.

Through physical exercises, Zookinesis achieves a "spiritual" end, that of true self-awareness. You can then examine the "play" of your life to determine in which ways that play is positive or negative. You can create a different play or story for yourself, one that is more healing for you and for others.

Sometimes we argue about competing philosophies, but they can all be different ways of saying the same thing. "Returning to God" is returning to your creative self – the artist of the fashioned creature. Let the created self go. Understand the whole process of creation so you can remember how you built yourself. What you learn from that process makes you a better creator. By remembering the process of creation, you get a better view of the creator. You can avoid completely condensing your attention into the created self so you are not holding onto it for dear life. Establish a relationship between the creator and the fashioned creature – a free, joyful relationship with no grabbing.

There is the story of the Zen monk who was being chased by a tiger. He fell over a cliff and broke one arm, but managed to grab onto a protruding branch with his other arm, hanging on for dear life. He prepared to gradually lower himself down to the ground but noticed another tiger at the bottom, waiting for him. Suddenly, he noticed a strawberry growing on the side of the cliff. He used his good arm to grab the strawberry and pop it into his mouth. In between life and death, let's not allow our grabbing to prevent us from tasting life.

We don't allow grabbing in Push Hands for this reason (besides that it is not mechanically useful from a self-defense perspective). This exercise teaches you how to have a relationship without grabbing or locking into a condensed state. Blending the unknown (your creative self) with the known (fashioned creature) is another meaning of the golden elixir. This unknown is called "The Great Mystery" among Native Americans. The sacred pipe ceremony is not just about thanking the "Great Spirit". The smoke issuing forth from one's mouth unites the Great Mystery with the known world. It represents the act of creation. Where that smoke goes is not under your control. The winds take it where they want. It unites with Father Sky and eventually may settle down to Mother Earth in all four directions. Creativity dances with the world around you just as the smoke dances in the wind.

The smoke is a messenger, carrying a prayer to the Great Spirit. But in this case the "sending out" is also the "receiving". You may think of the Great Spirit as being here or there within the known world, but its origin is the Great Mystery or the "dragon's lair" in Zookinesis mythology. It is from there the prayer issues forth and it is there it is received.

The ability to surprise yourself is the ability to be yourself. The fashioned creature should know when to step aside to allow creativity to come through. Even that creature doesn't know what creativity will come up with. If it does, then what comes out *is not* creativity. The good personality must not only be good to the norms of society but to "God" as well to step aside and allow the unknown to step through.

One of the most common instructions I give in Push Hands is to "not know" what you are going to do. If you are trapped in "knowing", then your responses will be limited to that knowing and I, as your partner, can get you tied up in your knowing. Your Push Hands movements should surprise you as much as it surprises me. In this way, the relationship between us reveals your true creative self. Imagine a relationship in which both people are bound up by trying to play the roles their culture has assigned them. They have become their roles. You can't do traditional Push Hands that way let alone live a joyful life.

You must allow each person to develop their own golden elixir and not require them to "drink yours". When the fashioned creature attempts to create other people in its own image, it is taking the place of the God of that other person. The fashioned creature is "known". God lives in the dragon's lair – the unknown – the emptiness. The known can only duplicate itself – it is not creative. Duplication is not power. Seat your attention in the emptiness of creation as well as in the product. That balance is the golden elixir. When pushed in Push Hands, keep your attention even throughout the body in order to maintain that relationship, rather than focusing on the partner's force.

In Push Hands it is important to not know where you want to go. Just concentrate on the principles of interaction, and trust them to propel you to success. If you lock into a position, you already have an idea of what success will mean. You do not trust the minute-to-minute interactions.

When I recently installed a "French drain" around my Tai-chi studio to divert rain water away, I spent a lot of time creating a 1/8th inch per foot downward incline so the water would flow to the drywell

72

and not get stuck in areas where the drain was level. I understood that it is the force of gravity that really does the work. This preparation allowed the gravity to work on the water. In Push Hands you yield your resistance in such a way that the partner's force is led to your center and down into the legs. Your work is in preparing the way – not in using your own force. If his force gets stuck in you that means that you have not completely cleared out the path.

In everyday life your character, your ability to perceive clearly, your knowledge base as well as openness, grounding, centering and balance are all preparations to allow your creative force to flow and make you powerful in a positive way.

Dreaming can be used to help us let go of negative, programmed behavior in our lives. While many people think that dreaming happens only during the night, this process is always with us, even in waking.

During the day our senses and everyday activities "outshine" the process of dreaming so it is hard to notice the dreaming. It is similar to the way the sun outshines the stars during the day so we can only see stars at night.

Whether during the day or night, there are two processes working in our consciousness that Taoist philosophy refers to as "Yin" and "Yang". Yang is the creator, forming ideas, assumptions, ways of perceiving the world and habits. "Yin" is the dissolver, melting those thoughts and habits so they don't become too ingrained. In Hindu philosophy "Brahma" is the creator and "Shiva" is the destroyer (or dissolver). Both are needed in a balanced and dynamic way.

At night Yin is stronger and so our thoughts and habits start to dissolve. This allows us to become more creative, like starting with a new canvas to paint a picture. During the day Yang is stronger and our attention is more trapped by our habits of thinking.

But day or night, there has to be a balance. The healthy function of consciousness requires that creation and destruction (I like the term "dissolving" better) play with each other. An unhealthy person may be too dogmatic and extreme or on the other hand, flaky and air-headed, easy to push around.

By noticing your dreams, you can sense whether Yang attention predominates (anxiety dreams), Yin attention dominates (can't remember your dreams) or if there is somewhat of a balance. It is important to notice the "dreaming within the waking", that is, this same dream process of creation/dissolving, during the day as well. If you can notice this process during the day, you can gain a great deal of understanding of your inner state.

Dreams are a description of the state of your elements, such as emotions and the body. If you can remember this while you are dreaming (as I try to do), dreaming can reveal how fear-based emotions, for example, cause your muscles to tighten. By noticing any battles among the thinking mind, emotions, the body, blockages to energy, etc., dreaming can become your teacher.

Zookinesis provides an analysis of the mechanics of attention, perception and thinking. It suggests that your attention can follow more than one activity at a time and that there is a part of you that can analyze the relationship between these several activities on a real time basis.

In modern times, this part of us has degenerated and that has resulted in the degeneration of perception. Our ability to perceive is limited when we can only be aware of one thing at a time.

Yet when we look at a scene, it seems as though we are aware of many things at once. This is true, as long as there is little activity and the scene is like a picture post card. But if there is activity, then we first look at one thing and then another. It is difficult for us to focus on two things at a time, let alone three or four things.

The martial arts have been affected by this degeneration so that there is now, one strike, one defense, one, two, one, two. It may be happening at a rapid speed but the fighter's attention focuses on only one action at a time. The "internal styles" are an attempt to preserve the multi-focus ability of the attention.

What is that part of us that can follow and analyze several things at a time? Is it part of the brain? Zookinesis has a different explanation. It describes our awareness as a multi-level system. Each cell and organ, each part of the body, has its own form of awareness –its own attention. This is known as the individual Tao. It is in the nature of attention to attract and connect just as it is in the nature of the thinking mind to divide and isolate. These two parts of us should work in balance but in modern times, the individual Tao has degenerated.

This may seem strange. You may think that since the mind has allowed us to become more individualistic, that the individual Tao should be stronger. But the very nature of this Tao is to align each part of the body with each other part, in a living relationship so that the individual Tao of the thinking mind doesn't subdue that of the body..

It is the part of us that seeks resonance in others. When I look into the eyes of an animal, the first thing we "say" to each other is that we are both aware, living beings. We resonate on that level. Then we can look for other similarities or differences.

Each part of the body seeks resonance with the other parts. If we can understand and appreciate the interactions of one whole creature to another, we can learn about the interaction of the individual Tao of the parts of the body and how that results in a multifaceted type of attention.

If we spend time interacting with specific types of animals, this can affect the quality of the individual Taos of the parts of our body. The individual Tao of the animal will resonate through our body and affect its nature.

In fact, if we work with several animals, then each part of the body will have a variety of qualities. Each individual Tao will be a combination of animal qualities.

This is the same with any endeavor. If you are exposed to several different styles of music, the music you produce (if you are a musician) will have more character. If you are exposed to several cultures you will be a well-rounded person.

Just as we should be able to follow several activities at once that are happening outside of us, we should also be able to follow the varying animal qualities of the individual Taos inside of us.

This may seem quite chaotic and not under any control but the cohesive nature of the individual Tao of the person as a whole organizes these various qualities in a creative way for any situation. As a simple example, when we are sparring, some students may fight in "monkey style" and others in "mantis style", etc. A good fighter will blend the animal styles creatively so that from second to second, that blend changes according to the needs of the fighting situation. Each style has its strengths and weaknesses so they are blended to take advantage of the strengths and minimize the weaknesses. It is as if you were several animals fighting against one opponent.

Within the body there is great activity as each cell and organ interacts with the others. In each person the quality of that interaction can be very different from that of the next person. This affects their health. If this quality is haphazardly imposed on the body through life's influences, you are helpless.

Zookinesis gives you an awareness of this process so you can gain creative control. The principle behind gaining this control is as follows: Control is not given to the thinking mind. Rather, the approach is to give as much awareness as possible to the student, of the mechanics of the individual Tao of the body so that it is as visible and obvious as are physical objects and their mechanics.

The awareness itself *is* the control. It is in the same way that we know that we must turn the knob of the stove to cook our food. We know what we want to do – eat. And we know the steps that are necessary to make that happen.

If what we want to do is relax, or to increase our energy or to heal ourselves, we will know the internal steps that are necessary. Many people are so disconnected that they don't know how to stretch or exercise. They need lessons. Animals don't need lessons. We have lost the awareness even of how to feel good. People are afraid to stretch or exercise because they may do something "wrong". They need to release the natural power of the body's attention (Body-Mind).

As an example, let's take the stare of a snake. We instinctively know that its stare is not merely the way it looks at you with its eyes. The snake's whole body is at attention, waiting for your next move. You can sense the power behind the stare.

Many people have told me that they feel intimidated by other people. What if they could acquire the snake's stare? They would never face intimidation again. The next time someone tried to intimidate you, that person would feel as if he were staring at a twenty-foot long python about to strike.

He would understand that there is an alignment of energy inside you that is more powerful than anything he understands. People are so shaken by the stare of a snake that it takes them a long time to recover. You might have no more overall power than your intimidator but your power is aligned and so is unshakable and unopposable.

Your ability to align the individual Tao within yourself goes a step further. You can also control the same process within the other person,

76

interfering with his alignment in a situation such as protecting yourself from intimidation or in sparring. This requires training with a teacher.

The energies within us are constantly being affected by our interactions with other living things, by changes in the weather and seasons, etc. When we start paying attention to these things, we realize that they affect our lives as much as money, health and love. When we are misaligned, we can be fearful, miserable and more susceptible to disease.

In modern times we don't have access to wild animals and so several techniques have been developed to teach this system.

Even sex has been used in ancient times as a training method. When two people are having sex, there is an obvious seeking of each individual Tao to unite with those of the partner. It is as if the two were one and so each Tao seeks the energies of the other as much as it seeks the energies of other parts of the same body. It is as if the two were melting into each other.

These two sets of energies can unite in an aligned way or it can be poorly aligned. When aligned, there is a sustained power between the two that anyone will notice.

Not only will they notice it; they will be drawn into the force of gravity of the aligned attentions. Zookinesis likens the force of gravity to the force of attention. The difference is that when the individual Taos within a person or between two people are not aligned, they tend to cancel each other out. When aligned they create an attractive force. This is something a couple that is practicing Zookinesis needs to be careful about. Gravity can attract a nice ripe apple, but also a repulsive, rotten one.

Other people will want that power of alignment, the power of a snake's stare. But they generally will not be willing to align themselves first. They just want you to do it for them.

There is a surface tension created by misalignment, a repulsive force of sorts. It is similar to why we don't fall into the center of the earth even though, on an atomic and subatomic level, both earth and we are mostly empty space. The surface tension keeps us apart. If earth and we could align atomically, I think we would indeed fall into the center.

You might ask, "If the individual Taos and their connection to other living things become stronger, doesn't that make the person, as a single individual weaker?" We associate strength with loudness and aggressiveness. While it is true that a practitioner of Zookinesis would tend not to be loud and aggressive towards others, this is not a sign of weakness.

The alignment and integration of the Taos within the body and with the environment creates a different kind of strength. When you speak or act, it is the voice of all the Taos speaking or acting as one. It is authoritative and sure. It is not based on an attempt to manipulate and hurt others to your advantage. It is based on creating harmony and alignment in the world and on an appreciation for the unique and individual spirit of each person.

When the person with the loud and aggressive strength meets the person of the inner strength, what happens? The aggressive person usually wants to overcome the more centered person. It is as if to say, "Look at how strong I am. I can overpower you." The aggressive person has already destroyed his own spirit and cannot accept that there are others who are still intact. It is an addictive need to destroy in order to feel better about himself.

How do you defend yourself against such people? First you need to know how they operate. The only way they can destroy you is by interfering with the alignment and connection of your Taos. In order to do this, they must connect your energy to theirs and away from your own spirit. This results in your spirit going into shock, as it is being exposed to a very damaged set of energies. When your body has been damaged in this way, its first reaction is to reconnect the individual Taos, in other words – to know yourself and to be yourself. The destructive person makes sure you only pay attention to him or her.

This is not done on a conscious level. On that level, the aggressive person may just be trying to be friendly or he may even feel love for you. This combination of love and destruction is a common emotional problem in our times.

I asked, as a child, "What is going on inside of other people?" and my interest in Tai-chi, Zookinesis and other training systems has been, to a large extent, to answer this question. The behavior of most people didn't make sense to me. Their behavior patterns seemed excessive and ineffective.

Heal Yourself and the World with Tai-chi

My training has provided me with a clear understanding of human behavior in order to be a teacher. Sometimes, though, finding a way to explain what I have learned can be difficult.

When I meet a new student, I try to understand them from "the root up". The way in which each part of the body is connected (or not connected) to the ground tells me a lot about what is going on inside of them. Your "root" means your base of support. It is the grounding on which everything is built. In Tai-chi forms, it is your base of support created by weight sinking into the legs and then into the ground.

In your life it is honesty. You could say that it is the ability to sink your attention into the truth, no matter how horrifying that truth may be. If you have lied to yourself from an early age, then all that comes later is built upon those lies. One lie can build a life of lies. It can make you comfortable with lying, and when you deceive others, you are easily deceived *by* others. These lies are often excuses as to why you were willing to sacrifice your dreams even if that dream is just to be loved.

There is a story I always tell of an old ship that sank in in New York Harbor and was buried under mud, which I alluded to before. Ships with cranes were hired to lift it but none succeeded. Finally, someone suggested that an empty barge be positioned above the boat at low tide. Chains were connected from the buried ship to the barge. When high tide came in, the buoyancy of the barge lifted the buried ship.

Honesty is like that barge lifting the boat out of the mud when the tide comes in. There is a trust that just by being honest with yourself and others, your life will be lifted.

If you have sacrificed your dreams to "fit in" you will feel empty and weak. You may seek someone with a strong personality to take the place of your own "weak" personality – to prop it up. You yield your life, your dreams and your creative spirit to him (or her). That person becomes your root. You might also use a religion for the same purpose. Any person or religion that acts as a substitute for your own spirit can destroy you. It causes your spirit to retreat from the spaces inside of you.

We say in Push Hands, that whoever controls the spaces, wins the game. The same is true inside of yourself. If your attention and creativity can penetrate and fill all parts of yourself, then you *are* yourself. No one can pull you away from yourself.

This is not the same as selfishness or self-centeredness. When you live in all your spaces, you feel life with the whole of you and then you are happy. When you are happy to your core, when you really know yourself, you tend to be kind to others. There is no craziness in you that hurts others.

It is said that those spaces within you are the root of your existence. Everything happens in there – truth or lies, jolts of thought, the flow of and interaction of creativity and attention and the flow of internal energy. That empty space is Tao – the dragon's lair. It is the root of existence. The "individual Tao" is what is in the space. When you are a master of emptiness, then you are a master of your own life. "Empty yourself", say the old masters, "...and nature will know how to flow through you."

Those who take advantage of your weak foundation, robbing you of energy are the basis of the vampire stories. They act like a street drug. Drugs deaden the painful spaces in you while at the same time, they destroy you. You know that they are destroying you yet you enjoy their effects. You keep telling yourself that one day you will stop but don't realize that you really don't have much time left. The drug makes you feel good and you want to feel good. You are not willing to go through a healing process to regain yourself because that would mean that you wouldn't feel good for a while. Hate can also act like a drug for some people. And just like a heroin addict, the addicts of this drug are willing to do almost anything to get their fix.

Healing must always start with the root because everything is built from that. The Tai-chi student feels pain in the legs for a year until they strengthen.

When two people, who both own themselves, form a relationship, then their interaction is different from vampirism; it is "soaring" that results from equal "interpenetration" (into each other's spaces). Your attention moves into the other's space as a guest, not a usurper. You interact with your partner in that space. You don't kick them out of their own space so you can live there instead. (You don't destroy their dreams and make them follow yours). Each removes the fears of allowing the other in by trusting in the honesty and integrity of each other. You have each examined your own behaviors, fears and stories living inside of you and have grown strong by understanding yourself. Your spaces are empty not because you retreated from them in fear but because your strength welcomes the other in and you "make space" for them.

Zookinesis describes the principle of "See yourself, be yourself, appreciate yourself".

See yourself. Understand who you are, physically, spiritually, your accomplishments, and your skills – all that you are.

Be yourself. Don't try to be someone else. Allow your uniqueness to blossom into the world. Let your unique qualities grow into their full potential.

Appreciate yourself. Value your spirit and all the ways you have struggled to become what you are now. Don't allow anyone to destroy that. Value other people who can see who you are, can allow you to be who you are and who like what you are.

Your world is made of spirit just as it is made of matter and energy. If you feel overwhelmed by life, take time out to strengthen your spirit, not to destroy it. Seek out those who value their spirit more than their bank account or the style of their clothes.

It may be difficult, in the world we now live in, to remember the value, the realness of your own spirit. As you work to gain more money, a bigger house, a nicer body – all great goals - you may forget about your spirit because it gets so tattered.

I remember that once, when I was a child, I was bringing an art project to my second-grade class. As my mother walked me to school, I insisted on throwing it away because the corner of the paper was ripped. It wasn't "perfect".

That painting was my spirit. It was damaged so I wanted to destroy it. That was silly even for a second grader, how much more so for an adult.

The solution to all this is to regain our sense of spirit. If we can perceive spirit as concretely as we do concrete, then we may be less likely to let it be destroyed.

In our culture, even God has become materialized – as a man in space, as his son on earth. Many no longer understand God as a state of grace, an experience of love and connectedness with all life.

My approach is to teach people to regain the senses that will allow them to perceive these things. It is a mechanical approach rather than a religious approach. It is more like a doctor curing a medical problem than a priest preaching fire and brimstone.

I see spiritual problems as a loss of senses that all creatures have as part of their biological natures. We are not superior to the animals in this respect. We just have the ability to "blind" ourselves while the animals don't. We are not more spiritual than animals – just more destructive.

Why does a destructive person want to destroy the spirit of others? He does not feel. His feeling has been replaced by thinking, anger and aggressiveness. Yet he longs for his spirit, as we all do. He may not like to see other people with an intact spirit because it reminds him of what he lost. Yet he wants to be around them as a substitute for having his own feeling connections to the world. He feels the world through them. He wants them for having their feelings intact yet he resents them for reminding him of his own deadness. He is therefore unstable in this relationship and can easily turn to violence especially if his partner tries to stand up for her spirit.

She senses this danger and it feeds her desire to destroy her own spirit so as not to upset the aggressor. And so, you have a mutually destructive relationship with obvious results.

Once the victim starts dying in this spiritual way, she will repeat the cycle with others. This is the basis of the vampire stories – blood represents the spirit. The wooden stake driven through the vampire's heart represents breaking free from this destructive cycle.

Internal or "soft" styles of martial arts require a radically different use of the attention than do external or "hard" styles. In hard styles (e.g. Karate, Tae-Kwon-Do and many Shaolin styles) your attention is drawn to the power of the opponent. You meet their incoming force with the force of your block. Whoever is more powerful and quicker, wins.

In internal styles (Tai-chi-Chuan, Pakua (Bagua) and Hsing-I), your attention is drawn to the empty spaces where the opponent is not concentrating his force. You (very quickly) melt away from their force and move towards an empty space next to him to deliver your own force.

In order to train to not have your attention captured by an opponent's force, you must first learn not to have your attention captured by your own habits. These habits were programmed into you or were just repetitive behaviors that you fell into. They are the opponent of your creativity.

The slow forms teach you how to make your attention more liquid so that it cannot easily be grabbed. You learn to connect your attention to the ground by starting each movement from your "root" so that your attention is not easily pulled out and controlled.

It is not controlled by your fear or anger. The tighter you are and the angrier you are, the less "space" there is inside of you to be able to function. Without this kind of space, you are forced to fight in a robotic way, becoming tighter and angrier. If you can give up your inefficient habits, let go of anger and spar in a relaxed way, then the martial arts can be very enjoyable and you will be very effective. While you are "empty" of habits, you are full of life and vitality.

The many ancient cultures I have studied all seem to agree on the secret to obtaining great wealth and power. They also agree as to how we have been robbed of our power as individuals. Even nature, herself blatantly reveals this power to us.

When I used to travel through the jungles of Central America to study animals, my favorite animal was the red-eyed tree frog. This crazy frog is about three inches long, bright green with white spots. Its sides are banded yellow and blue. The inside of its legs and arms are bright orange. Its eyes are bright red with a bright gold lace pattern membrane sometimes used to cover its eyes. Normally it stays curled up on a branch, showing only the green and white, which is a camouflage.

If an animal tries to grab it, the frog jumps, opens its arms and legs fully and leaps onto a nearby branch. The predator, faced with a moving flash of color, throws its attention to where he expects the frog to land, several feet away. Red-eye's trick is that it sends the predator's attention far away while it actually curls up on a close-by branch. In this way it controls the predator's attention.

The secret to great wealth and power is the ability to control peoples' attention. The secret to your own happiness is to understand that process and not to be controlled.

We all know that packaging sells a product. Many companies have spent most of their initial startup money on developing packaging. The manufacturers fight each other to have the stores place their product at eye level which makes it easier for you to grab the product and plop it right into your shopping cart.

We are trained to pay attention to the packing. It is much easier to make pretty packaging than it is to make a good product.

The key to great power and wealth, though, is not in manipulating people to buy your product. It is really in being able to discern the packaging from the product when it comes to who you are as a person.

You are not the habits you have picked up throughout your life that control attention. Those habits prevent you from being the "artist of attention" who blends Yin and Yang attention to achieve the Golden Elixir.

When you are a skilled artist of attention, you will be more effective in everything you do. You will understand that wherever your attention goes, your life follows. If it goes to its energetic connection to the vibrant energies of nature, to the experience of sharing your life with the human community, your life will be different than if your attention goes to the bright, flashy representations of value.

Yet, being in a more powerful, aware, integrated state, impervious to manipulation, you will be more successful in the material sense as well. You will be less susceptible to scams, able to stand up for yourself and be able to judge the integrity of other people. Since you will not fear failure as a slight to your tender personality, you will be more daring.

The development of your attention has been recognized as the key to success throughout the ages. My novel, The Doubting Snake, is an attempt to express this in an entertaining way. The specific training of the attention is hidden in the story line. Many ancient texts can be better understood as attempts to express this same idea. As the hero of The Doubting Snake asks:

"And if both the sorcerers and the people who run our modern societies have such power to affect peoples' minds, then what hope does the ordinary citizen have?"

Once your attention is freed from coercion the world will still be the same crazy place it was, but you can see the mechanisms behind the behavior of people and cultures and not get trapped in them.

Instead of identifying with a particular world culture you identify with the long line of people throughout history who were aware of these mechanisms. They were able to free themselves from the destructive habit patterns of the people around them.

Imagine yourself in a smelly, mucky swamp. You curse having to walk through this mess and concentrate on the smell and the muck. Soon you discover beautiful birds and insects. You feel the warm breeze and smell some flowers. Your attention is gradually drawn to the beauty of the swamp until even the smell and the muck seem an integral part of that beauty. You then enjoy being part of this scene.

In the same way, the world we live in is, to a large extent, the result of what we pay attention to. The news on television calls your attention mostly to the negative and horrifying part of our society. Yet the Public Broadcasting programs call your attention to the beauty. How do you feel after watching the news? How do you feel after watching nature programs? What factors in our society direct your attention to its horror?

Control over what you pay attention to is vital to prevent aging. This does not mean that you become oblivious to the problems of our world but that those problems don't destroy you. You must regain control over the dynamics of your attention and the balance of energy. This is where you start in Tai-chi and Zookinesis.

I know that in modern times Tai-chi has become just memorizing a series of movements and Push Hands has just become a shoving contest. This is true even in China itself. But the movements and the pushing are just the surface level of a very deep and beautiful teaching. The teaching of "immortality", as it used to be called, is about how to stay young and healthy and thereby actually extend your lifespan. It teaches you how to become connected to the world around you so that your consciousness may remain connected to the world even after your body dies. But the term "immortality" refers more to knowing that consciousness is immortal because it is an inherent part of nature. If your individual attention is connected to the whole you are living an immortal life.

Don't give in to the images of aging. Don't let those images implant themselves within you and direct your consciousness. Instead look to the agility, strength and beauty of wild animals and of athletes and allow those images to direct your consciousness.

I teach seated Zookinesis exercises to local senior communities and nursing homes. When I began they could barely move. Now we are beginning to do seated acrobatic movements. Each time I show them what exercise we are working towards, they laugh, feeling they could never do that. Yet a month or two later, they easily do the exercise. Many of them are over 90 years old. Zookinesis has given them a new perspective of what they are capable of. They are now headed in a positive direction – stronger, more flexible, more relaxed and more connected to their bodies. When you live your life in this positive direction, you are already immortal.

In Taoist philosophy the image of a pebble dropping into a lake is often used. The pebble falls down, inevitably reaching the bottom of the lake. But this act of letting go creates a splash upward and a radiation of ripples on the surface of the water outward. Letting go creates energy. In the body, relaxing and sinking into the legs creates a pressure that then bounces upward through the spine and outward through the center of the body, initiating the next movement. With each positive act we affect those around us in ways we may not even know. That positive affect comes back to us in ways we may not notice.

In the pebble analogy we may be sinking towards an eventual death but that splash upward and rippling waves outward still continue.

The Taoist perspective is that we are not only the pebble but the splash and ripples as well. If we are connected to our own creative attention and to the greater flow of attention throughout nature, healing energy constantly fills us. We have barely begun to tap our potential and can become stronger, more agile and, in effect, younger every day if we are willing to let go of the pebbles of ingrained habits.

When we are pushed in Push Hands and reach the "end" of our limits of movement we have to realize that "end" is just a concept. It is not the joint that has reached its end of movement; it is our mind that has gotten stuck. The habits of the mind are the limitation of the joint. We can certainly continue to move that joint as long as all the other joints also join in with the movement to maintain alignment. The reason the joint "reached its limits" is because it became disconnected from all the other joints. The mind's habits are the wall separating the joints. Each of us is like a "joint" of the earth.

People may ask me a technical question about one movement in a form. If it were a form I do every day I could use my thinking mind to answer. But if it were a form I haven't practiced for a while, my mind may reach the "end" of its ability to remember. Then I have to actually do the movement and watch what I am doing. The information is stored in the body much more securely than in the mind. When the mind gets jammed, I can switch my attention to the body to free myself and to remember the movement.

In the same way, much of your power is "stored securely" in how your attention is connected to your body and the natural world around you. As a culture, we are jammed in that way. We don't remember the details of that connection. Tai-chi practice leads your attention to that connection to "unjam" you.

When we practice Tai-chi and Zookinesis, it is essential that we stimulate the entire brain, including what is called the "reptilian brain", or "primitive brain". Rather than being primitive it is an essential part of the brain, dealing with basic survival. We gradually enliven all parts of the nervous system and that, in turn, enlivens the entire body. The result is that our very perception of the world around us is sharpened. We can perceive deeper levels and finer details of our senses and bring back senses that have been allowed to become dormant.

The process of bringing power back to the brain is most vividly experienced in Push Hands. But you can use the techniques of Push Hands in everyday life in ordinary situations.

As we practice Push Hands we experiment with "seating" our attention in various parts of the brain. As an example, we concentrate on the lower part of the brain that is the reptilian brain. However, as you are about to push the partner you may notice that your attention jumps forward which causes your entire body to lunge forward. This allows your partner to turn to the side and allow you to fall forward.

The dynamics of your attention can pull your own body off balance. An important principle in Push Hands is to keep your attention centered. This keeps the body centered. You generate the force to push the partner through "internal" movements of your body. This consists of moving individual joints and muscles *in relationship to each other* but now allowing the whole body to lunge back and forth. The result is similar to flexing and popping dancing styles in which the body undulates, sending waves of force through itself, but the body remains in a centered position.

This can only be achieved when your attention is centered. If your attention is concentrated in only certain parts of the brain, the frontal lobes for example, then it is already off center. You are already off balance as far as your attention is concerned and then your body copies that pattern of poor balance. The body reflects the pattern and quality of your attention. If your attention jumps around a lot, then your body will exhibit excess movement.

I guarantee that you will amaze yourself with how calm and powerful you feel when you keep the reptilian part of your brain (the lower, rear part) energized in interpersonal interactions. Rather than paying attention *to* the reptilian brain *from* the frontal lobes, try having the reptilian brain as the seat of attention and looking out from it. Make believe that right in front of the reptilian brain there is a window and you are looking out that window. The window is in the middle of the brain (back to front) and at the bottom of the brain. You may feel both your body and your breathing relaxing. You will feel more connected to your surroundings and more secure.

This exercise does not cut off your frontal lobes (the intellectual part of the brain) but includes them. Your attention will feel more centered within the entire nervous system. The quality of your attention will be more relaxed, sharper and stronger. Your body will be able to respond more accurately to the changing conditions around you. You can see that energizing the reptilian brain is essential for practicing Push Hands. It is also essential for living a more powerful and effective life.

You begin to look at the dynamics and qualities of attention in other people as if you were a healer diagnosing a patient. Your understanding of these qualities in others gives you a deeper understanding of their resultant behavior that in turn, gives you more options of how to respond to them. If they are off balance, then your own balanced state can help them to become balanced. Their attention responds to the qualities of your attention as one tuning fork vibrates when another one of the same vibration next to it is sounded.

On the other hand, you can avoid having your own attention thrown off balance by the unbalanced state of their attention. You see the underlying mechanisms of the interaction and can avoid the pitfalls.

It's amazing that simply by bringing the focus of your attention to a different part of the brain and "looking out" from there, you can change the whole dynamic of your personal life. It is so easy to try and the results are so obvious.

This is the type of training you would receive in what is called a "mouth to ear" transmission of teaching, such as Zookinesis. This means a tradition that is taught from teacher to student through long term, disciplined training, rather than from books or shallow training. There is a whole world of such training methods.

Once you become comfortable with looking out from the reptilian brain, you then create other foci of attention such as the Tan-tien, feet, hips, etc.

You allow your attention to sink to these spots to either energize or relax them as you do Push Hands. The patterns of energizing and relaxing in these areas create different alignments of the body and affect the flow of forces through the body. This allows you to send force out into the partner while keeping the body still. The result is that the partner is thrown back and it doesn't seem as if you did anything.

If you could *not* access the reptilian brain then you simply could not create and coordinate these multiple foci of attention because your attention would not be centered.

This is part of what is known as "Taoist alchemy" which is the basis of Tai-chi and Zookinesis. Taoist alchemy is the inner work to bring back your mind, body and spirit to full functioning.

From that inner point of view, you can perceive sources of energy that are normally invisible to us. You realize that our modern culture is not built on a foundation of "whole brain experience" or what I call "whole body attention". Anything outside of our cultural perspective is considered to not exist. And so, while we may have perceptions and feelings of these sources of energy, we tend to ignore them in order to feel emotionally secure. We need to feel that we are part of *this* culture. It is like a child grabbing onto his parent's leg, fearing to venture too many steps away.

The mouth to ear training allows you to take those steps and to understand the inner experiences which you have ignored up to now. In this way a whole new world is revealed which allows your life to make much more sense. Your culture, which previously caged your ability to perceive, now is seen in a wider context.

You can begin this training by yourself, simply by massaging the rear of your head several times a day to make it easier to seat your attention there. Remember that the goal is not to pay attention *to* the rear of the head *from* the front of the head. The goal is to "seat" the attention in the rear of the head (as an exercise) and then to eventually fill the entire brain with attention so that the attention is balanced. Paying attention to the rear of the head is only the first (but necessary) step.

When attention can fill the entire body as a result of balancing the attention, you can feel the energetic system that serves as a framework from which the physical body functions. You might also feel blockages to the flow of energy and how that jams the body's function. To heal means to unblock that flow.

One point in which I differ from many other teachers is that it is generally taught that there are a certain number of "meridian points", (points in the body that respond to healing in specific ways). From my experience, every point in the body is responsive to healing. The "official" points may be convenient points for acupuncture or acupressure and may be convenient to remember which points affect which systems of the body. But it is much better in my opinion, to feel the flow of energy so you can understand what is really going on in the patient's body, and respond to that "knowledge/perception".

To teach a large number of people, though, it might be impractical to get them to the point where you can enlarge their ability to perceive and function as healers. If the student is only willing to devote two or three years to training, then listing specific points, the conditions that "needling" them can correct and how to insert the needle, may be about as good as you can get.

If we look at our body as a machine, we can then push a few buttons to make it work better. If we look at it as a vibrant community of intelligence and energy, then healing requires deeper skills than pushing buttons or inserting needles.

Heal Yourself and the World with Tai-chi

Our culture looks at the universe itself as a big machine, forever destined to act according to predetermined physical principles that can be understood mathematically. We humans, according to this view, are the only part of the universe that has broken free from this mechanistic system. We are spontaneous and unpredictable. While our thinking minds may be the result of the biochemistry of the brain, there is an element in our make-up that breaks us free from mere biology. What is that element?

This element of freedom from the mechanistic, is represented by God or by Gods. The God of our culture controls it all through his will. The Gods, with their human-like personalities, reflect the interaction of power over it all with the frailty of human personalities.

We use our thinking minds to climb the ladder to God-like power only to find that we are trapped by the side effects of our meddling. How much more so must God be trapped by his own power? We hold two viewpoints simultaneously – God as the principles by which the great "machine" of the universe is governed and God as a human-like personality subject to human-like whims.

Science is an attempt to maintain the quality of the absoluteness of God, in the laws of physics, chemistry and mathematics while removing the element of consciousness, which is just a nuisance. Intelligence is considered to be just a side-effect of the complexity of the nervous system.

Compare this to a view in which intelligence has always been part of the universe. A person from this standpoint tries to perceive the intelligence in everything. This does not mean he tries to understand the physics and chemistry of the world around him. It means that he develops those senses that can directly perceive the element of intelligence in all things.

Intelligence, in this case, is also considered to be the result of complexity, but of the entire universe, not just the nervous system. The ability to be aware of complexity is the sign of intelligence in this view. That is why Tai-chi practices require you to be aware of every joint and muscle in the body, what state of readiness they are in, and how they move in relation to each other to maintain balance and alignment. You are being trained in this type of intelligence. Then when you use your other form of intelligence – thinking – you can use the same skills to compare many ideas to each other at each moment, so that your creativity gets stronger.

In the beginning, the student can do this by working with animals and experiencing the complexity of their attention and behavior patterns. She copies those patterns in her exercises.

Reptiles are especially good for this purpose because we usually don't consider them to be intelligent. When you have learned to appreciate the different nature of their intelligence you realize that there are different sorts of intelligence. Part of you can perceive the intelligence of a snake, for example, even though it differs from that of a person. You begin to learn to discriminate the continuum of types of intelligence and to recognize any particular type.

Intelligence becomes an experience rather than a calculation. It is a sign of awareness rather than of cleverness.

When you are aware of intelligence in this way you are aware of the spirit world. You "see" intelligence. You "see" creativity. You "see" spontaneity.

When a comedian sees a different slant on everyday life, he is aware of this intelligence. Everyday life can be thought of as "the machine" and the comedic view as "spontaneity". We go about our daily lives but the comedian asks, "why"? "Look at what you are doing!" he says. He is outside of what you take for granted.

The art of Zookinesis is the art of understanding what we take for granted. It is similar to what a comedian does. For example, we look at the world around us and see that it is a big world. Yet whatever we see is only a 3mm (about one eighth of an inch) spot of light on each retina (the area of visual acuity). The rest of what you perceive is the reaction of the retinal cells, the optic nerve and the general reaction of the brain. You learn to create the world by comparing one sense to another and through your experiences. Most of the world around you, including yourself, is a product of your creativity.

So, is the "physical" world what those two spots of light reveal or does it have more to do with your creativity? Certainly, creativity is as much a real part of the world we experience, as is matter. To many cultures creativity and light (sight) are on such an equal footing that creativity is represented by fire. Of course, the other senses are also partially a product of creativity as well.

Science by its nature is mechanistic and in its present form requires that we don't think of our universe as inherently conscious. The scientific effort at separating these two factors (the physical world and creativity) is very important. This effort allows us to better differentiate what creativity is and how it is different from matter and other forms of energy.

It is hard to know something unless you can isolate it and look at it. But this does not mean that creativity is actually separate from the physical world in real life. It is useful to concentrate one's studies on one or the other as long as you understand that, in reality, they are inseparable.

I call the corresponding study of creativity "The Dynamics of Attention". Push Hands is a very useful method of teaching this. You learn that attention has qualities and dynamics. It has "stickiness" or lack of stickiness. It can be thick and slow or light and fast.

If it is thick, an impression can be made in it so it can remember well. If it is thin, it can be agile but may not be able to retain memory. We try to develop both agility and the ability to retain memory.

The system of the elements was developed as a formal expression of the Dynamics of Attention. Each element is a general category of a dynamic of attention. The study of the elements is common throughout the world's cultures. In the West, for example, the element of fire represents creativity. Air represents thinking. Each element represents a large list of related qualities. The study of the elements is the study of the relationship of all the qualities of attention and the relationship of creativity to the physical world. We separate out the elements of our experience of the world, and we study how they work together to form the building blocks of our world.

When we do Push Hands, we find that creativity is very different from thinking. We can concentrate on all the mechanical aspects of the interaction – balance, state of tension of each muscle, etc. Out of this mechanistic awareness comes a "knowing." The body knows what it must do. This "knowing" comes from proper training which results in skill. Once you start to think, that jams up the whole process. The body's "knowing" comes of itself. The muscle "knows". The ligaments "know." The mind does not know. The body has an organic "knowing" which has much more "personality" than the thinking mind. In comparison, the thinking mind is mechanistic. The body's knowing is "alive." Its calculations are so intricate and fast that the thinking mind is, in comparison, a large dry rock.

You discover a new "aliveness" which is more intelligent than anything you have experienced before. Zookinesis wakens this intelligence to the point where it can recognize its "peers" in all things.

I used to have a slide projector. You would put a photographic slide in front of a light that would then shine through a lens and focus on a screen. A film projector does the same thing with thousands of stills.

Our sensory information is the slide. Our creativity is the light and the screen is the apparent three-dimensional world. But what about the real world we took a picture of in the first place? This is what is called, "the spirit world", when all of our senses are intact and we have a high resolution of attention.

When we hold a slide in our hands, we know we are not holding the real scene in our hands. But when we see a scene, we think we perceive the actual world. At best, it is a rough approximation. Similarly, when we think a thought in words, we "think" we have the whole thought that came to us. But when we perceive the "jolt of thought" as described previously, we realize that the words are only a rough approximation of a small fraction of the original thought.

There are legends of Tai-chi masters so powerful that when people touched them the people were thrown many feet away. It is said that the master's chi jumped out and threw the people. That is only a rough approximation of the truth. If you don't understand the dynamics of what is going on, you only see the result and have to make up your own explanation. The truth is far more fascinating.

Your body can sense the alignment of your partner's body and the dynamics of their attention. From those dynamics you can detect how they will be able to respond to your actions. A wave of expansion of your joints moves from the root (feet connection to the ground), up through the legs and hips, out of your body and into the body of the person connected to you. If more than one person has grabbed you, you can send a separate wave into each person. This requires that your own body remain still. If you moved much, this would weaken those waves of force.

This requires a decentralization of attention so that all the joints and muscles can create these waves, but also can adjust their actions to compensate for the reactions of the people who are grabbing.

I asked the student of one such master (a student who had been "thrown many feet") to push me. She did so and was similarly "thrown" back. I explained to her that this effect was more due to her poor body mechanics than to my great chi. She really pushed herself back. When we watched a videotape of her master pushing his students, it was obvious that his students all had very poor body mechanics. When you watch for the body mechanics of both the teacher and the student, you get a better understanding of what just happened.

The mind can be trapped into a machine-like state and, while it can invent technology, it cannot "see" the world as it is. A machine-like mind sees a machine-like world. You tend not to see anything that works differently from that mind.

True intelligence depends on understanding what you see. Understanding how the old masters could throw people a great distance depends on being connected to your own body so you can feel the forces involved. When you know these forces in yourself, you can appreciate them in the world around you.

In one sense, we have strayed from direct experience, attempting to duplicate it. Our lifeline has grown very thin. Zookinesis teaches us to first learn from the animals, that by seeing the intelligence within animals, you can retrace your path back to your own intelligence.

We must remember the fabric of our memory. There are two interweaving fibers. One is time – the memory of the sequential order of events. The other is feeling and how that changes from moment to moment.

Feeling memory is complex and involves the body. It stores a great deal of information. It is the memory of states of being which can be returned to at any "time". Time memory is also complex but involves the thinking mind. A moment in time can never be returned to because we think of our memories as having "gone away" to the past. It can only be recorded for reference. We create a timeline in our minds punctuated by specific events, like clothes hanging on a clothesline.

Continuum of Consciousness

The idea of time separates us from direct experience. When I watch the "Home and Garden Network", people talk about buying a new home to "create memories". They don't say they are buying a home to "experience life in a new way". They are already thinking of themselves as being old and remembering something that hasn't even happened yet.

How many people, especially these days, experience their vacation through the lens of a camera? Perhaps they feel they will soon be too old to go anywhere and experience anything. At least they have pictures of the past.

Animals have a memory as well. They remember the path through the woods. They remember the color pattern of an animal or plant that tasted bad. Perhaps they also recount their memories in their spare time. But that doesn't deplete their ability to be fully engaged in the present. It is this immediacy and total focus of animals that made me realize that my attention was not as connected to the present as it could be. An animal demands that you are fully here and connected to the interaction. The thinking mind acts as a diversion of attention, like the way the social media on the Internet sucks your attention.

If you concentrate on the feeling of the interaction with another person you will find a large world of experience having nothing to do with thinking great thoughts or time travel in your mind (thinking about the past and future). There is a difference of engaging and satisfying the mind in the interaction, and engaging and satisfying every cell of the body. Children at play engage every cell of their bodies.

Tai-chi trains you to be fully present in the "real world" even as you also engage the thinking mind. It does this by teaching you to use less energy for each, and be more efficient. You learn not to "grab" at thoughts and not to "grab" at what you see and hear. There is a gentler relationship with your own mind and a gentler relationship with the world around you.

There is also a gentler relationship with the flow of energy in the body. You trust the energy to "know" how to flow. You trust the mind to be honest and simple so that it doesn't twist itself with deceit. Honest words don't need to be calculated. You trust the body to function well in a relaxed state and can resist the temptation to tense up in order to feel strong. This results in trusting the world around you.

Heal Yourself and the World with Tai-chi

Your honest, simple mind can easily detect deceit in others. Your relaxed body doesn't get worn out by stress. Releasing your manipulation of your body's energy, joins that energy to the world so you are no longer just an isolated object fighting against other objects.

The mind and body no longer battle each other for energy, as if they had to take turns. They are now integrated, support and energize each other. You are a whole being, not just a random collection of parts. You can now interact with a wild animal as an equal.

When a potential student hears that Tai-chi teaches you to develop internal energy ("chi"), he immediately thinks of science fiction stories of shooting rays of energy to conquer enemies. We take very sophisticated ancient training and make them seem silly. The term "internal energy" refers to the way that what is going on inside of you influences what happens in your life. It means that your state of health and emotional balance is the most important influence on your power to improve your life.

Some students want to learn to concentrate and direct their energy. I teach them to release their energy and let it go where it wants. The students want to gain power. I teach them to stop interfering with their natural power. Some want to live in a beautiful house. I teach them to become alive in their bodies.

When you are alive and vibrant, your consciousness seeks to expand and to connect with the world around you, and so you live in the world, and are alive in the world. It is your living energy, merged with the world around you that makes that world beautiful. When you withdraw your feelings from the world around you, the world itself feels dead. When you withdraw your feelings from your body, your body feels dead. Your life then becomes divided, one part withdrawing, and the other part wanting to be released so it can join the world.

You then seek to acquire things of the world. In this way you can remain separated from it, yet claim ownership over part of it. Owning something takes the place of really being part of it. Your relationships with people are no longer based on releasing yourself to the other, and receiving them, but rather on agreements and arrangements.

You originally withdrew to protect yourself from the unpredictable behaviors and intentions of others, yet wound up damaging yourself by being disconnected from the vibrancy of life. Tai-chi and Zookinesis teach us that the state of withdrawal is so prevalent in our society (and in many others past and present), that we have forgotten how it feels to be connected.

Some of us have even forgotten how to let another person completely into our souls. We have "hesitant" relationships. Some people call it "transactional relationships". Tai-chi and Zookinesis teach the art of "letting go" (releasing). At a certain point you feel the flow of energy within the body. You realize that you are "holding" that energy, or we say, "locking it up". Even our attention (consciousness) seems to be locked into patterns of thinking.

At another point in the training, that energy suddenly "jumps the fence" and seeks to merge with your surroundings. It is a startling moment because you realize how much "locking up" the energy has hurt you previously. Your consciousness now joins the "consciousness of nature" just as the water of a stream joins the water of a river and then the water of the ocean. You feel a member of life. Your thinking and behaviors are no longer so patterned, but are more creative. Once your consciousness fills your body and the world around you, your life is felt more intensely.

Every cell of your body is like the string of a stringed instrument, which is played by the beauty of the world around you. Your attention is attracted to beautiful things and thoughts rather than to worries and anger, and so your life goes in a new direction. This is all accomplished by learning how to release your energy ("chi") and consciousness and let it go where it wants. You will feel like you were a caged animal that has now been let loose into its natural habitat. The cage of fear is no longer your home. I had a rabbit who lived in a cage in the house during the winter. When I let it loose from time to time, it sought the "shelter" of a stool I use to hold a plant. The rabbit stayed within the four feet of the stool. It has been let loose yet sought the security of something that looked like his cage.

When the student's energies have finally been released, there is a tendency to seek a new "cage". He seeks philosophies and "truths". Tai-chi is not really a system of truths. It is a way to become re-connected to nature and to other people. It is a simple, practical teaching that does not get involved in abstract philosophy. The goal is to understand yourself, as in the saying, "See yourself, be yourself, appreciate yourself." Appreciate your biological aliveness and how you are connected to nature. Appreciate the creative efforts of others and be sympathetic to their lack of perfection (as well as to your own). Understand that other philosophies are also a way of understanding yourself and releasing you from self-imposed prisons. Don't seek them as the security of yet another cage. Seek nature in your surroundings and in people. Step out of your own way so that the now invisible world of creative energy can be perceived. Let that be your new home.

Remember that nature is creative. Nature is vibrant. Tai-chi also teaches that nature is conscious. The qualities that you seek for yourself are already in you because you arose from nature. When you release your energy, your attention, to nature, you enter the flow of creativity, vibrancy and consciousness. As much as you release, that much and more flows back. The teaching of "letting go" is the path to power.

The training of mobile vantage points is the most difficult for students yet provides the greatest insights into healing and gaining power in one's life. It allows you to identify and release chronic behavior habits and tensions, and to utilize the power of the body and mind to its fullest. It allows you to understand the behavior of other people so you can be a better healer and teacher, and you can be more comfortable interacting with people.

This training begins with the leap of faith of considering attention to be a universal force. Attention affects what it is part of as does any force. It certainly interacts with our nervous system and other systems, resulting in the individual feeling of consciousness we experience. The history of our development as individuals and as a society includes the various ways we have learned to interact with this force.

So what is a "vantage point"? It is the place where consciousness is most condensed within your body. For most people it is in the eyes and the head in general. We also hear and speak from the head. There is usually little consciousness in the rest of the body. It is also concentrated in the process of thinking. There is little consciousness in other perceptions such as the kinesthetic sense.

Even our hearing and sense of smell are so bombarded in modern times that their sensitivity has been greatly reduced. The rest of the body is directed by the vantage point of the eyes and by the dynamics of the thinking process. This is where we feel we live. In pre-modern cultures other senses are recognized, so that Tai-chi speaks of sensing "chi" and other cultures speak in similar ways.

As we practice Push Hands, we learn that we can sense the state of balance within our partner and even how his body prepares to carry out an intention to push even though our eyes are closed. And so it becomes easier to accept that we have a "sense of chi", the sense of connection within ourselves and between ourselves and others.

What is the thinking process if it is not consciousness itself? Thinking is the interaction of programmed habits of behavior and instinctual responses to consciousness. While the nature of consciousness is to connect, the nature of thinking is to disconnect. You separate yourself out from what you consider in order to judge it. Consciousness is union. We experience a back and forth tug of connecting and disconnecting from what we perceive and thereby gain a sense of self.

The head-oriented awareness works in one dimension. It is aware of one thing at a time. The body-oriented awareness is aware of everything that is going on at the same time. It is three-dimensional.

In order to achieve great skill, the student must develop a harmony between these two types of awareness. You can think of it like a map of a mall. The map shows where all the stores are located and also shows where you are in that map. You need to know both in order to get to your store.

We have become a society of "where we are" awareness but have lost our awareness of the "map". Our schools don't teach labor history, women's' history, art history, the history of the human mind (cultural anthropology), financial history, etc., and so we don't know where we came from. The history of religion and its interaction with science would be too controversial to teach in schools.

We certainly don't learn how we humans have become so stiff, so sick, so angry, so stressed, and so anxious, etc. But when we practice Tai-chi we have to delve into these issues and recognize the patterns of behavior and tension that have been programmed into us. We have to recognize how they have power over us and by doing so we learn who "we" really are.

Heal Yourself and the World with Tai-chi

We have to learn how the dreams we had as children have become co-opted by the agendas of those who control our society. The path to achieving great things is to let go of the ropes that bind us to their agendas and allow your dreams to empower your life.

This doesn't necessarily mean quitting your job. It means understanding your own behavior. Which behaviors are a reaction to your fears and which emanate from your creativity and your joy?

This is true even when practicing your Tai-chi form. Are you pushing yourself through it to feel you have accomplished something or is the form organically emerging from inside of you and expressing itself? In the latter case, the thinking mind has to sit back as if it were the audience and allow the play to take place without interference. Sometimes it is useful to create a form spontaneously so you can use the principles of fluidity and grounding but not worry about the specific movements.

In many cases it is not the lack of skill that holds you back from a beautifully performed form but the unwillingness of the vantage point of the thinking mind to yield its one-dimensional control.

When we do the spins, for example (in "kick with heel" and "lotus kick") there is a tendency to bring your attention up as you spin, which makes you unstable. You have to trust that from the vantage point of your center, you can "see" everything about the mechanics of the body. The spin comes out of a small circle in the center of your body. It takes trust that the other parts of the body will work properly when you are just working from the middle. It is just like the trust that if you live your life honestly, you will be better off in the long run. Being centered, physically or in how you live your life, allows you to perceive more clearly and fully.

I remember as a child understanding that I was controlled by behavioral habits and that is partially why I started learning Tai-chi and other healing systems. (The other reason was that I was physically restricted by severe scoliosis). One summer I went to summer camp. I thought that this would be an opportunity to re-invent myself. But unfortunately, my habits came along with me.

This made me redouble my studies to be able to discern, understand and influence those habits and to understand why they have such power. How can I still function without dragging them with me?

In Tai-chi we say that it is an interaction of intent and letting go. If you can intend by relaxing in your form or Push Hands, for example, you can be more creative. This means you push by relaxing, not by tensing. In order for your energy to move forward, your back relaxes. Each movement is initiated by a relaxation. When I punch, I am concentrating mostly on letting the muscles in my back relax and drop. This sends energy forward. In this way you unite intent with letting go. But most people tense even with the thought of pushing or punching. Tai chi pushing is really a trick to get you to marry intent with letting go.

As I grew up, I learned to let go of the self that was created by the people around me and found there was a natural self, yearning to come out. I learned to stand up for that self – for its experiences and perspectives. By doing that I was able to find other people and teachings with similar spirits. That self was like an intent, but one that did not live in the thinking mind.

Intent doesn't have to emanate from the thinking mind. It can emanate from any part of the body or the body as a whole. When you are riding a bicycle, intent to stay balanced doesn't really come from the thinking mind. You are not constantly thinking about how each muscle has to act in order to stay balanced. Muscle memory keeps you balanced and the intent to stay balanced is in the body's natural need not to fall. That intent powers the actions of the muscles utilizing their training.

Students can learn to condense consciousness in other areas besides the thinking mind and eyes but it is very hard to "melt" consciousness *from* the thinking mind and eyes – to let go of those areas.

The student must place the racing horse of his consciousness at the starting gate of his belly but must not keep the horse tethered to the thinking mind and eyes. In this way his vantage points (condensed consciousness) are under his creative control. Breathing in then lifts the gate.

Creativity itself then becomes his basic identity – that is, the interplay of intent (Yang) and letting go (Yin). He does not need to grab onto the branch over the cliff (as in the story of the monk who was chased by a tiger).

Holding onto that branch is like the grasping of the mind to find a secure place, a secure opinion, a secure sense of self. The less creative he has learned to be, the more he feels the need to hold onto that branch.

To abandon his fixed vantage points is an uncomfortable prospect. It feels like an attack on his identity but is really an attack on the trapping of his identity in the cage of habits. Even a wild animal, used to being in a cage, won't leave the cage if the door suddenly opens as in the case of my pet rabbit. He is used to the security of the cage. It takes time for him to be willing to leave that security.

I can see how hesitant my own students are to step out of their cages, but when they do even for an instant, they laugh at how silly they were to be willing to remain trapped. They laugh at how easy a technique is once their vantage points are mobile. And it feels so good to have those vantage points move, like the opening of a door once the rusty hinges are cleaned. You feel a refreshing breeze flowing through the door.

In fact, laughter is a very powerful tool to decrease the power of the habits. When a comedian looks at an everyday event from a different viewpoint you laugh. You never thought of it that way before. You see it from a different vantage point.

When you are sparring and your opponent completely protects himself with his arms, all you have to do is tilt your body and now you can see his defenses from another angle. From that new angle there will be gaps in his defenses. (You could also just punch his arms of course).

That is why we often laugh when we get hit in Tai chi sparring. We thought we were protected but our sparring partner just changed his vantage point. It is like a Tai chi joke.

A vantage point gives you leverage. If your leverage point is at the center of the body when you do a form, it is easy to move. When you push a partner, you must know the best leverage point to push from and your attention has to be there. If the attention sits at a vantage point different from the required leverage point for the push, the mechanics won't work.

The movement of consciousness from its condensed, fixed position, to a more fluid Yin state and towards another location is called "intent". The destination of intent may be outside of your body such as when you push your partner. It is the movement of your vantage point, letting go of the previous vantage point and the resultant effect on your body, that sets you up to push. To accomplish the push there is an expansion of energy from that new vantage point to both the target (your partner) and to the ground.

This intent resides within the body. If your intent comes from the thinking mind, you are bringing your habits with you. You are going to summer camp but remaining the same person you were before. The push should be a transformation of yourself. By transforming yourself you transform those around you.

In my push hands workshops I demonstrate pushing someone without moving – just by breathing in. This is probably the most confusing part of the workshop for the participants. How can I push someone without moving?

I am moving but the movements are internal. By moving my vantage points, each muscle and joint readjusts in subtle ways. Breathing in creates a "car air bag" effect knocking my partner forward. Even if I do this in slow motion, you can see my partner slowly being uprooted and losing balance until he falls. All the while I seem to be just standing there, doing nothing. It is all about the internal dynamics.

When people see a Yang style Tai-chi form, which is slow and even, and then see Chen style which is more active physically with quick changes of movement, they assume that Yang style is for meditation and Chen for martial arts. Actually, they are each for both purposes.

It is just that Yang style is more "internal". All the dynamic movements of Chen style still take place in Yang style but you don't display the movements externally. When you are fighting you don't want your opponent to see what you are going to do. You want every one of your moves to be a surprise to him.

It may seem that we would learn Chen first and then bring it in more internally to Yang style. But in my school, we learn Yang first. We first empty our cup (let go of habits) before re-filling it with something else. Yang style emphasizes letting go so that each technique is not encumbered by habits. The emptiness (of habits) allows the technique to be performed cleanly. The quality of emptiness forms the core of both initiating and letting go.

You might think that in an "empty" state you will no longer be able to think or to have a set of morals. But this is not true.

Creative thinking which involves the full consciousness of the body doesn't require an undue condensation of consciousness. It does require an even distribution of consciousness throughout the body. Too much condensed attention in thinking or in the physical head can jam creative thinking and can also cause headaches. It also reinforces habits.

Letting go can empower thinking. When letting go allows your Yin attention to connect with others, your moral sense is heightened. You recognize the universality of your consciousness. Rather than letting go of morality, you let go of the illusion of your separateness.

Creative ideas pop up instantly. It then takes your thinking mind time to write it down. But writing it down is not the creative thinking itself. Emptiness allows creative thoughts to pop up. It is like a whale in the Arctic that needs a hole in the ice to pop up and take a breath. If there are no holes in the ice, the whale dies. Don't let your creativity die. Nurture emptiness. Imagine how happy the whales are when there is no ice. They can leap into the air with their whole bodies.

One of my students was in such agony from a punch to his shoulder that he had to sit down, shaking his head from side to side. Yet I only gave him a light tap. The reason that he felt the light tap as a powerful blow gives an important clue to Tai-chi as a martial art and as a healing art.

I struck him at the moment he was about to punch me. At that instant his attention condensed into his punching arm. By striking the area where his attention was condensed (the front of his shoulder), I shattered the attention. Only a light tap was necessary to disrupt the attention because his attention was so condensed.

The instant shattering of a condensed attention is so disruptive that people usually interpret the experience as physical pain. Yet when my student actually thought about whether his shoulder really hurt or not, he realized that it didn't hurt at all. There was no real physical pain. It was all psychological pain interpreted as physical pain.

In our culture, we are taught to condense our attention into a single point in the head. When our attention is locked into one part of the body or into a habit of thinking or acting, the attention is not really functional and it becomes delicate. A locked attention is dead and can break as easily as a dead twig.

One of the main reasons Tai-chi trains you to be fluid in your movements is to develop a fluid attention as well – one that can move, vary in its qualities and dynamics. This is essential in fighting but also in living one's everyday life. The more rigid you are, the less functional you are and the more easily your attention can be worn out or broken.

When practicing a Tai-chi form, allow your attention to sink down into the ground, as if you are a lotus plant (water lily), floating in a pond with your roots deep into the mud below. As you breathe in, your attention flows up through your stem (up the body) and into the "lotus flower", which is within the chest at the sternum (breastbone) level. Continuing to breathe in, the lotus flower opens and so the front of your body flows up and then opens out to the sides, like an opening flower.

The opening flower then lifts your head that is the center petals of the lotus. Breathing out, the front of the body sinks, the sides of the chest drops to the center and your attention returns to your roots.

This process will bring fluidity to your attention so that it can never be frozen again. Frozen attention makes you vulnerable and ineffective. As the reality of life tugs at your attention and your attention resists the tugs, life seems like a struggle. You feel as if you are at your "wit's end" because the requirements of the dynamic mobility of your attention is greater than its actual abilities.

Once attention is freed from its rigidity it instantly has all the energy it needs. It becomes more balanced and easier to move – just like the needle of a compass. The needle is so balanced that it can spin around easily. But if you move its fulcrum even a tiny bit, the needle will fall over and not move at all.

Breathing as if you are a lotus flower is a very valuable form of meditation even while standing still (as long as you allow your body to sink down and expand upward as described above). As we get older there is a tendency for our attention and thereby our bodies to condense. The lotus flower meditation helps to prevent this aging process.

Remember that what you may interpret as frustration, anger and even physical pain, may just be the result of a rigid attention which is not up to the task of functioning properly in our complex modern world. Tai-chi teaches you to break free from rigidity.

A newborn is completely dependent on the people around him or her. The behavior patterns of the people around him gradually imprint themselves on his behavior. At a certain age he begins to exert his independence to break free from the control others have over him.

As an adult we must balance our connection to our surroundings with our creative individuality. The skill of creating this balance is key to our power and fulfillment in life.

A musician in a band, for example, must have skill both in playing his instrument and in allowing the other band members to play their instruments through him. In this way there is a balance between synchronizing his playing with the others and creatively leading the music.

Each musician "gives life" to his or her instrument and feels that his fingers, his breath (depending on the instrument) and even the instrument itself have a life of their own. He feels that the instrument is playing itself and interacting with the "aliveness" of the other instruments.

In this way playing in a band is similar to raising a child. There is a struggle between the feeling of control and the desire to let the instrument or child have a consciousness of its own. At a certain point you feel that you can just sit back and let the instrument play itself. At a certain point you can allow the child to control his own life (maybe when he is in his thirties).

When you get involved in any relationship you go through this same process. Each person has issues of controlling or letting the other person control and they hopefully learn to blend together. You reproduce your early childhood with each relationship. So the quality of your success in balancing letting in external influences vs. developing your independence as a child will greatly affect all future relationships.

It may be difficult to remember how you developed as a child. Children's memories are recorded as "states of being" not as events in time. Accessing each type of memory requires a different mechanism of your attention.

There is an exercise you can do that shows you how to use your attention to access childhood and even fetal memories. I use this exercise to prove to my students that there are indeed dynamics to their attention. In order to perform a specific conscious act, you must use a specific dynamic of attention. These dynamics are the "secrets" that ancient teachers taught to their advanced students. It is a large part of Zookinesis training.

To do this exercise requires that you have some basic awareness of the feeling of attention itself and its movements. It may take years of training to get even to that point.

So here is the exercise.

Remember an event in the past. Note how each part of your body feels as you are remembering the event. Is your attention concentrated in one part of the body more than another? Write it down. Do the same for several events. You will see how even just remembering an event can control the dynamics of your attention and affect your body.

Next, keep remembering the event and change the distribution of attention in your body so that it is even – front to back, side-to-side and top to bottom. You may then feel new memories emerging. Allow them to, without comment or reaction.

If we can become aware of these dynamics, we can develop skill in their use. We can use this skill to become much more aware of the world around us and how to interact with it.

We will see aspects of our everyday world we were not aware of before. Infant and fetal memory can be accessed so we understand how we tried to make sense of this world and fit into it. Some of the solutions we came up with were useful and some ineffective. To what degree do we shut out the world around us and how does that affect us? To what degree are we too vulnerable and how does that harm us?

Once we gain awareness of these mechanisms, the awareness itself is the solution to the problems. It is as if someone's eyes were shut and he kept walking into things. He spent his life remembering where everything was so he wouldn't bump into them. But the best solution is to just open his eyes.

Learning about the dynamics of attention is like opening your eyes. Then you can easily balance the interplay of letting influence in (Yin) and exerting creative influence out (Yang).

There are exercises to develop each of these two parts of the balance. When you practice your Tai-chi form, initiate each movement from the center of the body – the hip and lower abdominal area. Then let the movements flow outward through the legs, the torso, arms and head. This will develop the outward flow of creative energy (Yang). Imagine that you are in a pond and someone drops various sized and shaped rocks into the center of the pond. The dropping of each rock is like an initiation of movement because it creates ripples in the water that flow outward and a splash upward.

For the Yin aspect of this dynamic, allow the legs, torso, arms and head to yield to the initiated movement and reproduce its quality of energy. You will be like the water itself that yields to the force of the falling rock.

The water on the surface of the lake is completely smooth at first as the water is relaxed. It is like a musician who stays in the proper stance to play his instrument. He is not grabbing the instrument with tension as if to protect it from the influence of his band members. He does not feel territorial about his instrument but holds it in a relaxed and open way.

On the other hand, his stance is not sloppy. That would interfere with transferring his creative energy to the instrument. He is open and connected to the other players influence but also connected to his instrument so that it is receptive to his influence.

He is open and receptive to his entire history of development as a human being because he knows how to remember. So the quality of his music is expressive of his entire life.

He can see how his life can really be described as a quest to learn about this balance of the dynamics of attention. It is about the development of his soul.

When you know your soul, the audience knows it, whether you are a musician or just a regular person interacting with another person. Your soul is really the musician playing you and it plays all day and night. For that reason, it would be very helpful it if played well.

Zookinesis and Tai-chi-Chuan are not only teachings, but teaching methods as well, both arising from Taoist philosophy. You can only understand the deeper aspects of a teaching by understanding the teaching method.

From my point of view, I reach back to help the student along the path. I wonder about their inability to walk the path by themselves. Yet I can appreciate the student's dilemma. Just when he feels he finally got it, he finds he has only taken one more step.

Zookinesis teaches you to copy the patterns of internal energy and the dynamics of attention and movement of animals. It is thus a shamanistic training, allowing you to merge with what I call the "continuum of consciousness." This is the level of experience at which all living things are interconnected. It is the basis of life itself. It is the foundation upon which the individuality of each of us stands, appearing on a shallower level, to be separate, one from the other. Without awareness of the foundation, the illusion of separateness seems like a fact.

At each stage the student is asked to perform relatively simple movements. He is faced with habits that prevent him from carrying out those movements in their simplest, mechanically efficient form. Against the simplicity of those mechanics, the student's habits starkly stand out. The student must enter into a relationship with his own habits.

Theoretically, he should be able to let go of them but they have a life of their own as if they were separate animals. They are obviously part of him, just as all living things are part of life and as all people are part of humanity.

Our habits battle us, as other people battle us, as nature seems to battle us. The method is to become aware of the common foundation of the student and his habits. That common ground is the dynamics of attention. Attention is the life of a habit and the life of a person. Once you are aware of the level of attention you have hands-on access to the habits. You can change your relationship to them.

A habit is a pattern of behavior from a past situation just waiting to be readjusted again. A habit can last three seconds or a lifetime. The habit doesn't want to die. It wants to remain in control of you even if it was created many years ago.

When you learn Tai-chi and the principles of its mechanics, you are aware of the new situation (the new understanding of body mechanics, for example). You want the old habit to "die" and the body to function properly.

Rather than one awareness battling another (the old battling the new), the student learns about the mechanics of awareness itself by watching this "battle" take place. Freezing the hips when you prepare to take a step is such a habit. Turning your head to look ahead to the next movement is another. The student knows what the mechanics should be – and they are very simple – but the habits insist on exerting their will.

He can laugh at the habits as one laughs at the antics of a child. You don't expect a child to be skilled at a complex task. As you practice Tai-chi you notice your "past selves" (your habits as fixed at various times in your development) attempting to do the task. This helps you to know who you are now. I have found that at a certain point in the training your old habits just start boring you too much and you lose interest in them.

When it is time for you to physically die, you remember your whole line of development and remember that you are really the foundation of life and not the habits. You can return to that foundation more easily, even happily.

Just as you focus on various tasks throughout the day, you have focused on this life as a whole. You may wash the dishes, then read the paper, then clean the house, etc. You focus on each task and forget the others. Then you remember that you have other things to do. Similarly, you focus on this life until you are old, then you "remember" that you (attention) have other things to do. When you are truly free of your habits you can enter the spirit world easily.

In Zookinesis teaching, you practice entering the spirit world while still alive so that you incorporate it into your life. Then death is not such a catastrophic transition. Awareness of the spirit world puts your life into perspective, shows you that you are attention and that attention is immortal. The meaning of "spirit world" is just the world as it is without the distortion of habits and with full attention.

When we practice Push Hands and "hide our intentions" beneath the other person's movements, we are in effect, copying their patterns so they can't see us. They can't distinguish their own movements from ours. We let their movements dance through us and so we don't battle them. Our attention though, extends to the center of their balance, and when we push them, this line of attention simply expands into a push.

111

Your attention moves freely ahead to their center while their habits dance through you.

The movement towards your goal is not thwarted by the circumstances of the world that seem pitted against you. You move like water around obstacles.

If you were to concentrate on the partner's force moving into you and did battle with it, those forces would define your interaction. By allowing each muscle and joint to yield to that force while smoothly continuing your journey to his center, your own goals define the interaction.

Allowing the partner's force to define the interaction is death to your own spirit. To reach beyond his force is to trust that your spirit is greater than everyday battles. Letting his force go by is like allowing the wave on a beach to flow past you.

The student sees himself controlled by a habit. He understands what he must do to evade a push yet sees himself doing the opposite (moving his body into my force, for example). He wonders, who is doing that habit. Is it I? Why am I under the control of that habit?

When he allows an animal pattern to take over, he is introducing a powerful force into his body that can deal with the partner's force without battle. Those patterns of animal behavior are based on the principles of yielding and connecting.

His isolation as an individual is no longer the most pervasive force in his life. He participates in the flow of force to release his goals to their targets.

When the relationship of mind and body started to shift, with the influx of such teachings as Tai-chi into the West, part of our culture started drifting to a new direction. A culture's description of God is the definition of the relationship of mind and body. Is God terrifying, demanding and destructive or the compassionate creator? Is God to be feared or played with? Is God related to historical events or to states of being? Is God separate from you or part of you? It's all about the relationship of mind and body.

I have found that in all mystical teaching I have been involved in there are three basic principles. It is called, "The Three Statements" in Zookinesis. The first is that attention is not the same thing as what you are paying attention to. Attention is a force in itself and doesn't just refer to the direction your eyes are facing. We are aware of what our attention connects to, but usually not the attention itself.

The second statement is "You are attention". The basic nature of any living thing is attention. It is our awareness of the experiences of life.

The third statement is "When you know attention, you know your origin". (In other cultures, the saying would be "you know God"). This means that the creative force moves and shapes attention, creating the dynamics of attention. If you know attention itself, when it is still, then you know the movement of attention, which is creativity. When the student truly understands the three statements, he understands the whole of Zookinesis.

In the Gospel of Thomas, Jesus said that the sign of the "Father" (God) in you is movement and rest (the dynamics of attention). Christianity equates consciousness with "the light". We are all the light. The essence of each living creature is "the light" or attention.

Wild animals are the purest connection to the foundation of life. Attention and creativity *are* life. Allowing many forms of life into us is the key to a full and fulfilling life. When I studied the patterns of consciousness of the many species I worked with, I realized that it could not just be an intellectual study. I had to allow myself to be affected by them in order to really understand them. It is the difference between "knowing" a person because they are your friend or "knowing" about a person you heard about.

Another value of allowing animal patterns into us is that it humbles us. We no longer see ourselves as above animals. We are just next to them.

The arrogance of individuality taints the beauty of creativity. This means that when we use our points of view and our strong personalities almost as weapons to overpower others, we disconnect ourselves from the flow of creativity, from our connection to the foundation of life. A culture is a balance of each of us trying to get what we want vs. uniting together to strengthen our community. In modern times we have seen corporate executives cheating their stockholders, religious leaders trying to prohibit gay people from marrying and political parties engaged in vile personal attacks. It seems as though we are all fighting each other over our little area of turf. What sort of relationship between mind and body does this suggest? Is your God simply the relationship with the bigger stick?

The culture and even God are not the issue. The best way to heal people and cultures is to unite mind and body. Culture and the definition of God will follow. When you unite the internal culture of your body, you begin to heal the greater culture. Your own healing will resonate with others.

I saw a program in which a Bonobo chimp had been taught to follow spoken instructions. The trainer's head was covered so she couldn't give cues of her intentions to the chimp. She would say, "Open the bottle of soda and pour it into the glass. Put the glass into the refrigerator. Put the vacuum cleaner outside".

The chimp followed the instructions exactly. When I teach my students. I also give them instructions. I may say, "Relax your back, expand your sternum and bring the expansion through your arm to push me."

The student then proceeds to tighten his hip, lift his shoulders, tighten his back and do everything except what I asked. And I'm not even covering my head.

Sometimes I wish I were teaching that chimp – it would be easier. Human students have to be first taught to develop a balance between mind and Body-Mind before they can actually do anything.

Sometimes a student needs to break free from the teacher. He has followed the teacher and his teaching faithfully but now needs to make them his own. Yet there is a strong momentum to stay connected to the teacher – if nothing else than for the friendship that has developed.

The deeper the student has delved into the teachings, the more it has affected him, and the stronger the means the student must use to break free and establish his independence. This time in both the student and teacher's lives can be unpleasant, disruptive and, if not handled correctly (on the part of the teacher), detrimental to both.

The teacher has to let the student go yet make sure the student knows that he retains his respect and friendship for the student. Often the student abandons the teachings themselves for a while and gets caught up in the mundane pleasures of the world. He feels all his studies were a waste.

Or the student may feel he has gained skills far beyond that of his teacher and doesn't need the teacher anymore. This is all an attempt to regain independence and freedom – the same process a child goes through.

The Tower card of the Tarot, a burning castle tower that is falling apart, can represent this period. People jump from the tower to escape the flames. This is the most spiritual card in the deck for it shows this period of transformation of the student.

This is the apocalypse described in the Bible. It is like a butterfly emerging from a cocoon. The shell of the cocoon must be left behind. This shell is the blind following of the student. He must instead, incorporate the teachings into his own life.

The "second coming" is when the teachings merge into your life, when you become the teacher. Then the student can return to the teacher to begin higher-level training.

It is like with some computer programs. You load them into your computer and then you must turn the computer off and re-start it for the program to work.

In the New Testament, people try to trick Jesus into saying something against Rome. Should they pay taxes to Caesar? He explains that Caesar is depicted on the coins of those times so "Give unto Caesar that which is Caesar's and to God that which is God's."

It is important to distinguish outer power and inner power. In either case it is essential that one's power derives from oneself. If you look for others to give you power, they can easily take it away. The student has to let all the lessons learned settle into his being before it becomes his power. Lucky is the student who can go through this process without abandoning or delaying his training.

The Zookinesis "art of soaring" is one of its most powerful teachings. A student learns to merge his system of internal energy (chi) and even his consciousness with those of other animals. The effect is to radically transform the student to be able to "enter" the body of a client, if he is a healer, and examine that patient from the inside. In this way he can affect a much finer healing. I have worked with several of my students to be able to do this and they are always astounded by the improvements in their healing ability.

My wife, Jean used to teach classes in the "foam roller" which is used to relax and stretch the body. You lie on it along your back or across your back and roll from side to side. When you lie on the ground before using it, the ground seems hard. After a session the ground seems soft as if you are melting into it. The ground hasn't changed, of course. You have changed and therefore your relationship to the ground has changed. Now you can merge into the ground.

When you massage someone, her muscles seem tense. "Soaring" serves the same purpose as the foam roller in that it allows you to "melt" into those tense muscles energetically. It is like a push in Push Hands in that you allow the resistance of those muscles to the massage to move through you just as the Push Hands partner's force moves through you. Your attention continues moving into their muscles as you allow their resistance into you, just as you continue to push as the partner's force flows into you. The result is that the muscles will relax.

In an interpersonal encounter you allow the attention in your eyes to be Yin, as you do when practicing a Tai-chi form. Then you can feel any energetic tension in the other person and allow it through you and into your root. You release your Yin attention into them at the same time. Your receiving of their energy will connect you to them so that the release of your attention will move into them. This allows a very positive connection that relaxes the other person.

You are not harmed by their forces moving into you as long as you let them be grounded. It is only your resistance to those forces that harms you. Their pressure into you is like a masseur's finger pressure into your tense muscles. If you release those muscles you get healed.

I used to trade massages with a Shiatsu practitioner. He was very aggressive. His thumbs were going to go into me whether I relaxed or not. I quickly learned to relax. My resistance to his insistence was painful. When I let go, he was able to work on me very deeply and got rid of a lot of tension.

The art of soaring results in not getting disturbed by the way our world is, and yet being able to exert your own influence to improve it. The forces arrayed against you don't create anger or fear inside of you – just a smile, and a call to action.

The student of Zookinesis or other Taoist practices perceives a world filled with attention, flowing in dynamic activity. His own consciousness is completely connected to all others and it is easy to move the focal point of his attention anywhere along the "continuum of consciousness".

Heal Yourself and the World with Tai-chi

Zookinesis shares this type of awareness with many other ancient training systems around the world. The goal of these systems is to allow the student to experience this level of perception. In working with live animals, Zookinesis is similar to some South American Indian spiritual systems in which you "journey" with an animal. This means that you place your consciousness inside an animal and let it take your consciousness with it. While this may seem a bizarre and primitive mythological belief, it is everyday reality when you perceive on this level. We modern people may look down on this way of experiencing the world around us and pride ourselves in our isolation from nature. But that isolation has led to the deterioration of the body and mind (and natural habitats), and the lack of inner peace in our times.

In modern times we make a similar connection of consciousness to mechanical and electronic devices. How much of children's minds today are imprinted by the mechanics of the cell phone?

The idea that only one way of perceiving the world around us is "correct" is itself, I believe, a very primitive and shallow belief. It deprives us of the fullness of human experience and of the biological vitality that is our birthright as biological beings. It also blinds us to the very real dynamics of attention and the dynamics of internal energy. Our inability to perceive these dynamics makes it impossible to organize our lives to maintain the health of these energy systems. Our consciousness and chi are pulled, twisted, depleted and damaged every day without our knowing and then we wonder why we are tired at the end of the day.

Many teachers of the modern versions of ancient training are completely unaware of the original purpose of those trainings, to teach students to become aware of this level of perception. That level of perception has been lost for the most part and only the shell of the teaching remains.

Some of those teachers have privately admitted to me that they don't even understand what they are teaching but they do it to earn a living. I'm afraid that genuine teaching, in all of these systems, is in danger of dying out. The main reason for this is that these teachings have become a form of entertainment. Teachers have to become showmen and emphasize the hype and glitter in order to gain students.

117

Without advanced students to practice with, their own abilities, which originally may have been genuine, gradually fade away. In each generation, the students put in less and less effort to learn until the teachers have no real abilities or awareness.

The culture stops valuing this awareness, this connection to nature. Yet within each of us beats the heart of our original biological awareness, our original vitality, witnessing its own gradual death. The place this awareness lives within us is a place of despair. At every moment, it calls out to us like a prayer to God. But we don't answer because we don't understand what is going on. Isn't it hypocritical to pray to God when we don't answer the prayers of our own soul? Our culture denies the existence of our true nature and values us only as pieces of the great machine of the economy.

When we wonder if we have the time or the energy to get involved in a practice that brings us back to ourselves, our dying vitality ask, "Why do you even have to ask?"

We live in a rich world of life, filled with conscious energy. Yet when we look at the world, the only things we notice are the speeding cars and the exciting television screen. We have lost the ability to see conscious life itself.

We humans are designed to soar, in our own way, as the eagles above us. The choice we have as individuals and as a culture is to decide what it mean to be human. You can decide that for your own life.

A healer must determine the state of his patient's attention and heal that first. For most of us, attention is like a piece of meat discovered by a pack of hungry dogs. It is ripped apart and devoured by whatever distractions are around – sights and sounds, thoughts, emotions, advertisers, etc.

The art of healing is to first recognize this situation and to know that attention is who we are. We cannot just let it be ripped apart.

Attention can be weak or strong. It can be agile or stuck. It can be trapped or free. It can be evenly distributed in your senses, your thoughts, emotions, energy and body (your "elements"). It can also be more in some of those parts of you and less in others. In other words, it can be balanced or unbalanced.

Attention can be Yang (aggressive), Yin (passive) or balanced between those qualities. It can be fragile, solid, rubbery, flowing, rigid, etc.

You need to find a central spot within yourself on which you can "stand" and balance the elements of your being. We call this spot "the passive observer". The name itself should be enough to give you the feel of what it is.

From this state, you experience the physical world around you in balance with all the parts "inside" of you. You do not view the physical world as primary and your other parts as secondary. All parts are equal in importance. You live a balanced life.

You may ask, "If I need to balance all the parts of myself, who is this 'I' who is doing the balancing?" And therein lies the purpose of spiritual development – to discover the answer to that question. It is a spiritual type of "growing up."

When I was a toddler and was at my grandparents' house, my mother gave me milk with a bottle. She brought two rubber nipples with her for the bottle. One was all chewed up and the other new and too stiff. I was perplexed because I didn't want to drink from either one. My little mind just didn't know what to do.

Someone suggested that I drink from a glass. I tried it and drank from a glass ever since. I felt so grown up.

Balancing the elements is like this. At first your attention is ripped from one thing to the other. Once your attention is balanced, you have a whole new perspective. You have "grown up". You proceed in life as a whole, with all of your parts integrated. This is the meaning of the ancient saying, "Make the outside like the inside".

When practicing Push Hands, there are two people at first. Each tries to conquer the other. As you allow their force to flow within you and yours to move freely inside of them, there is now just one arena of action. Within that arena are many joints and muscles, many intentions and tensions, alignment and misalignment, balance and imbalance, energetic smiles and calls to action. The "outside" (your partner) has merged with your inside and revealed a world of interactions on the level of Body-Mind. It is the thinking mind that creates the inside and outside, the "push or be pushed".

You still push whenever you can but now there are two teams with many players interacting. The game allows your attention to "see" more and to be more intricate. It trains attention to merge with the body on a finer level so that the body is no longer "outside" of "you". Your partner's energetic system is no longer outside of you. You learn that the more you separate from your partner to conquer him the less effective you are in the game. By merging the two into one you can push him more easily.

The purpose of Push Hands of course is not to learn to push people over but to train the attention. It also teaches you that the "I" has as much to do with connecting as with separating and to keep those two principles in balance.

Push Hands also reveals your dead spots that the partner uses to push you. As force is applied to a dead spot you can see that it is not responding. You practice allowing his force to move through that spot so the deadness can be dissipated. This not only enlivens the dead spot but also connects it to his force, transmuting his force into energy that is just passing by, like the mist passing through a valley.

The same principle applies to momentum flowing through your body as you practice your forms. The only way you can release the momentum upward and outward (on the in-breath) and downward (on the out-breath) is if the momentum meets no resistance from any dead spots. The momentum becomes your Push Hands partner.

The Zookinesis animal exercises are designed to balance your attention within and surrounding your body. Your attention becomes a sphere, centered in the Tan-tien, that area just below the navel, inside the body. There is just as much attention to your back as to your front, to your left as to your right and to the top as to the bottom. As you practice the movements, attention remains balanced.

Your skill in each exercise is remembered by each muscle and joint. Attention is decentralized so that the attention of an elbow regulates that elbow and the attention of a foot regulates that foot.

Our government is divided into federal, state, county and town. In a similar way our attention is divided into each organ, muscle and cell, and each regulates its needs in harmony with the rest. This is the natural state of a living thing. In modern times we've got it right when it comes to governments, but not when it comes to our attention.

You may allow your attention to become distorted a little bit only to pull it back to its balanced position. You may "allow" distractions to pull attention but you do it for creativity's sake just as if you were to make believe you were falling off balance (as in drunken forms) only to regain your balance.

Creativity is the issue of balance, off balance, re-balance. To be creative you must have a strong sense of balance, whether physically, musically or in a painting, etc. That is the beauty of Push Hands. You try to deceive your partner into thinking you are off balance so he tries to push and then you throw him off balance instead. Push Hands is very creative.

Yet the balance of attention is but one of its qualities. Another is agility and focus. When we work with attention it can be too diffuse or too focused. The proper state is decentralized but not washed out. Each cell, organ, each bone and joint has a central focus of attention so that attention is spread out and focused at the same time. This creates a state of agility.

Most peoples' attention is drawn to whatever is the strongest sensation at the moment, be it a feeling, sight, smell, thought, etc. But in Zookinesis, we need to be aware of subtle experiences as well and not allow the strength of a sensation determine the amount of attention it receives. Otherwise we will be controlled by the loudest, brightest, fastest, etc.

When our attention is controlled by the extremes, we become extreme (in our personalities) and have no rest. We need quiet, meditative times and we need a meditative center even during active times.

Just as the baby knows to suck milk from its mother's breast in order to live, each part of us knows to suck attention from the surroundings to sustain the flow of attention through us. The parts of us (the elements) do not derive their life from the ego – the identity – but from the creative, intelligent energy of attention, which flows through the whole world.

Each part of us knows how to draw attention to it, just as we know how to take a breath of air. Sometimes people are so debilitated that their parts cannot draw natural attention very well and so they have an inordinate need to draw attention from other people, especially from those who have such energy in abundance. I have discussed the harmful consequences of this before.

In the Gospel of Thomas (#29) Jesus said that when a body becomes enlivened by attention, it is a wonder. But when attention becomes aware of itself because of its connection to a body, it is a wonder of wonders. In that same gospel (#50) Jesus explains we come from attention (the light) that "came into being of its own accord". The light becomes manifest through the image, for example our self-image, which draws attention to it.

In this perspective, attention is an energizing force that is drawn to emotions, thinking, the body, etc. and fuses them into what we are. It is the glue that makes the various experiences of life into the one being we think we are.

Thus, the movement of attention is towards our elements. From this point of view, spiritual development is to allow a counterbalancing movement back to the source of attention that is called, "God" or "The Father" in Christian philosophy and in Taoism is called, "Tao" – the emptiness from which all emerges.

The materialistic view of the world is that the body is all. Emotions, thinking, memories and all the other elements, are the result of chemical and electrical actions of the nerves. The body exists. Mind and emotions don't exist in and of themselves.

The non-materialistic view is that each element exists independently and it is the energy of attention that binds them together. When the body dies the other elements don't necessarily die with it. At death the body decomposes into different forms and shapes, but our emotions, thoughts etc. are constantly changing as well during our lives.

The body is not all. There is another "all" that includes the body and other elements as well. This is an ecological system in which the physical world is one element. The spirit world represents the all-inclusive world, one in which all the elements exist equally.

When your attention is evenly distributed among all the elements, your way of life changes because you see things in a different way. You see your connection to all life and your satisfaction in life comes from that.

One perspective doesn't oppose the other. You can hold both the materialistic and non-materialistic point of view as you would have both reading glasses and sunglasses to see through. You are seeing the same world but you use each pair of glass for a different purpose.

A teacher teaches these things. A teacher of Tai-chi, music or anything else, teaches the same thing. An instructor teaches different things. A Tai-chi instructor teaches Tai-chi; a music instructor teaches music. But a teacher uses his particular skill as the path he brings the student along in order to gain insight.

If you were to go to people teaching music, pluck a string and ask, "Tell me about the sound", you may get different responses. One person may say, "That's a middle C". Another may say, "That's a magic carpet that can carry your soul on a journey." The first is an instructor and the second a teacher. Teachers recognize each other because their paths lead to the same destination. They all come from that same magical land.

Such training systems help you understand the source of your power as a human being and how to channel that power in your life. The basis of this realization is the relationship between consciousness and the physical body. Imagine a glass of water sitting on bone-dry earth. Sitting on the earth is a little seed. This is the situation most of us are in.

In this situation it is obvious that if the seed ever were to grow into a plant, the water in the glass would have to be spilled so that the earth could absorb it. The desiccated earth is our body. The water is our attention (our consciousness). The seed is the aliveness and power inside of us.

The whole approach of Zookinesis training (or any Taoist training) is to understand that attention is not the eyes. It is energy just as gravity or electromagnetism is energy. Our bodies have evolved within the environment of these energies. Our bodies are even pressurized with about fifteen pounds per square inch of pressure, to counter the tremendous air pressure around us. In every way, our bodies have evolved as a response to the energies around us. In the same way, our minds have evolved in this environment. Consciousness (attention) is an energy in which the body has evolved.

We know that the water, in the example above, needs to be absorbed by the earth. The water sitting in a glass does not help the seed. The water must lend its very nature and substance to the earth to create life.

In the same way attention must be absorbed by the body so that every part of the body can become "moist". The attention "knows" how to be absorbed by the body. The body "knows" how to absorb the attention. To let the body absorb attention, you must let go of attention rather than holding it rigid. The rigidity of attention makes the body rigid. Rigidity separates attention from the body. That is why we practice to relax the body and to relax the attention – so that the two can merge.

When attention and the flesh merge, tremendous power and awareness floods a person. At first this may feel threatening. "How could poor little me have such power?" The tendency is to "objectify" the power, to call it God or a spirit channeling wisdom through you. We project our own power onto images we have learned just as we originally objectified attention itself by thinking of it as the eyes.

When the body absorbs attention, you realize your connection to the source of attention. You can perceive the energy of attention in the world around you. While the world you perceive is the same old world, it seems very different, very alive. Your body feels very alive and you feel yourself beginning to heal. You feel each cell like a baby bird desperately calling out to its mother for food. Each cell of the body wants to receive the energy of attention and calls loudly for it. You begin to "hear" those calls or rather you feel the body trying to absorb attention.

We naturally know how to pull attention through people. This is important to strengthen the attention of babies. In Zookinesis it is called "Threading Attention" as if through the eye of a needle. Everybody tries to get the baby to look at him and respond to him. This strengthens the baby's attention. The baby connects its attention to our own behavior patterns. We innately know how to do this. It feels good. But if you are trying to absorb other peoples' attention because you are internally disconnected, that doesn't do you or the other person any good.

When people objectify their attention to an unusual degree and are unusually disconnected, their attention will be concentrated directly in front of their faces. They will have a "crazed" look. Some of those people make very good salesmen because the customer is accosted and overwhelmed by the salesman's energy and they will buy anything to end the assault. This is really a form of violence.

Heal Yourself and the World with Tai-chi

I believe that violent people are very disconnected and their behavior results from a misdirected attempt to reconnect themselves. But since they objectify their feelings they will attempt to connect to other people, often in very inappropriate ways. They are desperate and don't know how to heal their disconnection. If someone displays a quality they know is missing inside of them, they may resent that the other person has what they don't have. The violent person has become lost from himself and doesn't know his way back.

When the attention is concentrated in the front of the face, its energy pulls the body forward as you practice Tai-chi. You tilt the body forward in forms and lean into the partner in Push Hands. The head may even start each movement of a form so that it pulls the rest of the body along.

Just as a movement should start from the center of the body and its relationship to your root, attention should also be centered and grounded in the same way. Then the thinking mind will receive continuous nourishment from the flow of attention of the whole body and the surroundings. That's when cleverness gives way to wisdom.

When attention merges with the body this also connects you to the same energy of attention that permeates the entire earth and all of its inhabitants. How do you use this connection to make your life more powerful? To explain this, remember that when the attention is rigid, this makes the body rigid. Patterns of the attention affect the body. On the other hand, behavior patterns in the body, such as patterns of tension, affect the attention. It is their separation that causes the rigidity. They are like two sets of patterns fighting against each other. Once they are connected, they are just moist earth – they are organic – and life can begin to grow.

If you maintain a positive image of what you need in life, that image will resonate in other people and in general, in the energy of attention around you. The ability to affect the larger energy of attention to help your life depends on how connected your attention is to your body.

This is the great benefit of the Zookinesis exercises. Without that connection, you just struggle. You can't beat the whole world into submission to accede to your demands. But you can connect with the energy of consciousness (attention) that permeates the world. Each act of self-healing will be magnified by that connection. When you try to heal others, your efforts will likewise be magnified by your own connection. Life becomes easier and a lot more effective.

Some people make the mistake of just trying to use what is called, "The Law of Attraction", that is, to send out those images of what you want, but without first connecting their attention to their bodies. This is utterly useless. It is only when the attention and body merge, when you stop objectifying attention, when you become fully connected to the larger energy of attention, that you can have any effect.

Some deserts only receive a few inches of water every ten years or so. But as soon as it rains and the ground becomes moist, a thick carpet of colorful flowers appear within days and the desert comes to life. It is like a miracle. The Zookinesis training is like this. Before this training, you are like a desert and then soon your life blooms with beautiful colors.

When practicing Tai-chi form (or any other activity in life), it is important to distinguish the two parts of "Mind" or what I call "attention". A Tai-chi saying is that, "Mind leads, body follows". This does NOT mean that your thoughts tell your body what to do.

This saying is a clue to the real relationship between attention and body. There are two aspects of attention when you are practicing. One is knowing the movements and mechanics behind the movements. The other aspect of attention is its ebb and flow, its expansion and relaxing. This aspect is like the ocean currents. The "knowing" aspect is like a scuba diver who wants to get from here to there and get things done. He still has to yield to the ocean currents, which are much stronger than him.

The flowing aspect of mind is not fixed at one spot, such as in the head. It does not give orders to the body. It flows, and the body responds because that is its nature. Attention simply flows here or there; it sinks or expands. It is Yin. It is the job of the other aspect of attention, Yang, to exert influence on the body so that the movements are specific. But Yang attention does not interfere or overcome Yin attention.

Another saying is that "The one begets the two, the two begets the three and the three begets the ten thousand things". At a beginner's stage of training, the Yin and Yang aspects of attention and the body are fused. Everything is tight. There is no relationship among these parts of us. In order to have a relationship, each member of the relationship must be free and independent yet coordinated with the other. If any one member is frozen, there is no relationship. If each is completely independent, with no connection, there is still no relationship.

Yet that fused, locked state is the condition of modern people. In order to develop relationship, you can practice the form in this way: First allow your attention to move towards where your body will go, and then allow the body to move there. It will be like laying down railroad tracks so the train can travel.

"The one" can be thought of as the locked state. "The two" can be thought of as releasing the grip of Yang attention on Yin attention so they are independent. The three is the relationship between them - your ability to function in mind and body so you can accomplish "the ten thousand things". It is the water moistening the earth.

Every day the Yin aspect of attention tries to "break its chains" and flow but we are so unused to that that we tighten up right away to stop it. If you know this, and look for it in your everyday life, you can attempt to extend the time that Yin attention is free by not reacting against it. Then you will have a chance for a real relationship between the parts of attention and the body.

When you first begin your Tai-chi practice you bring to it the state of attention you have. But that frozen state makes it hard to learn Tai-chi. So you either do Tai-chi stiffly, or you struggle to do it in a flowing way. The only way you can really do Tai-chi well is through a transformation of attention itself, allowing for the relationship described above. That new state of attention then stays with you all day. You bring it into your everyday interactions and you find that, not only does this new attention help you in your Tai-chi practice, but in your everyday life as well. And that is one of the great benefits of Tai-chi.

Consciousness sinks as well as expands. It sinks into every cell of the body. It expands to connect the body to the natural environment. When these two dynamics of consciousness are evenly balanced, images can resonate throughout your being. Allow your creative spirit to be in charge of these images. If the images are controlled by others you will be trapped into their agendas. Allow the beauty of nature and of human artists to sound the gong in your life to call you to your vision.

With this balance your consciousness is in a constant state of flow, inward and outward. This keeps the body healthy and young. As you breathe in, the balance of flow favors an outward expansion, connecting you to the world around you. As you breathe out, the balance of flow favors an inward sinking into the body. So there are pulses within the balance of consciousness.

The dynamics of these pulses are taught in Push Hands. As you push a pulse begins from the center of every part of your body outward into the partner. A pulse also begins from the feet into the partner. At the same time, his resistance is allowed to move into your body, into the feet and the ground. The evenness of these dynamics is the key to your power.

If you are aware of and creative with this process, you can compensate for the ways your partner tries to prevent you from pushing him. There is a tendency to "harden up" when your partner resists and abandon the creative process of keeping the flow of consciousness even. In this way, when consciousness meets resistance, it condenses and dies into the idea of winning. Push Hands is taught to convince you never to abandon being creative with the interaction of consciousness and your body. Don't let the "hardness" of the world around you, deaden you.

When we do Push Hands, this state of not being trapped is called, "neutrality". This is a state of not resisting and not even having an opinion about what the partner is doing. You just "unwind" your tendency to resist or attack, to attach or separate from the push. You seek neutrality even though your habits pull you away from it. Unwinding from your habits is what initiates your push – not your mind or emotions. This allows you to see the difference between your habits and you. You created the habits or were an unwilling victim of patterning, in which the patterns of the society become part of you. Push Hands is designed to convince you that you are not your patterns.

Emotions and thoughts are the condition and interactions of every part of the body bubbling up to your perception. When that bubble pops open it is hard to resist grabbing onto it. Grabbing is the reaction of your habits to the revelation of your internal state. What you experience is as much your behavior of grabbing as it is the bubble itself. The Tai-chi student learns to watch the bubbles pop but not grab, in order to learn about his internal condition.

Che Guevarra, a Latino revolutionary said, "The first duty of a revolutionary is to stay alive." While you may not agree with his politics, this statement can be understood on many levels. When you grab, your attention dies.

This is why Tai-chi-Chuan, as a martial art, does not emphasize techniques, which are condensations of principles. We teach creating each technique in the moment and appropriate for the moment. We teach you to flow with the "opponent" and control the relationship, and to keep your consciousness alive in the body.

One of the primary effects of Tai-chi and Zookinesis practice is to keep the body and mind young. The basic principle about how this can be accomplished is the balance of Yin/Yang energy in young vs. older people. When a baby is born, according to these principles, it is all Yang energy (expansive). As you get older you become more Yin (compressed). Your body shrinks and your mind becomes more rigid. The body and mind are most powerful when the compressive energy (Yin) exactly balances the expansive energy (Yang).

As an example, if a joint gets injured and the ligaments, tendons and muscles around that joint are damaged, the body starts healing. If you just sit around and don't move the joint a little, the repair job will be affected by the immobility of the joint. The repair will be compressive, which means that you will have little flexibility. This is why physical therapy is needed to stretch the muscles and connective tissues around the joint so you will maintain flexibility. When you stretch and use the joint, your body then knows how that joint is to be used and it repairs the joint with that "in mind".

I healed a torn knee this way, without surgery (torn ACL and medial meniscus). Tai-chi theory explains that the body does, in fact, have a mind (Body-Mind), which is aware of what needs to be done and intelligently adapts the repair to the needs of that part of the body.

Stretching and using the joint would be considered Yang (expansive), while giving the joint adequate rest would be Yin. You need a balance for a good repair. There is another factor for the repair job to come out right. Children, as noted above, are more Yang than adults (in general). They will run around without worrying about the possibility of injury. They love to move and use up energy, while adults like to sit and talk (in general).

If your body is repairing an injury and you are the type of person who doesn't do much and doesn't have much to look forward to doing after you get better, then your injury may not heal as well. We all know about athletes who get injured on a regular basis and have many surgeries. They want to get back into the game as soon as possible. This Yang attitude helps their recovery. They can't wait to get better. The Yang attitude of mind helps physical recovery. On the other hand, if they cut their recovery short and go back to the game too soon, they can re-injure themselves. They also need patience. So again, a balance of Yin and Yang attitude is essential.

A researcher had just come back from Ecuador where he met a man who kept marine iguanas (from the Galapagos Islands) as pets. They were housed in a fenced in area in his back yard. At that time, and even today I believe, zoos were not able to keep marine iguanas alive in captivity. So the researcher was sent to find out this man's secret. What did he feed the iguanas (which normally eat algae on rocks under the water)? He fed them scraps from his table along with scraps of vegetables he got free from the local market. "But this is not the natural food for marine iguanas!" complained the researcher. The man explained that he loved his iguanas and they loved him. They were very happy. So it didn't matter what they ate, as long as they were happy. Food going into a happy iguana, he explained, turns into a healthy iguana.

The point of all this is that an iguana or a person who looks forward to and is excited by each day is in a healthy state of being. A person who whines and worries about each day is in an unhealthy state of being. The excitement of life adds Yang energy, which can compensate for the tendency to become more and more Yin as you get older.

It is similar to relaxing to initiate a push in Push Hands. You are using relaxation to generate force. The principle here is turning Yin energy (relaxation) into Yang energy (the release of your energy upward and forward). When your partner pushes you, you take that Yang energy and sink it downward into your "root", compressing your legs. You have turned his Yang energy into your Yin energy (compressed legs which is potential energy). As you are grounding his Yang energy, you are sinking your own body into your root and then releasing his stored energy plus your own back into the partner.

And so Push Hands is the art of transforming Yin and Yang energy in a continuous flow of motion until one person gets the upper hand due to greater skill (not due to greater strength). You learn to balance and use Yin and Yang so the body stays relaxed yet powerful. This keeps both the body and mind young. In everyday life you can stop for a moment to assess your balance of Yin and Yang. Do you feel your body and mind compressing or expanding too much? Is your attention more in the grabbing mode or in the letting go mode? You will learn to develop a balance that will keep you healthier and younger.

You may say, "What if I don't have anything to look forward to?" This reminds me of an experience I had when in nursery school. I was always happy. A girl came over to me and asked, "Why are you so happy?" I couldn't figure out why I was happy, so from that time on, I wasn't happy anymore. My state of unhappiness led my mind to contemplate unhappy things so as to explain why I was now not happy. It took many years to remember that turn in the road that led me in the unhappy direction.

We used to do a ceremony at my Tai-chi school called, "The Forest Wine Ceremony". Each person took a turn to say something they were thankful for. Then all took a sip of wine, placed their glass on the floor and their hands on the floor on either side of the glass, and bowed. After a couple of hours, we were mentally grasping for things to be thankful for but always found something.

Chapter 3
The Inside and the Outside

"The inside and the outside – they are made of the same flesh". This is reportedly the cry a student of Chan (Zen) cried out when he reached enlightenment. It is an apt description of the basic principle a Tai-chi teacher tries to teach to his students to bring them to their first perceptual breakthrough.

Every discipline of personal development is based on the principle that, to change one's life, you need to change what is going on within yourself. What else can we do? We can't change the whole world around just to our liking

We learn how perfecting proper body mechanics allows us to perform physical tasks easily. Learning about the mechanics of our attention allows us to be effective in interpersonal relationships and in navigating our lives. As we discover the physical and mental behavior patterns that presently fill us, learn which ones are effective and which interfere with our power in life, we can reconstruct the very mechanisms we use to live our lives.

And then we discover that much of the way we perceive the world around us is really a reflection of the patterns of behavior within us. As we become more creative in gaining Tai-chi skills, the world itself seems to change and not be as threatening or as cold. The student discovers that much of what he took to be the cold reality of life was just the projection of a story he was telling himself, onto the world outside.

At this point he realizes that part of that story was his identity. To really gain power in life, to be able to drop the behavior patterns of battle and self-destruction, you have to allow that story about your identity to change. And then you become just a simple person.

In another Zen story, a Buddhist student brags to his Taoist friend that his Buddhist teacher can create miracles. "With a movement of his arm he can make an entire dinner appear in the middle of the forest. He can knock over a band of robbers with one breath. He can clear a valley of fog with one in-breath." The Taoist student was not impressed. "That's nothing compared to my teacher," he said. "What can your Taoist teacher do?" The Taoist student replied, "When my teacher is hungry, he eats. When he is tired, he sleeps."

To what degree do the stories we have been told, affect our perceptions and our behaviors? We trust that pieces of paper (money) have great value and then numbers in computer memory have great value and then learn, as we have lately, that there is nothing really backing up that value. These are stories we tell each other to help our lives run smoother. But we have all learned what happens when some of us no longer believe those stories. Perhaps we need to base our lives on stories that are not "built on shifting sands".

We must begin by understanding the stories that we have based our lives on. To what degree are health, loving relationships, and a feeling of connection to the earth important in our lives? And to what degree does the quest for money overshadow these values?

If you tell yourself a new story, a healthy one, that story may resonate with others and become their story. The power of life is to be the storyteller and not just the actor portraying someone else's story. Transform the inside to transform the outside. This is what every Tai-chi student must realize at deeper and deeper levels.

A beginning Tai-chi student just tries to "cover ground". He moves from here to there, lifting up from the floor, stepping and landing his leg back down on the floor. Then he is told the story of sinking into the ground and shifting his weight underneath the floor. His tailbone anchors beneath the floor to bring his weight from leg to leg. And so, the "story of shifting weight" is now about what happens beneath the floor rather than on top of the floor.

He begins to see that what happens above the floor – the movements of his body – is a result of what happens beneath the floor. All of his joints and muscles are connected to this "root" beneath the floor and so the body above converses with the root below to create the flow of movement.

His attention has stretched, encompassing more territory, even outside of his body. Yet he is acutely aware of how his body's mechanics in cooperation with gravity create the root, and how the dynamics of the root in turn, affect the body. He no longer moves "from here to there". His movements are now the result of that relationship.

His movements reveal the story he is telling. That story is not just about mechanics; it is a story about who he is – a living being in relationship to a larger living being and with the forces and cycles that connect the two.

When you visit another culture, you realize how differently other people see the world. We tend to feel that our "modern" world-view is the most correct because we are the smartest people who have ever lived on the earth. And yet, the fact that we are willingly destroying the life support system of the earth creates questions about how smart we really are. The way in which our life-style is destroying the life support system within our bodies also calls into question our dedication to survive even as individuals.

Tai-chi practice is a way of introducing into the modern world, the concept that each of us is an ecological environment, completely connected to the larger ecological environment. How we balance the internal ecology with the external ecology should be a large part of our "personal culture". If we can experience our bodies as living and conscious, rather than just a machine that carries our head around, we can begin to restore our health.

Our modern culture is based on the isolated individual, each of us fighting against all the others. To maintain this feeling of isolation we "condense", that is, we tighten ourselves physically and mentally, turning ourselves into a walled city. The world outside of that city can be raped and pillaged, can be turned to cement as long as the city itself is protected. It is an illusion. We feel that, as long as our lawns are green, the rest of the environment doesn't affect us.

According to Tai-chi principles, the destruction of the natural world and the destruction of our own physical health, arise out of the same mind-set. When we practice Push Hands, for example, there is a tendency to use physical strength to push the "opponent" over. It is common for someone, being pushed, to grab the arms of the pusher to avoid getting pushed and thereby be able to say that he didn't really get pushed.

Push Hands is a game of transformation. It is based on not using tension but fluidity. It is based on allowing the push of your partner to be absorbed by your body, the force distributed among all the muscles and joints, and then transformed to go back to the pusher. Your role is to transform the force that comes to you. In this way you learn the connection between your inner self and its connection to the forces around you.

In Native American tradition, the "vision quest", or in Australian aboriginal tradition, the "walkabout", is a chance for a young person to spend time alone in nature and find his "vision" in life. That vision helps him understand who he is and how he will transform the world around him – how he will heal.

Tai-chi practice is both the vision quest and the healing. It transforms you, revealing who you are, and it can transform those who see your practice. Many people say that they have seen someone do Tai-chi and one day they would like to learn it. To effect change in others, the Tai-chi student needs to do Tai-chi so well as to transform peoples' "one day" into "now". You know that you have achieved a certain level of proficiency by how quickly "one day" gets to "now".

When we are connected to our bodies, we are also connected to the entire physical world in the same way. The way the chi of the environment flows through each part of our bodies affects the state of attention of that part. In this way, our own individual consciousness dances with the flow of energy of the earth, keeping pace with its cycles. A Tai-chi form or Zookinesis exercise is that dance.

When we practice Tai-chi massage, we sense how the chi is flowing through the person we are massaging. We can detect blockages in that flow and correct them. We can also detect blockages within ourselves and correct them. In this way the flow of chi of the environment flows cleanly through us, connecting us to the client, helping their bodies to synchronize to the larger flow of energy.

Each part of the body becomes a window through which to see the whole pattern of chi of nature. When the whole body is enlivened in this way, it is as if we can see out of every pore of the body and perceive nature intricately.

When the student becomes connected to nature in this way, we say that he has come home. He now remembers his original state and great health returns to his body.

Those involved in the martial arts aspect can perceive what is going on inside the sparring partner and can respond to his move before the move even begins. The sparring thus becomes a contest of how clearly each partner can perceive the pattern of chi and attention of the other. It is also a contest of how connected each is to his own body so that every part of his body can instantly respond to the partner's moves. The sparring partners seem to be like two leaves swirling around each other in the wind. This healthy state then stays with you in your everyday life and brings joy to every moment of life.

The dance of the dragon and tiger is a common theme of Chinese art. The tiger represents external (Yang) power such as physical tension and large movements. When unbalanced, it is like the angry response to the actions of another person. While we may think of the power of a tiger as brute physical strength, a tiger in reality is very flexible and relaxed, even when fighting. I can attest to the fluidity and relaxation of wild cats due to my many years of experience importing and working with wild animals. The tiger is not completely external in its power. It balances and blends the external, physical force with internal fluidity and relaxation, which is Yin power.

The dragon represents Yin or internal power. Its very depiction in drawings is of a long, swirling, graceful body yet you can see that it has great power and blends some Yang force in its movements. The Yin within Yang of the tiger is the black spot within the white "fish" of Yang, and the dragon's Yang within Yin is the white spot within the black "fish" of Yin, in the Yin/Yang symbol.

In martial arts, fluidity allows you to explode your force from your root in the ground (the weight of the body sinking through the legs), up through the hips and out of your fist or your foot. Your force is explosive, penetrating the outer layer of the opponent (their skin, bones and external muscles) and explodes within their body cavity. Your power is Yin turning into Yang.

Think of the dragon hiding in his lair – a deep cave within a mountain. It is a vast, empty cave yet you can smell and feel the presence of a dragon within it. While the dragon is hidden in emptiness you dare not disturb it.

The tiger's home is the forest itself. He wanders about and when tired, just lays down and sleeps right there. The tiger's power is "in your face" while the dragon's power is hidden. Tiger style of fighting is very aggressive and overpowering. Dragon style is deceptive and evasive. You can't understand how you were hit, but you feel the effects.

Yet to be a whole, powerful person you need to blend the two kinds of power. The teachings of Tai-chi and Zookinesis use movement to train you to blend external and internal power, not only physically, but in relationships, in business and in your approach to life.

Using relationships as an example, the external power would be how you view the other person by using your senses. How to they look, how do they talk, how do they physically feel, etc.? Yet we all know that there is an invisible connection between people that we call "chemistry" and it is not only sexual. It is a connection among all people. Much of how we react to someone is a result of the feeling we get through this connection, an "internal" connection that is not obvious. It is the job of proper training to make this connection as obvious and clear as the other senses.

You will then discover a whole new world of dynamic activity of "chi" which is the energy connecting all living things. Once you understand this energy and how it relates to the "external senses" such as sight, life becomes a lot easier and more effective.

So the dance of the tiger and dragon is a constant dynamic blending of our external awareness of the world and the internal awareness that is missing in modern cultures. You may already realize that your personality is more Yin or more Yang. You may pay more attention to what is going on inside of you or more attention to external activity. You may be more passive or more aggressive.

Your power as a human being is at its maximum when the internal and external power is most balanced. A person who is mainly external wears himself out. A person who is mostly internal has a hard time organizing himself to actually get anything done.

In the drawings, the tiger and dragon's eyes are both wide open and you can feel the energy flowing between them. It is this magnified energy, flowing between Yin and Yang that we can tap to become powerful.

This is the dance that empowers life. Ancient art encoded great principles of ancient teachings even before there was written language. A teacher who is part of a direct lineage of training understands the principles behind the outer appearance of the training. Tai-chi forms, for example, are not just a question of memorizing a sequence of movements. Each movement is a deep reserve of layer upon layer of meaning. These exercises are the ancient libraries, but you have to know how to read them.

And so Tai-chi and Zookinesis exercises are like the dance of the tiger and dragon. They are right there in the open but their true significance and power lay hidden.

Connection is the first issue that comes up in Push Hands. It is not enough to just start by touching our arms to each other. Something else has to take place inside us. We have to release the boundary between us so that the entire interaction is us. Our attention now must be evenly distributed throughout that interaction to seek balance. Once we interrupt that wholeness with a mental attitude, we get pushed. If our attention can live inside the partner more fully than his own attention lives inside him, we are in complete control of the interaction.

During the yearly Tai-chi Farm "Chang, San-feng Festival" people practiced Push Hands with each other well into the night. I remember one guy there, a small guy with a little white woolen cap. We connected our arms to begin and I instantly realized that I had to pay full attention, while with other people I could be lackadaisical. His attention so infiltrated my body that mine had to completely infiltrate his or I would get pushed right over. We stayed in the same position for a long time, neither of us daring to move. After a while I realized he was resting his head on my shoulder. During our fifteen minutes or so of Push Hands we did move a couple of times and finally we both were exhausted. It was one of the best Push Hands experiences I have ever had. I still don't know who he was.

The great benefit of learning to "live within" your body, your partner's body and your surroundings is that it gives you alternative perspectives that allows you to respond in new ways. If the seat of your attention moves from your head to your whole body, this changes your feeling of who you are. If it moves from you to the center of the dynamic of an interaction, this changes your investment in that interaction. If it moves to the whole environment, it radically changes your sense of yourself to be a "cell" of the body of the life of the earth. You then have more of an investment in the health of the earth and you understand how your personal health affects the health of the earth. Your relationship to the world is not to hold it at a distance. The world' is an identity to become.

In Push Hands, such a change of your inner state changes the desire to win into "waiting for a bus", which is very fulfilling as you watch your partner struggle to use his strength to try to push you. You then look at the people and situations around you in this light. Are they "waiting for a bus" or struggling to win? Are they battling their way through life or connecting to it? Are they "hiding in their heads" or do they live in their entire body? The path to maintain your own health and fulfillment becomes clear.

When a teacher tells you to "just not be there" in order not to get pushed, he means that switch from winning to waiting for a bus, from condensing in order to feel powerful, to your energy being even to deprive your partner of power. When people tense up, lift their center of gravity and resist, it is to feel powerful, but it is not effective against a skilled Push Hands student. This student may provide force against his partner in one direction just to lure him to resist but then push from an entirely different direction. The lure of resisting is the bait to hook the "fish".

When you release momentum in the form, a viewer can sense that release. Since they don't understand the principles of release, their mind interprets what they see as your body moving further than it really does. When they try to duplicate what you have done, they move their bodies in excess. Rather than energy flowing out of the arms and the arms remaining relatively still, they move their arms around a lot. The mind interprets the eye's data but without actual experience.

Once you have that experience you see the performance of a form differently. If you live in your whole body you see things out of that window. In this case the mind can provide additional insight by understanding the principles behind the movement. But those mental principles are only useful when matched with the actual experience of the flow of energy. Living in the body and its connection to the earth is a very different world of experience.

The Inside and the Outside

A basic principle of Tai-chi is that "the inside and the outside reflect each other". Your internal state and the world around you are in a dynamic balance. If someone wants to argue with you and you stay calm, they will usually also calm down. This is because their understanding of how they are behaving has a lot to do with your reaction to them. They "see themselves through your eyes".

In Push Hands this is called, "mirroring". There is a tendency to copy your partner's internal state. If they are tense, you tense up as well. You mold your behavior to his. Once you are free from this addiction you can really do Push Hands in a creative way. This then affects your everyday life.

Some students are "tricky". You can feel the wheels of the mind turning to figure out their moves. If you respond to each trick with a counter-trick you are getting caught up in their mind-set. You can instead provide a harmless space for them to carry out their tricks. Every muscle of your body connects to their actions with very light pressure. When he exerts his pressure into your body, each of your muscles acts as a cushion, dampening his movements.

If you interpret his pressures by assuming his psychological intent then you are responding to a whole set of emotions and intentions, rather than to just a pattern of pressures. Responding to your impression of his psychological state is "mirroring".

While you don't do your form as you work at your job or go shopping, the effect of your practice brings fluidity and aliveness to your "inside" which carries on in everyday life. The result is that the "outside" seems just as fluid and alive. Before my students enter the studio for a Push Hands class, they often stop to look at the garden. When they leave, they look at the garden again to see how the "outside" has changed. In this way they know how the class has changed their "inside".

When I was a zoologist and first studying Tai-chi, the way I would practice Push Hands in class depended on which animals I worked with that day. I had to conform my "inside" with the behavior of that species so that it was comfortable. That pattern of behavior stayed with me when I went to class, so that each class was different depending on which animals left their energetic imprint on me. Fighting class was the same. Years later, I would have my own students spar according to which animal style we were working with at the time. Practicing the animal styles helped them have the same experience I had with the animals. When I still had a large collection of animals, I would bring them into class so the students could get a firsthand experience.

The practice of allowing the energy of an animal to penetrate and influence your own energy, I call "interpenetration", because your own energy also affects the animal. You can't learn anything from the animal unless you let him into you and he lets you into him. If your identity is in a vault, this can't happen. The same is true with people.

This is what my students saw in the garden as they left Push Hands class. They interpenetrated with the garden. They expressed it as the garden being more alive. This is because *they* were now more alive inside. Your experience of the physical world changes. The sensory data coming into the brain may have been the same but that data sets off a chain of reactions of the whole body, if the body is alive. That chain of reactions is part of the world we experience but we project it onto the sensory data. The outside data and the inside reactions form the only world we experience. Tai-chi training is really the mastery of that process.

When my wife Jean used to teach the "foam roller" classes, we learned that even our experience of the hardness of the world was partially a reflection of our own hard bodies. After the class, the floor was just as hard as before but our bodies were softer. When we moved off the roller and onto the floor, we were experiencing a new relationship. While the floor "refused" to change, our own internal change turned the floor into a soft mattress. We could use this experience in Push Hands to deal with partners who "refused" to give up their tension.

Our experience of the physical world is really about our relationship to it. If we come to it with a "hard" body (or personality), the world is hard. If we create a "relaxed" body (or personality), the world is relaxed. The personality is our lens through which we see the world. We may still face "hard" realities but they are more effectively dealt with if you are dynamic and can deal with change.

If your Push Hands is all about resistance and tensing up, you will be strengthening internal battles. The personality that develops, (even "the peaceful Taoist"), will reflect those battles. It will be artificial (your understanding of how that "peaceful Taoist" should act). Your personality will respond with a phony "niceness" that will create a warped maze inside of you.

Alternatively, Push Hands that emphasizes merging with the partner, develops a personality that reflects the dynamics of your connection to others. It is not a "character" in a play that you have to memorize.

When I was younger, I realized that I was duplicating music. As I heard music, I repeated it in my mind, so listening to music wasn't as enjoyable as it could be. I learned to let go of repeating what I was experiencing and just allow the music to affect me. When my mind let go of the music, it really became music. I allowed it to change me by trusting it and could appreciate the creativity of other people. I remember when my first Tai-chi teacher, Herb Ray, played a few licks of jazz on his guitar. This was new to me. It felt strange yet made sense in a new way. And that different sense then became part of me, even though I am not a musician. I had to allow the jazz to change me – to make room for something I didn't even understand on one level, but something inside of me understood it.

Jazz is dangerous in a way. It leads you into unknown paths. You can't "duplicate" it in your head because it is not predictable. It is dangerous to the process of your attention becoming mechanistic – of living your life as a predictable actor on a stage. If an actor is unpredictable (like Robin Williams was), then his fellow actors have to be more creative. In the same way, if each part of your body is conscious and creative, its fellow parts also have to up their game. This is what the practice of Tai-chi should be doing to you.

Everything I have described above is expressed in Chinese as "sung". On a simple level it means sinking into the root. If you sink into your root you are sinking into the earth. Since everything else is connected to the earth, you are "sinking into" everything else. To sink, you must let go of your "holding". You hold in order to judge and to feel strong. I held the music in my mind and had to learn to let it go so I could merge with it.

When you are a small child you see adults relating to each other way above your head. Then you grow up and you are in that "high" world. The last thing you want to do is be "down there" again. You have arrived at your final destination. Your attention, your energy and your body try to stay up there and are locked up there. Even our mythological imagery describes "down there" as bad and "up there", "a higher plane" as good.

The concept of sung is part of the concept of "aligning heaven and earth". On a simple level this means that your whole body, the parts higher up and the parts lower down, are all part of you and important. The flow of motion and energy should go through all your "parts". Not only that, but this flow should continue down into the earth and up towards the sky. This is essential for health. The release of energy upward and downward is as important as the circulation of energy within the body.

There is a saying that Taoists breathe in through their feet. This describes the process of clamshell breathing. The diaphragm pulls down, drawing breath into the bottom of the lungs, which presses into the legs. This compression results in a pulse of expansion up from the root, sequentially expanding the body (but the root remains anchored). Your lower ribs, then your upper ribs expand as the breath fills the rest of the lungs. It feels as though you are breathing in from the feet, adding to the feeling that the feet are the "gateway to consciousness".

I used to take students to a steep stream in upstate New York for camping. It was strewn with large boulders and smaller rocks. We would walk up and down the stream during the day. At night we took flashlights and ran down the stream full speed. We could only see where the light of our flashlight was aimed but we had to land on the rock so that our foot conformed to its angle. As we landed, we had to prepare to jump off to the next rock so that the pressure of the jump was perpendicular to the angle of the rock we were on, or the rock would slip out from under us.

This trained all our joints to respond to our feet instantly. (I wouldn't recommend this exercise for most people). Surprisingly we never fell – except for one student who found the only flat spot in the area. When he walked on that flat area he tripped and fell. His feet weren't used to walking on flat earth. You can't think when running a stream. The body consciousness takes over.

The moment the feet land on a rock, all the joints and muscles have to sink into the rock ("sung") so you are feeling its angle and how slippery or loose the rock may be. When you leap off of it, that leap has to start from the "root" you have created in the rock. You and the rock connect and interpenetrate so your response – your leap – is informed.

Healers have to "feel" inside the client with a gentle touch of the surface of the body or perhaps some gentle pressures. It is common in modern healing systems such as generic massages to keep your energy separate from the client so that you don't "absorb" any of their "bad energy". But this makes you very ineffective as a healer. If you first heal yourself and know how to keep your flow of energy clear, you can connect with the client to heal them more directly. The very experience of connection itself can heal by reminding the client's Body-Mind of the experience and of its own existence.

Remember the Gnostic myth about Sofia (meaning - seeking wisdom or human spirit) who was searching for God. On her way she gave birth to the demiurge (an ignorant, false god). Leaving the demiurge, she continued on her way. The demiurge, looking around and seeing no one else felt that he must be God. In a very simplified way, you can see this myth referring to each of us who has lost the connection to each other and the world. We "see" no one else around us even though we see many people, so we feel isolated and feel we are the only one that matters.

Our thinking mind concludes that it is the only part of us that is intelligent and so has to run everything. The source of its consciousness, the Body-Mind, is beyond its perception because the thinking mind only wants to look at itself. Its isolation determines the culture of the personality and that culture then tries to impose itself on the body and on the connection to the rest of the world.

Tai-chi massage dissolves that culture of isolation. Providing a deep feeling of connection to a client is a very spiritual way of healing. Physical and emotional healing emanates from that, even long after you do your specific healing.

When I was studying at Cornell, I felt like I was always on the outside of human society, looking in. There seemed to be a transparent wall between me and everyone else. I even went to Phillip Berrigan (an activist priest, brother of Daniel Berrigan), explaining my feelings. He said he didn't understand and just gave me a bible, which I still have.

Through my studies and practices of aboriginal cultures, including Taoism, I discovered the joy of connecting with other people. These studies gave me a language to describe my situation and the "mechanics" to heal. I feel that many people today are in the situation of isolation and that is what allows us to act coldly and cruelly to others. Traditional Push Hands has been the most powerful of those "mechanics" of healing for me.

Each season affects us internally, leading our bodies into a new path. It is nature's version of jazz. As we move into spring you might expect to become more energetic. Yet many people feel tired at the change of each season. The spring brings pollen and even if you are not allergic, your body fights against pollen's foreign protein and this requires a lot of energy. This points to one of the most basic principles in Chinese medicine. The body is like an ecological community, with each of its types of tissues like the many different species of plants and animals in an ecological community. As the spring changes the face of the landscape, so it changes the face of our internal landscape. In modern times we try to maintain a constant environment in our houses to overcome the changes in temperature, humidity, etc. outside. Yet, no matter how much we control our environment, our bodies and even our minds and emotions are at the mercy of environmental and seasonal changes.

This is why many cultures have festivals for each season, welcoming these changes and preparing us emotionally for the fact that we are entering a new phase of the year. We can do the same, for example, by spending a day in a park for no other reason than welcoming the spring, or spending a day planting seeds.

Land used to be part of the soul of each person. Now we move from place to place. Isn't your bank account more part of your soul than the land you live on? The bank account moves with you. "Moving" the Native Americans, "moving" the Jews during the Babylonian and Roman Diasporas and "moving" black people from Africa, detached them from a large part of their souls. The land was part of who they are. It was part of their emotions.

We may like to think that our bodies are machines that we own, but the Tai-chi perspective (and that of most ancient cultures) is that the body, mind, emotions and spirit are all interweaving living energies. The impression of us as a single identity is a reflection of the relationship among all those "elements". When that relationship becomes rigid (because we cling to a rigid identity), we cannot adapt to the changes in the seasons of the earth or the changes in the seasons of our lives. Rigidity leads to battling against the changes in the environment rather than adapting.

There is an old story about a Zen teacher walking with his student in the woods. They saw an old man fall into a rushing river and the student was about to run to save him. His teacher stopped him. The student asked, "Why are you stopping me from saving that man's life?" Soon they saw the old man emerge downriver unharmed. His teacher said, "That man is a Zen master. Where the river flows in, he flows in with it. Where it flows out, he comes out".

Take the time to notice and acknowledge changes in the seasons and the weather. Allow your "elements" to adapt and participate in those changes so that your internal environment becomes vibrant and alive.

The timing of the body's functions is a result of the variability of the environment. This type of timing is in competition with clock time. Another type of timing is the synchronicity of the behavior of a population of people as their individuality interacts and develops the pace of the community. When these natural paces are replaced, the body loses its timing, and the functions of the body are divorced from its own biology. This affects us emotionally creating an underlying battle. That can undermine our health because it reaches so far into our biochemical make-up.

Our emotional state normally helps our bodies synchronize the pace of its functions with the surroundings and vice versa. Emotions could be said to be the result of this synchronization or problems with that synchronization.

If the body is not allowed variability to maintain homeostasis (a dynamic steady state), it breaks down. That's why the pace of the form should not be interfered with. Clock time is not the arbiter of the pace of the form. Don't rush a move. Don't let your attention jump ahead.

If the body's internal conditions are in a balanced relationship with the environment then the emotions will reflect that balance. The condition of the environment will be an important part of your feeling of well-being.

The emotions shouldn't be like an investment portfolio where you invest in some emotions and are against others. Emotions shouldn't be the blood spent on the battlefield of the thinking mind. Release your

146

emotions to the natural world so your body will be mechanically coherent with natural forces. Otherwise your mind will stand apart and issue forth its opinions as to how you should feel. It will figure out how you're supposed to feel and impose that on the body.

Connecting your emotions to the world rather than to the mind does not interfere with your conscience as a human being. It allows emotions to feed you accurate information about the world around you and synchronizes your behavior with timeless values that create maximum harmony in a community, whether human or ecosystem.

The altar is a table with several objects representing our "elements". The objects are manipulated in ways that represent our inner work. Some people project their internal elements onto another person and use them as the altar. Their manipulation of the other person is a way of working out problems within themselves.

They do this because there are some parts of themselves they consider to be "bad" and some "good". They are afraid of accessing what is going on inside because that will call up "bad" feelings as well as the good. By associating with someone who is a reflection of their "bad" qualities and projecting their "good" qualities onto them they can work out their attempt to grow within the other person. They are duplicating their internal state onto the other person rather than onto a table altar.

If they are mistreated, they don't consider the other person to be a jerk because he is just part of this sacred process of using an altar, but of course, it is a misuse of that process.

Using another person as an altar never works out well for either person, unless both are doing it with awareness and great skill. If you could face your insides directly you wouldn't need an altar.

Dreams are also an altar. You project what is going on inside of you onto the dream images and they take on a very real appearance. The person you may project onto is like a dream. They are both being used as altars and both seem real. When you wake up you realize the dream was illusion. You remember who you really are.

When you face yourself, you wake up from your illusions and realize the beauty you thought you saw in the other person was really inside of yourself. Then you are prepared to find someone of equal beauty.

The Inside and the Outside

Doing things in a sacred way means understanding the relationship between the inner and outer – "As above, so below" as the pagans say. We understand that everything is connected and how we can affect an inner transformation by changing something on the outside or by representing it on the outside.

In Tai-chi we say, "large circle form, small circle form". The large circle means that you do the form with large movements, very externally, so that you can really see what you're doing. When you work out all the mechanics of the movements with the large circle form, you then try to bring those mechanics more internally.

The form is the altar. It serves to display all the imperfections of your attention and energy flow and of the connection between mind and body. Correcting the form transforms those imperfections inside of you.

This technique of displaying internal states externally to more easily work on them is termed "magick" in Western spiritual traditions. This allows you to understand how your internal work can transform the world around you. Practicing the form is a kind of magick. When using the form, you know what transformation you want to achieve and you play it out on that altar.

Attention is a part of who you are. You are your body, your thinking mind, your memory, your will (the drive to do things), your emotions and some would say your spirit. These are all parts of you. Certain of these parts may be too weak or too strong in relation to each other.

Attention is such a weak part of us that we don't even think of it as part of us. Internal energy is also part of us – a part few of us recognize.

Our future is becoming clear – faster pace of life, increasing emotional distance between people, less healthy food choices and increased stress. It's now more important than ever to understand how choosing the future of your personal life can be different than going along with the future destined for you by our society.

In 2013 an Australian farmer's crops were infected by pollen from a nearby genetically modified organism (gmo) farm. This farmer's organic status was revoked and he went bankrupt.

I watched an episode of "Dangerous Grounds". In this reality show a coffee grower visits dangerous areas to buy gourmet types of coffee beans. In one area of Brazil the farmers have to keep 24-hour guard around their villages to protect themselves against agribusiness. The farmers claim that thugs from agribusiness keep trying to sneak into their villages and shoot them to take away their land.

In many ways our food, and the earth in general, is a battleground of people who wish to live simple, healthy lives and those who want to rape the earth. We can certainly help to protect the earth by joining ecological groups but we also must protect the earth in another way.

Our bodies are part of the earth and part of the web of life. We can protect our bodies and our minds from a sort of rape by the violent patterns within our culture. We can make sure that destructive patterns, which may have invaded us (like the gmo pollen), are rooted out and discarded. The fears that make us distance ourselves from other people and groups can be recognized and the power of those fears over our behavior, dissolved.

This is what Tai-chi and Zookinesis practice does. They give us the tools to bring our original organic consciousness back. The teacher explains what has happened to us internally and guides you back to being human. The Tai-chi massage quickly melts away years of tension, fear, trauma and self-destructive patterns to free you to live a better and more enjoyable life.

Learning and practicing these exercises is just as important to protecting the earth as working politically. They teach you to control your own personal future so you can better contribute to a better future for everyone.

The body's systems are completely connected to each other, so that a change in one affects all the others. The conditions around us, affect the inside of us. A gloomy day will affect you emotionally, while a cold windy day may lead to illness. At least I have found this to be true for me.

So how can we change external conditions to affect the biological systems inside the body? This principle is called, "resonance". It is like the vibration of a tuning fork vibrating another tuning fork or shattering a wine glass. It is like the cadence of the waves in the ocean lining up just right to create a rogue or "killer" wave. Tai-chi and Zookinesis use patterns of movement and breathing to create cadences and qualities within the body that the body's systems gradually follow.

That is why sequential movement of the joints is so important. Each joint, in turn, duplicates the pattern of movement of the hips, which create the movement. This trains each joint (and the muscles

149

controlling it) to be able to duplicate patterns of movement. It is like the students in a gymnastics class who stand in line to each take their turn to perform an acrobatic technique. If the body were to move as one rigid unit, with no internal movement, those joints wouldn't learn anything.

The mandala of Hindu and Buddhist traditions and certainly any other great work of art can also heal us. When we see Thai dancing or a great Tai-chi form, we are moved deeply even though we don't practice these movements. But something inside of us is impressed. Native American dance and singing is, in some cases, specifically used for healing. Those artistic or dance patterns are felt by the body even if you are just sitting and watching.

In all these cases the healer is the person who is the master of the "gate" between the internal mechanisms of our bodies and minds and the "external" conditions of the world around us. He is the "gatekeeper", a name often found in mythology. Such a healer understands that most people are unaware of the intricate connection between what we call internal and external. In fact, to a large extent, the differentiation between internal and external is not even real when it comes to how we actually function in everyday life.

Such a healer, often called a Shaman, does not live in the world of here and there, you and me. He lives in the world of connection, because he understands that the principle of resonance, of how every aspect of the world around us that affects the world inside of us, is where the action is. He sees a world in which every part of life on this earth, affects every other part of life on this earth. It is his life's endeavor to learn how to use his particular skills (artist, cook, Tai-chi teacher, parent) to positively affect the people around him.

When I first began to write I heard that writing can heal. I thought this meant that you should write about how to stay healthy, such as eating right. But my earliest teachers explained that it is not so much in what you say as to how the reader's body, emotions and spirit follow, flow with and react to the way you write. If I claimed to be a Tai-chi practitioner, they explained, then the healing principles of Tai-chi should be embedded in the very manner in which my books were written. When I re-read ancient writing from several cultures, with my teachers' advice in mind, I found they indeed were written that way.

150

In writing my books, "Movements of Magic" and "Movements of Power" I first asked myself, "What journey am I taking the reader on? How does that journey heal?" The journey is to see the world around him as a Shaman would see it, that he is a fully alive being in a vibrant world of biological energy. His adventure would allow him to take a second look at his everyday life and relationships so that feeling fully alive and healthy, feeling fully connected to the people and other living things around him, were the central purpose of life. The books needed to stir the internal biological memories of those connections so they could no longer be sidetracked by the lust for material goods. They needed to show to what extent that lust for objects is just a suppressed longing for and replacement for, more deeply seated needs. And of course, the books needed to serve as a path to achieve that more shamanistic way of life.

In "The Doubting Snake" novel, I went a bit further. My goal was to represent the path of recapturing one's power and spirit in life as the journey up a jungle river. As you battle your way upriver, do you have to leave your dreams behind? Who controls your journey and even your very mind? Whose stories can you believe and which are meant to deceive you? Which paths will lead you to your own power?

In ancient societies, "rites of passage" were required to bring children through severe experiences to prepare them to become happy and productive members of society by giving them the skills they need to survive. In modern times, books have replaced these rites of passage.

Isn't this how all fiction is supposed to be written? By the choice of words, pace, attitude, imagery, character and action, the author can create a healing "pill", with a power only limited to his writing skill and with no detrimental side effects. The book can adapt itself to a wide variety of ailments because it works to strengthen a person on many levels and allow his own body, mind and spirit to do the healing.

Such a book is like the pole a plant climbs with its tendrils. Is the pole sturdy? Does it lead to sunshine or shade? Pay attention to the poles your tendrils attach to. It is like seeking a Tai-chi teacher. Spend time to make sure the teacher is competent. There are only certain qualities that make a pole useful to a plant. It might be a beautiful pole but if it is not sturdy and does not lead to the sun it is not useful to the plant.

151

The Inside and the Outside

Trusting the skill of the attention is one such pole. If your thinking mind orders the body around you don't have that pole. The uninterrupted flow of momentum is another pole leading to the sun. If the body is used to express your emotional state, you don't have that pole (unless you are in a play). It is the flow of momentum itself which is the state you are trying to achieve, rather than the feeling of winning, or of having tried your best, or being strong, or being weak, etc. Those poles lead to darkness because they trap your spirit. They are connected to outside forces that determine the criterion for those attitudes.

The sun is up in the sky. It is in the plants that turn its energy into food and wood. It is in the weather that is affected by its warmth. The pole we are seeking leads the tendrils of our energy umbilical, to nature - not to attitudes. That nature may be within our own bodies, the world around us or within other people. When you surround yourself with nature, when you seek the natural spirit within others, you are using the poles that lead to a better life. Then just let nature take care of the rest.

Remember that if you are not kind and forgiving to other people, you probably treat yourself the same way. We have learned to mistrust other people, and usually for good reason. It takes a great effort to trust again without being taken advantage of.

When sparring, we do not hide our heads but trust that our skills will allow us to duck. As soon as we have ducked, we are right back in. We know the partner will try to hit us again but we keep a positive attitude towards our own skills and the partner's skills. If we were to just hide, we would not learn. Learning sometimes requires getting hit.

Chapter 4
Mythology – Being the Creator

In an internal martial arts system, the smaller your movement, the more powerful it is. The goal is to send your energy into the other person. If you can do that without using up that force in your own movements or in tensing up your body, you can send almost all of your force out. In external martial arts systems, the body tenses up to provide solidity. There can be no small subtle movements within the body and so the body has to use large movements.

In an internal system such as Tai-chi-Chuan and Phantom Kung-fu (the system I developed), each muscle is under your control and is kept relaxed. You can move several muscles and joints just a tiny bit each to result in the strike so that the overall movement of the whole body is very little.

Power comes out in a spiral pattern from the ground up through each joint. This spiral pattern magnifies the force. At the moment of impact, the body tenses just enough to prevent the arm from collapsing and to allow the force to flow through the arm. The internal martial artist is aware enough not to tense up even the slightest bit more than is necessary.

It is the degree of his or her awareness, to be able to make such subtle adjustments in just a fraction of a second that results in power. If the martial arts student can make his concentration fine enough to make these tiny adjustments, he can be powerful. And so there is a general saying that the smaller you can make your attention (the higher resolution), the more powerful you are.

153

As an example, if you think that a punch is the thrusting of the arm forward or turning the whole body to thrust the arm forward, then you are only aware of the arm as a whole or only the movement of the whole body. If you think of a strike as a quarter turn of the spine and a slight upward quarter turn of the hip, your movement will be much faster, more connected to the body and to the ground and more powerful. As far as your attention is concerned, you will be striking from the ground up and from the inside of the body out, which is the proper mechanics for sparring. External stylists generally keep their attention on the outside of the body, keeping their bodies rigid. Most styles of course, are a combination of internal and external.

When you can bring your attention to a point you become very powerful. When you can work with many of these points at once then you can really start to learn. Internal stylists also learn to bring their attention into the joints and muscles of the sparring partner so that he feels completely connected to the partner. In this way he can feel what the partner is going to do before he actually does it.

The martial arts practices have their greatest benefit in everyday life. If you can take this training into dealing with other people, with business strategies, with goals in life and with your health then your life can become powerful.

A few examples will explain. It is very easy to get caught up in the emotional patterns of other people. This is because most people cannot bring their attention into the subtle changes of feeling inside their bodies. If your attention were everywhere inside of your body and at the same time was inside of the other person, you could tell how the other person's emotional patterns were affecting you. You could see the mechanism of how your own feelings and reactions change due to the other person. You could then take control of that mechanism so that you do not copy their emotional patterns or even react blindly against those patterns. You can remain centered and examine how you can be most effective.

In the martial arts, each partner tries to control the behavior of the other, confusing them or freezing their attention. In everyday life, many peoples' emotional and mental patterns are so chaotic that they constantly damage the people around them. It is important to be so aware that you are immune to that damage.

On the other hand, your own behavior patterns from the past, may have taken control of your present behavior. When you react to a situation it may not be in the most effective way or even the least bit logical. If your attention is so pinpointed that you can feel how your own patterns are affecting you, then you can get beyond them. They only have control if you can't see them, if you feel you *are* them.

That is the most powerful effect of developing the fineness of attention. We have come to believe that our identity is the patterns of behavior and reactions that have programmed us. Most people have really lost the awareness of themselves. When you reach your original creative, connected self, there is great calm and joy. But most people are trying to follow the "breadcrumbs" home, meandering through the thick forest in search of themselves.

The finer your attention, the more you can see the mechanisms that control your behavior, the more you can see what is not you and the quicker you can discover the source of your creativity, of what makes you a unique individual.

At that point you can see that while we are all unique individuals, we are also completely connected to each other and to nature. At that point we can finally love fully and let go of anger and resentment that may have been seething inside us for many years – about issues long since gone.

I have also found that in business, you are able to get to the heart of any negotiation and better understand the issues that bother the other person. Very often in business negotiations the other person is not saying exactly what they want. They're trying to be coy. It is important to sort out the issues so that you immediately understand where the other person stands. This makes for more effective negotiations for both sides. If your attention is strong and can follow many lines of discussion at the same time, it is easier to sort out the underlying themes and get to the heart of the issue.

You may feel that it is unpleasant to deal with people who are completely controlled by their programming. Remember that the programming is not who they are; it has captured who they are. You can address yourself to their creative consciousness, which has been imprisoned. The creative consciousness is eternal; it is the same being that is at your own core. By addressing yourself to this being, you help it to remember who it is.

Recognizing the imprisoned being within the bars of programmed behavior can be difficult. You gain this skill by releasing your own imprisoned self from its programming. Then you can understand the dilemma of the other person.

Training the attention in this way is not easy. The Tai-chi forms and Push Hands exercises and the Zookinesis exercises teach the attention to seep into every crevice of the body, to follow many patterns of energy and movement at the same time and to constantly re-adjust the body and mind to changing external conditions. It is said that it takes five years of Push Hands training to be able to consider yourself to be a beginner. This is because the condition of our attention in modern times is so poor. Our attention can be considered to be in critical condition. To bring it back to even normal health takes a lot of work. But the result of that work is not only a more effective life but also great health and joy.

There are two reactions to practicing Push Hands among my students. The first is laughter. They laugh at how dead their attention is compared to how healthy they know it can become. The second is shaking their heads and saying that they can't believe how stupid their bodies are. They know what they should be doing, but the attention is so rigid and so programmed with useless patterns that it is a great struggle to free the attention. It is as if their attention is entangled in a net.

And yet, as a teacher, I see that they are making great progress in every lesson. It is just such a long journey back home!

You can go through the rest of your life knowing and being yourself and enjoying the thrill of living or trying to follow the breadcrumbs through the forest as if you are lost.

When I first began studying Tai-chi and Zookinesis, the 1960's were in full bloom. The theme of the times was to try something new. The music, Eastern traditions such as Tai-chi, exploring space, love-ins and all of the social movements gave us hope that a new world was about to emerge. There was energy among people, a concept that we could and should create our world rather than just complain about it.

It may seem that we are now back to the "grind" and the 1960's is long dead. Yet there were hundreds of thousands of people who sought to retain that creative energy throughout their lives. I have met many people who, each in their own way, try to bring that peaceful, creative energy into their communities.

Yet there is no getting away from the fact that the theme of our times is survival. It feels as though time, money, energy and creativity are in short supply. Is it possible for people who lived through those times to bring back the excitement, the vigor of their youth?

According to Zookinesis principles, creativity is the most important factor in reviving our health and energy. When you are involved in the creative process, something you are excited about, energy somehow comes to you and you forget about all the aches and pains.

Your creative energy and your renewed enthusiasm for life then charges up people around you and ignites their creative energy. It doesn't matter if you paint, write, do Tai-chi, play music, etc. Bringing a creative activity into your life, if even for a short amount of time per week, is very healing for yourself and your community.

Have you stopped doing something creative because you "didn't have time" or because you think you lost your skill? Some people have the idea that if they cannot be great at what they do, they shouldn't do it. They give control over their lives to other peoples' opinions (or the expectation of their opinions). We pay people to make music for us. We pay people to play sports for us. Music and sports were invented for everyone. They are not just a contest but part of the enjoyment of life.

I believe that as a society, we have forgotten this. We have, to a large extent, become parts of a machine and not part of the energy of creativity that is the basis of life itself. We are, like the Star Trek "Borg", part human and part machine. The question is, are we becoming more machine or more human. This is a choice each of us can make. We can make it every day and every week.

Dobby Gillis, in the "Dobby Gillis Show" (many years ago) once said, "Have a dream and live it." Are you living your dream or have you forgotten what it even was? I have found that just by remembering your dreams, you can bring new energy into your life.

Why not spend just a half hour a week doing something you would never have considered, something from your dreams long past, something positive and creative?

You may be wondering, "If your ability to be changed gives you power, then who are you? Is there nothing that is constant?" There is a "you" that is constant and that is the relationship of consciousness to the body and that connection to the environment. That is a living, constantly active relationship, just as an ecological environment is a constant yet has many species within it and many dynamics of energy. Nature is a creative interaction of seeking balance and evolving. So creativity is the constant. In its attempt to connect to others, this "you" creates a personality that is constant, so that others can identify you. It is like a bird feeder with a place for the bird to stand and eat. If there were no such stand, the bird would have to keep flying in place as it ate and we don't want the birds in our yard to be so inconvenienced.

The identities we create make it easier for others to relate to us. If we take this created personality too seriously, it may damage us. We may focus on sustaining that personality rather than on our health and the beauty of our relationships.

It took me a long time to learn to let go when someone poked fun at me. I knew they were joking but it was, after all, an attack on that sacred personality, which was I. Through my training, I found out it wasn't "I" – it was a created identity. If that personality made me feel pain, when the other person had good intentions and was just having fun, then I had too much investment in the personality and not enough in the enjoyable connection to my friend. The personality was no longer an artistic creation but had become an object, a thing – me. I realized that in order for the personality to have power (to improve my health and happiness), it had to continue to be the artistic creation of the relationship of consciousness, body and its connection to the environment.

There is a Taoist saying, "The one begets the two, the two begets the three and the three begets the ten thousand things." At first there is the personality. When we realize the personality is a creation of the interplay of consciousness and body, there are two. When that interplay then interacts with the world "outside", there are three. At this point, when you move from identifying with the created personality to "being" the whole interplay of your experience of life, you *are* all of life and you become kind. As the Buddhists say, you see consciousness within each living being and you know it is the same consciousness that is in yourself.

The Body-Mind is the artist and perceiving its internal conditions bubbling up to your whole person consciousness shows you how you are being created moment to moment. If your thinking mind plays nicely with the Body-Mind, then it can have some say about your life.

The thinking mind can learn to be creative. It learns to balance the two styles of interacting with the world. You can live your life mythologically, in which case stories are the basis of your life or scientifically, in which case hard facts are that basis or usually, a combination of both. If we are to be truly free people or even just effective at Push Hands, then we must understand this dynamic. We must know who is the artist and what are the inks. Consciousness develops in an individual by what it creates. You could say that the personality is created in the image of the creator. Its tentative nature (art is always being revised) should not make the personality feel vulnerable. If your thinking mind grabs onto the personality and fights to keep it from changing, it is like two people in a dream fighting each other. Each person is created by the sleeper. The fight just represents an imbalance in the sleeper, maybe emotional distress over the events of the day before.

If you can see your need to fight against other people, even while awake, as that imbalance, your focus can be on righting the imbalance rather than on gaining more strength to defeat other people. This is the idea behind traditional Push Hands. Your tendency to "fight" the partner indicates your imbalance. If your response to a push is to always seek balance, you neutralize the fight and remain centered.

I tell my students that when it comes to your movements in Tai-chi, you are capable of anything, even though you may not feel competent now. Trust that the Body-Mind is a great artist. It can even heal itself. It knows what is wrong and can make it right. It can do that in your physical body and in your life. Let that consciousness play the melody and the thinking-mind play the back-beat. They are both needed – each just has to know its place in the overall piece of music.

Attention and the physical body are living things. The fashioned creature is art (not to denigrate art). When the artist returns to her work, creativity is stimulated. Your work in Tai-chi is to let go of destroying yourself. Remember the creator – that is you. Keep fashioning the creature – it could use more work.

When you are pushed, it is not the fashioned creature that is pushed – it is the body. The former sees the push as a threat to its existence. The latter experiences a push as an opportunity to be creative – it is just force given to you to use. Your partner would prefer to push your fashioned creature and its struggle for survival, not your body and its creative consciousness. The body is just as happy being here as there. The fashioned creature doesn't want to be where the partner is pushing it, wherever that might be.

The key to Push Hands is to be just as happy there, as here as long as you keep your stability. Some people feel they need to be powerful in order to be happy. You learn that you need to be happy in order to be powerful. This doesn't mean that you just get pushed around. As mentioned before, as one side gets turned by the partner, your other side moves towards her, pushing her, so that she really pushes herself. You are happy to allow her to push herself.

But here is the problem. Who gets the credit? You have let go of "rule" by the fashioned creature and so your Push Hands doesn't come from its need to gain credit. The Body-Mind doesn't know anything about credits – it just wants to have fun. Your life is no longer a dictatorship in which the dictator claims credit for everything. When your body and consciousness are working naturally and therefore effectively, then nature itself gets the credit for inventing you. In other words, you learn to be thankful.

You are thankful that the same process of millions of individual plants and animals in an ecosystem living in harmony, also takes place inside of you. How many human cells, beneficial bacteria and even beneficial viruses live in your ecosystem? Somehow, they all know what to do and they are usually pretty good at it. What interferes with that harmony? It is the "poor art" of the fashioned creature and its dictatorial, aggressive nature, vying for control of your life to increase its power that weakens the body's ecosystem. Of course, there are other factors but the basic battle created by your personality, its artificiality disconnecting it from nature and its struggle to subdue its creator, is the major factor.

The Gnostic Christians felt that God was like a "bridal chamber" or space within which creation takes place. The Christ represented formative consciousness – our individual human lives and thinking ability that creates the patterns of our lives. The Holy Spirit represented creativity that allows for change so you don't get too "fixed" in your ways. The Christ and the Holy Spirit were like the groom and bride in the bridal chamber creating your life. They accepted creativity as the center of one's life rather than blind obedience.

As you practice form, each part of your body may want to do it differently than before. From your normal vantage point – your feeling of who you are – you just watch the dynamics of energy, created by each part of the body, "painting" the form in a new way each time. And yet the form still has to conform to the Tai-chi principles and the movements have to be correct. The body consciousness knows how to be creative within those principles, as an artist knows how to be creative with the same colors of paints and the same brushes she always uses.

If you do not allow your body consciousness to paint a new picture each time, you are not doing Tai-chi. You are like one of those people hired to duplicate dozens of the same painting to sell cheaply. If you don't breathe fully in and fully out, and fully release, the body just duplicates. Your form is being "fixed" into place with no input from the body consciousness. When I look at someone's form, I want to see the dynamics and qualities of the release. If there is no release, I feel the student is just saying, "I did this move and now I will do the next move. There! I did the form."

So your identity is no longer a set of habits that must be defended but is now a fluid and dynamic relationship between your consciousness and body. You can easily discard a habit because it is not you. In fact, most habits are a burden you have been carrying around. When you let them go, you feel lighter. Rather than living to acquire money and power you live to become lighter and freer. If you can make a few bucks in the process, so much the better.

The consciousness of our culture becomes more disconnected with every technological advance. When I was young, people in my neighborhood sat in wooden folding chairs in front of their houses in the evening. They were just watching the sunset and "kibitzing". When I moved to my present location in the 1970's, people were always out, taking care of their gardens. They walked a mile to get the newspaper every day. When I asked them why they didn't go to a more nearby store to get the paper they just looked at me as if I were crazy. Nowadays people aren't outside so much. They hire gardening companies to keep their lawns green (using herbicides). The idea of walking, even to a nearby store is beyond their comprehension.

A local comedian told of the time his children wanted him to buy a 3-D television. He said, "Just go outside. Everything is in 3-D." It's great to be able to get information immediately wherever you are, to send emails, etc. But there are some changes that are changing our basic nature as human beings, making us forget what we are and what we are part of.

Creativity is unknown. Who knows what it will come up with next? It is your true self. Your true self is unknown. So to trust in yourself is to trust in the unknown. While the origins of creativity are unknown, the processes may be known. It is like a vast sea. We can't see what is underneath but we can go fishing. The type of bait we use will determine the fish we will catch.

Our bait will be a pattern. It can be a pattern of behavior, music, movement, thought or anything. The important thing is the nature of the pattern itself. This pattern will coax out the creativity – the true self. If you wish to coax out an animal you can do the form. Animals will sit and watch you.

Creativity is like a curious animal. It can be coaxed out with bait but you cannot look at it directly or it will disappear. You can move with your pattern and allow creativity to dance with you but not grab it as a partner and lead. If you lead, it will be from your habits and your programming and the creativity will cease to exist. Be coy and make believe you hardly notice it.

One day you will discover what this creature is really attracted to – and that is your will. When you discover that you may turn against it and chase it away. But the creature is like a skinny cat you have given milk; it just won't go away. So you have to develop a relationship with it, not getting annoyed that it is always trying to "drink your will" to get stronger.

When you can look directly at it and it won't disappear, then you are at a stage where you are willing to share your will. The same is true in any relationship. It can't always be just about you. Your creativity creature and your thinking mind (home of your habits) are now both drinking the milk. As you are working on your notes, the creature may have other ideas and lay across them to get petted. Yielding your will to develop a relationship is the basis of Push Hands.

Since this creature is really your own self there comes a time when your mind wonders, "If the creature is myself then what is it that is opposing the creature and which is developing a relationship with it?" It is the original self-control you were taught as a child which has gotten out of balance and it thinks of the original creative being as the enemy – as that which gets into trouble. A second person – the "good" person was substituted for the natural person rather than the original person developing a creative relationship with the norms of our society. You can know the rules and still be able to play within them. You don't need a second person – a fashioned creature – from which that "nasty" creativity has been removed.

Having a creative relationship with our societal norms keeps you human and keeps you "good". If you are just a pawn of the society, the fashioned creature can be the culture's spokesperson even when the culture itself turns "bad" because your identity is tied to the current norms, not the underlying principles of being human. These principles are indelibly printed into our creative self because that self is connected to millennia of human evolution.

The patterns of Tai-chi and Zookinesis coax out those underlying principles so you will have to deal with them. The resulting balance of wills within you allows you to develop healthy relationships with other people.

The quality you admire in another person can be a pattern that attracts creativity. The energy of that quality can strengthen you. Don't become dependent on it or it will weaken you. Let that quality grow in you. Remember that everyone is a combination of many patterns, some positive and some negative. Learn to distinguish which specific quality you want to strengthen inside of yourself so you don't adapt the wrong patterns. Be selective.

When practicing the form, you yield your will to the intelligence of the body yet your mind keeps track of the sequence of movements. You are balancing creativity – the body's intelligence, with norms – the mind's intelligence. The resulting relationship creates an internal community that is coherent, vibrant and joyful and is able to engage in life with joy. You are now the gatekeeper between the internal and external community. Neither community battles the other. The gate is open and energy flows through both ways. Each side enriches the other. The inside and outside reflect each other.

The "norms" in sparring are the mechanics. You are trained to move, to transmit power and to neutralize power, based on real-life physics and physiology. Yet within the seriousness of sparring there is playfulness. This allows sparring to be joyful. There are many styles of sparring based on animal movements. Imagining yourself as those animals calls forth their behaviors from your creativity, which energizes the body. You are uniting imagination (of the animals), creativity and "hard nuts and bolts" physics and physiology to produce a result that does not involve the thinking mind. That mind's role was in your training but now you have to let it go. If the mind still tried to be the puppeteer of the fashioned creature you would be counteracting your own power.

The Body-Mind is that creativity connected to the body without the interjection of the thinking mind. As Body-Mind encounters the culture's training and learns to channel and limit its behavior appropriately, it is introduced to the story of that culture. This story explains who we are, where we came from and what is expected of us. Yet our biology has its own story of who we are, where we came from and what is expected of us.

We are biological organisms, cells of the earth. We came from a lineage of animals dating back to the simplest single-celled animals. We are expected to enhance the health of the larger organism – the earth. In a larger sense your creative spirit is the whole of the universe entering your individual life at each moment.

Each culture has another, different explanation. How the two stories harmonize determines the health and joy of its members. This book is, to a large extent, an attempt to do just that.

The dragon as mythological creature probably originated with the monitor lizards of Asia, Africa and Australia, which grow to 14 feet long (depending on the species). Discoveries of dinosaur remains may have added to the myth.

The monitor lizard emerges early in the morning to sit on a rock, tree branch or any area exposed to the sun. Even a small hole through the forest canopy will do. As the sun warms up its body the lizard stirs and begins to search for food.

As a pet they are unequalled - friendly, intelligent and playful and yet they don't need constant stimulation and attention. A monitor can rest for long periods of time as long as its belly is full.

The dragon is a symbol of our inner power and knowledge. Its transformation from sleeping to stirring to activity describes the development of the student. The sun, which warms up the dragon to activity, is the creative intelligence. Such mythological symbols are useful to study. They provide an easy way to understand the principles of Taoist practices such as Zookinesis and Tai-chi. These are the metaphors or symbols I use to teach. This section is an example of how to use these terms, which represent internal experiences.

Try the exercises that are suggested. The purpose of this section is to show you how something which at first seems meaningless, can become very meaningful if you actually experience what the myth describes. Much of this dragon set of myths describes breathing techniques which are designed to allow you to see inside of yourself.

A lizard that has not been warmed up is easy to capture. They just don't have the oomph to get away. A student who is not yet aware of his dragon nature is easy for the world to capture and the slave of peer pressure.

While the lizard is cold it lays flat, pressed close to the rock to create as much body surface area as possible. This helps it to absorb the sun's rays. Luckily it is usually camouflaged and hard to see. When it is active it is easier to see but almost impossible to catch.

The dragon within us is also very hard to find. We must warm it up first and look for something that stirs. The Zookinesis exercises warm up the dragon and indeed a series of exercises go by the name of "Laughing Dragon". I do these exercises before any other chi-gung.

They work in several ways. In one sense they take advantage of the fact that our structure and behavior reflect to some degree our entire evolutionary history. Nature doesn't create brand new species all at once but builds on what she already has through small changes. Evolution is a bumpy road, sometimes jumping forward quickly (in geological terms) and other times lumbering slowly. But all changes are built on what came before.

So there is a history inside of us, a record of what came before. We can tap into that and experience feelings and behaviors related to previous stages in our evolutionary history. This helps us to appreciate where we came from and where we are now. It is similar to remembering your life, how you grew and developed to get to where you are now. That helps you appreciate yourself and all you've learned. At each stage of life, you related to the world around you differently based on your limited understanding and skills at that time.

When we feel the energy pattern of other species, by working with them or doing animal forms, we learn to appreciate their perspectives and how they relate to the world. "Laughing Dragon" Zookinesis exercises help you peel the perspectives of your own evolutionary history and feel some of the skills and inner knowledge developed at various stages.

This is important because it connects all those stages together and makes you a more whole organism. If we were to wake up one day with amnesia, we would want desperately to know who we are, what skills we have and what are our opinions and ideas. Yet we have amnesia in a biological sense and don't know who we are organically. The "Laughing Dragon" series stirs these memories so that you notice them and remember who you are.

Now you have access to a treasure chest of skills and perspectives. It is a wealth beyond imagining, certainly worth more than a chest full of gold and jewels. It is the treasure of bringing your body back to life. Some people are interested in past life memory. This is past species memory!

If the body is deadened, its experiences of life are dead. Our language and culture are based on that deadness. A description of the dynamics of breath and energy, as experienced from an aboriginal peoples' point of view can seem like fiction or poetry even though it is a straightforward description. There need not be a competition of which view is right or wrong, just what is right for each of us. We can even hold both points of view, understanding their origin and effects.

There is an element of trust in reading descriptions of life experiences that originate from other cultures. The goal is to be able to experience in this way yourself, not to replace your usual way of "being in the world" but to realize that there are other ways. In this way your experience of the world around you is expanded.

When I do massage, I understand the role of breathing. Breathing pulls life energy into your body. It is not just a question of the exchange of oxygen and carbon dioxide. Breathing is the device by which you can channel life energy through you.

There is a momentum to the breath - an inertia. You can "grab" some life energy from anywhere around you and pull it into yourself. Or you can pull it from one part of the body into another. When the breath is used in an active way like this, it is the "dragon breath". In

Yoga it is called Kundalini training. It is likened to the uncoiling of a snake through the spine.

You can also draw energy out of the body and let it "settle" on something else, let's say a plant or a rock. After the dragon breath has settled and seeped into the plant (breathing out), you then breathe in again. This draws back your own energy that has mixed with the plant's. You then relax and breathe in a normal slow manner as the resultant breath settles back into you and you "taste" the plant's energy. This is why, in some cultures (e.g. South American Indians), healers say they can sense which plants to use for healing.

Don't just take my word for it; try this, but try it as if you mean it. I have described the process of "choosing to believe" in *Movements of Magic*. Practice the breathing exercises with full belief and trust. The result is not vague. It is a natural thing for people to do. It is as natural as exchanging carbon dioxide for oxygen.

This process is used during massage. The patient's energy is constantly being monitored through your breath to assess the effects of your work.

But the breath can itself be used to actually do the massage. The experience of breath and internal energy form a composite experience. On an advanced level the breath/energy "goes into" a muscle for example and manipulates its energy to relax the muscle. In this case you are considering the other person's muscle to be part of your own body and working on it as you would within yourself. You are manipulating the qualities of that energy, how Yin or Yang, how viscous or watery, how hot or cool, etc. The energy has many qualities just as does physical matter.

It is through affecting the qualities of energy that you do your healing. I have been surprised by the energy qualities of some people. They are startlingly obvious and easy to feel. Allow your fingers to lightly stroke someone's skin. Try that on several different people as you do one of the breathing exercises. Notice any differences among the people.

The breathing really illuminates these differences. When you experience how your own energy has been affected by the other person, breathe in, allowing that new energy to fill your body (assuming you feel good about that energy).

Your breath can be used like a fly fisherman casting and retrieving his line, as you send out your breath, let it touch and then whip it back into yourself. You might let the breath settle onto something on your out-breath and then let it continue to settle while taking a couple of normal breaths, then draw it back with another dragon breath. What is really settling onto something is your chi and your attention which is so connected to the pace of the breath that is feels that the breath itself is settling onto things.

What makes a breath a dragon breath is that it is used to manipulate energy. That life energy is the dragon. It is interesting that in the Middle Ages European mythology, slaying dragons was considered to be a good thing.

When you live in a natural area, breathing in to smell becomes important. Each time you breathe in, you assess the smells and get a picture of what's out there. The nose is a very useful part of the body. It not only breathes in oxygen, but also provides a very detailed picture of what creatures are in the forest, where there are sources of water, which plants are in bloom, which person or animal walked by a pathway, etc. In a city or suburb, you don't appreciate the nose as much.

Smells can be intoxicating and stimulating. They can greatly influence behavior. So here is another world that has atrophied for most of us - the world of smell. Would you be embarrassed to smell your date? It is a very natural thing to do yet it seems uncivilized and rude. If your date and you feel comfortable smelling each other then I say you are meant for each other!

For some reason our breathing process has taken a real hit from civilization. Most of us breathe in a very shallow way, in the upper chest. It is healthier to take full, deep, slow breaths.

The lungs and the skin are closely related (as is the lining of the digestive tract). Simply by breathing properly, using the breathing exercises mentioned in this book and smelling your mate you can greatly improve your health, especially of the skin, lungs and digestive tract. Proper breathing can also improve your blood pressure by calming you down.

It also serves as a central focus for your practice of Zookinesis, Tai-chi or Yoga. As you practice your exercises, notice if your breath is deep, slow and relaxed at all times. If there is a particular position that interferes with the breath, examine that position.

Notice the breath as you go through your daily activities. Are there any movements or emotional responses that tighten the breath or bring it up into the chest? Use breathing as a biofeedback for proper movement and to understand your emotional behavior.

Once you find some interference with breathing ask yourself what you can let go of to allow the breath to be more relaxed and lower in the abdomen. Can you let go of some tension or even the behavior of fear? What internal programming causes you to tighten up your breathing due to outside circumstances or inner thoughts?

You will gradually find there is a relationship between your breathing and your behavior. The reality of this relationship controls the flow and movement of chi.

As you practice your exercises you may feel as if something is surging through your blood vessels like water rushing along a river after the dam breaks. This is known as dragon blood and is the rush of biological memories that have been released, pushed along by a surge of energy. They are the memories of feeling your own body and its internal communications system of chi. This energy is released whenever there is a connection on the continuum of consciousness within you. It is a version of soaring with an animal but in this case the cells and organs of your body are connecting to each other.

When the surge occurs, it is important to be very quiet within yourself and not get excited. Be the passive observer watching a scene. This will enhance the connection, allowing it to be more permanent. You may even taste something strange, as there are chemical changes in the body. This may be termed, "tasting the dragon's blood." When you taste the dragon's blood, the dragon itself is not far behind.

Some Zookinesis exercises are to find the dragon. They teach you to develop your inner senses and allow your attention to travel through the internal channels of chi. Another important skill is to spread your attention out like a fine even mist, using Yin attention, so that you can become aware of anything stirring.

The best time to find the stirring dragon is just after the rush of dragon blood (the stimulation of chi), which clears out a lot of debris. If you are calm, the energy will calm down and settle, making the inner scene easier to see. It is like the little sandpiper birds scurrying around the sand after the wave goes back, trying to find sand worms.

In this case you simply stay still, feel how the energy is settling and notice where the energy is absorbed. You will feel certain spots within your body absorbing the settling energy and stirring it around. Those spots indicate parts of the body which are most connected to the flow of chi.

You will find that the dragon's blood flows through these spots most easily. The result of all this training is that the entire body should become permeable to the flow of energy. Every spot should be interconnected.

More Zookinesis exercises allow you to "release the dragon". We do not capture it as I would capture a monitor lizard and bring it home as a pet. Your dragon has already been captured and your job is to discover the nature of the trap and eliminate it. Traps are built on many levels. As babies we learn the ideas of the culture that contain within it, many traps. The anxieties and fears we suffer that create tension, are another form of trap. Lack of self-confidence, atrophy of body parts due to lack of use, atrophy of the dynamics of attention due to lack of use are all traps.

I saw a Facebook post recently in which a rat brought a pencil over to a rat trap. It triggered the trap and got the cheese. Even a rat knows how to avoid getting trapped.

We must "see" the traps as well as seeing the dragon. I will describe techniques to open your body to the flow of energy. Even though these descriptions may not mean much to you now, you can try them as best as you can and trust that they will lead you to new experiences of healing.

When you find the spots within you that can absorb and use energy you will notice other spots that cannot. Pay attention to the differences between the two types of spots. Breathe into both and see what happens. This means that you breathe into that part of the lungs closest to that spot and relax the muscles around that spot. If a deadened spot should stir, then relax and stop using the breathing technique. Allow it to settle and then stir it again with the breathing. It is not good to stir it too much at first.

You may feel a tiny surge of "blood" from the deadened spot that has been stirred. This may be termed the "baby dragon's blood". It will grow up as long as you continue your practice.

"Baby" is a good term, for one of the traps is getting psychologically stuck at an early stage of life. In certain ways you may have grown and matured yet in other ways not. Your body, on an energy level, is affected by this uneven growth and this affects the ability of chi to flow through those parts and connect them together.

It is as if only certain muscles were developed. The undeveloped muscles may hinder your activities. Anger and self-righteousness can be felt in those undeveloped spots. You may notice that when you are angry in life those spots will feel bad. It is as if emotions like whining live in those spots and hold you down to an earlier phase of your development.

A very effective technique in releasing the traps is to take nearby open spots and connect them with your attention and breath. Build a highway between them with your breath by breathing into the parts of your lungs closest to these spots. Someone else can help you by pressing their fingers on or near those spots so you can focus your attention. Keep the lungs between the two open spots evenly inflated, including the dead spot and that spot may open. Keep all the muscle between those two spots relaxed. Of course, this is all easier said than done. Practicing this breathing technique will improve your skill in all chi-gung exercises.

The most important technique is simply to observe the dead spot and bring your attention as close as possible, keeping it steady. Breathe slowly and steadily. This brings energy to that spot in a non-threatening way.

You may become aware of the psychological or emotional make-up of the trap, or you may not. The trap may just break up and go away. Don't try to follow it and figure it out or it may trap you again. Just say a quick goodbye. The dragon, to express its power not to get caught in traps, will smack the trap with its tail to give it an extra push, as if to say, "I don't even care what you are made of, just go."

If you do realize the trap's emotional make-up, that's fine. Just don't indulge in it. See it and smack it. Then go back to concentrating on the spot to clean out any remaining 'pieces" of the trap. It is also important to spend at least five minutes in quiet meditation after doing these exercises and to do another five to ten minutes of mild stretching (emphasis on "mild").

Traps are made of assumptions and fears. Sometimes you assume that you should be afraid or that you should be sad. Try to find any spots in your body that are caught by the trap of assumptions and fears. Sometimes, laughing at them can act as a smack.

Releasing your dragon from the traps releases a lot of energy. Let the energy go where it may. Remain quiet and calm as the energies swirl around you. As you practice the Zookinesis exercises, allow the released energy to flow with the momentum of movement. You are linking this internal energy with physical momentum using your kinesthetic sense (sense of motion). Many of these exercises involve drawing momentum up from the legs, letting it flow through the body and out into the environment. Your internal energy will piggy back the momentum. As the combined energy flows up, you breathe in strongly. When it reaches the skin, your breathing becomes a bit less forceful and at the same time you release that energy out of the skin. We call it "igniting the dragon breath" as if it were a blowtorch forcefully shooting out of the skin.

This feeling of ignited and expansive energy can be accomplished by relaxing the back at the same pace as you breathe in. This causes the top rear of the head to lift, which then stretches the spine. Make sure to breathe in equally to the front, back, top and bottom of the lungs (using clamshell breathing). As your attention reaches the skin all around the body, and your breathing in begins to slow, relax the entire skull and face (even as you are lifting the top rear of the head). The relaxing of the skull and face, lifting of the top rear of the head, relaxing the back muscles and the breathing in slowing down – all take place at the same time and at the same pace. This is the procedure for igniting the dragon breath. It will feel as if the breath is igniting and shooting out of the skin. This may result in one or two seconds of physical shivering.

Remember that the actual breath slows a bit at the moment the dragon's breath ignites. When the dragon's breath has shot out completely, you breathe out, making sure to take at least one regular breath before using the dragon's breath again. This is for safety purposes so you don't wear yourself out. Normally you would wait at least 30 seconds between dragon breaths.

This exercise is used for several reasons. The first is to help connect all the opened spots together so the whole body may be open. The second is to exercise and strengthen the will, as you would strengthen steel by repeated heating and cooling, to make a sword. The third is to maintain a connection between your creative spirit and the physical world. As long as you can send out the dragon's breath with these exercises, you know the connections are open.

Another purpose is to let go of excess Yang in the body so it may relax. This is especially useful when you are stressed. Still another purpose is in "freezing" the attention of a Push Hands or fighting partner.

It is a very useful practice. When it is perfected you are energetically connected to the environment and the exercises take on a whole new dimension. Every cell of the body is a channel for the dragon breath and has the ability to connect intimately to other forms of life. You become vibrant yet calm like the forms of Tai-chi. You fully experience the vibrancy of life. It is best to practice with a teacher or at least have access to a teacher to ask questions as you practice these exercises.

Now the dragon is warmed up. Its head is raised high and it looks up at the sun with thanks. The dragon wanders around the countryside, king or queen of its territory.

These are exercises of wisdom. They let you "be still and know that you are alive". They teach you to connect your inner sanctum to that of other people. This is the place to which you may have retreated as a result of your fear. Now it is a place of meeting, where all the life energies around you meet within you and there, share their knowledge and unique perspectives with you. It is like the marketplace of life, bustling with friendly chatter yet calm and quiet in its feeling of safe, comfortable friendliness. You are providing a safe center in which life may proliferate and flourish. From this center, life flows outward again, enriching you and all life.

Your Yin, calm center allows life to become vibrant and the Yang movement of energy outward allows that vibrancy to fertilize all levels of life. The "lair" or home is one's personal space. It is the ability to be still in the midst of a storm. When people are frantic around you, it is the ability not to get caught up in the insanity. When someone demands an immediate answer from you, it is the ability to take your time and think for a while. It is the ability to create space just as you create activity. Space within you allows others to enter you. Within space, life energy lives.

It is the expectation in the eyes of an animal when it first sees you. The balance of emptiness and outgoing energy is a vital issue in Zookinesis. You can practice that balance with animal staring (a Zookinesis practice). If you are balanced, a monitor lizard will stare at you for quite a while.

An exercise to help achieve this is similar to the Tai-chi form movement, "strike ears with fist". Use "clamshell breathing" as you allow your body to be moved by the breath. Breathe in from the bottom of the lungs to the top and also breathe out from the bottom of the lungs to the top. This will create a wave-like motion of the body so that you roll up on the in-breath and you roll down on the out-breath. As you breathe in the shoulder joint rotates forward, then the elbow bends, and then the wrist rotates forward until your open hands are at head height just in front of you. The breathing in and resultant wave of motion of the body creates the rotation of the arms. At the end of the in-breath you use the "dragon breath".

As you breathe out, the arms continue their rotation, but this time rolling back to the body until the hands move in towards the Tan-tien, the tips of the fingers pointing to the Tan-tien and about one inch apart (fingertips lightly touching the belly). Your body relaxes slightly forward. Then let the arms move to your sides and bring the body back to a vertically aligned position as you take another breath in and out.

When we talk about opening spots in your body that are blocked, we are really talking about opening the energetic connections between the parts of your body. It also means allowing energy from your surroundings to flow through your body. Your consciousness is now more influenced by those connections than it is by maintaining blockages to the flow of energy. With your chi-gung practice you are clearing a path between the inside and the outside, or more poetically, "the dragon ascends to heaven," or the "union of heaven and earth".

This living energy network becomes as solid to you as the physical world. As your physical and emotional tensions, which cause you to tighten, ease, you feel lighter – even weightless. As you work with this weightlessness you realize that perceptions and experiences in and of themselves do not a world make. Creativity or how we organize these experiences is important too. The physical world and the spirit world are ways in which we organize our experiences.

"Dragon ascending to heaven" is the ability to perceive and experience with lightness and creativity. It is the ability to bring joy into your responsibilities and not resent them. The mythology of your life makes it simpler. Rather than battling your way through life and getting worn down, the story of your life is the path you clear between the inside and outside. It is like running a Bread and Breakfast in which new visitors rent rooms every week. You get to meet interesting people and hear their stories as you provide a base from which they can explore your neighborhood. Allow yourself to become a Bread and Breakfast for others – a space where strangers become friends.

Tai-chi is often called an investment in loss. You invest time in your Tai-chi practice to lose the tight hold on the particular world you created. In this way you don't need to desperately cling to the product of your own creation. You can identify with yourself as creator.

The dragon is the creative power inside of you that is part of the creative force of all life. Release the dragon and let it find its way home. Release your inner power and remember who you really are.

The dragon's lair is a very important concept in Zookinesis. It is the emptiness filled with potential. Imagine a big dark cave filled with unusual smells and mists - but no physical dragon. It is completely empty.

Yet you know the power of a dragon lives there. As you approach, your body trembles with anticipation. You know nothing physical is there yet you wonder what kind of emptiness houses the spirit of a dragon. You can consider it to be Tao, the mysterious emptiness of Taoism. It is the place of wisdom, of knowing how the universe works and fits together and yet, there is nothing to know. It is the center between contradictions.

The dragon's lair is the home of your power animals. This phrase refers to the creative yearnings of your individual spirit – the seeds of your growth as a human being. They need stillness as the seeds of a plant need earth, water and the sun. Each works its way through your life in an attempt to blossom, finally showing its innate beauty. They stabilize your life with purpose and energy. If the thinking mind tends the garden of these seeds, your life will be powerful. If it replaces your creativity, allowing the seeds to die, your life will be weakened.

In the Chinese system, the "element" of Metal represents animal spirits and Body-Mind. It is the ability of all levels of life to communicate. It is sometimes thought of as the balance of Body-Mind and thinking mind. Earth is the physical world as revealed by our senses. It is the physical body. Water is the ability to be flexible, to change and merge. It is our emotions. Wood is life, the alignment of heaven and earth. It is the cycles of nature and our evolution as a person. Fire is our energy, our will, and our determination. It is the joy that comes from dragon fire igniting dragon breath and filling the body with warmth. There are many correspondences to each element, including parts of the body, seasons, time of day, internal organs, senses, colors etc.

Each culture based on this method has a slightly different set of elements (usually - earth, air, fire and water) and different correspondences with each. The attempt is to create balance in our lives and have a language to discuss how you may be out of balance. And what is it that is being balanced? The answer to that is really - attention. If we neglect any part of ourselves, that part will atrophy. If we stop paying attention to our health, we will become unhealthy. If we don't pay attention to our electric bill, the electricity will be turned off.

Some of us may be too intellectual or too emotional, not aggressive enough or too aggressive. In ancient European tradition the body is earth, the intellectual aspect is air; the emotional is water and aggressiveness (will) is fire. This is certainly an oversimplification. The elemental system is the basis for Chinese medicine, and diagnosis of ailments are made on the basis of the elements.

The importance of this system lies in understanding what controls our lives and how to regain control. As an example, one of the first parts of my training, as a child, was to try to figure out why my mind created a particular sequence of thoughts. Why do we think the way we do? Certainly, the immediate situation we are faced with plays a role, as does all our past experiences and education. Then we say there is something else - our individuality or you could say, our creativity. We think of our opinions, our way of expressing ourselves, and our storehouse of ideas as the most important part of our identity.

Yet how much of the sequence of our thoughts comes from this creativity and how much from what our culture - advertisers, religions and political parties - instill in us? I'm sure each of us is amazed at the thought patterns of some people we meet. We know people who simply parrot what they've heard.

To what degree are our thoughts based on what we think we should think, depending on what groups we feel we belong to? Are our thoughts merely a reflection of our identity? And what makes us decide which groups we belong to? We like to feel that the thinking comes first. We think things out; come to intelligent conclusions and then it may be apparent that we are more "liberal" or "conservative". But from what I've seen of people, the identity often comes first and the thinking follows.

To the degree that this is so, our minds are a handle for those groups to control us and remove any hint of our individuality and creativity. The sequence of our thoughts is not a reflection of who we are but the categories we belong to.

According to the elements, there is a problem with metal (or Air). We need to balance this element with more water (fluidity, change) so it doesn't get stuck in patterns. Dry wood can be broken easily and so can a person who is so concerned with his identity that he gives his mind over to those from whom he wants approval. They can make him do things he doesn't want to do.

The dragon's lair is the place where all the elements are balanced. It is still, yet ready to explode with potential. Notice the way a monitor or another lizard acts, as it is about to grab its prey. A chameleon is a good example. It is camouflaged as its background and flattened vertically, like a leaf. Its toes, two fused on one side, three on the other side of the foot, firmly grasp the branch.

Its gaze on an insect is unwavering. Its eyes bulge out in anticipation as it waits for the slightest movement of its prey. One eye may rotate around in its socket to watch out for danger but the other remains fixed. Its mouth is open and its tongue is ready to shoot out.

It may stay in that position for a few minutes, every part of its body and mind focused on its task. But you would never see it in the forest, even if it were right in front of you.

All of a sudden - zap! - and it's all over except for the munching. The lizard was still but focused. Its whole spirit was ready to act yet not fidgety. It could have remained still for an hour if need be.

The dragon's lair is like this. It is an empty space within you. Yet it is ready to go. It is ready to rally all the spirit animals to run down the court and drop the ball in the hoop. The spirit animals work like a basketball team, each member an individual yet their activities are completely coordinated. They are so integrated in their movement that they act as one being - us. Yet no one would ever know that all that potential lurks inside us because the stillness makes that person almost unnoticeable.

His invisibility is his power. This power can be likened to humbleness. This person does not seek status, but focuses his eyes on his own development as a person. The prey he seeks is his own deficiencies. He focuses on them like the chameleon, and waits patiently for his spirit to learn its lessons. His version of zapping the prey is to laugh out loud at those deficiencies – laughing at himself as if he were watching a foolish character in a movie. By being kind to himself in this way, by forgiving himself his foolishness, he learns to be kind to others and to forgive them.

All the spirit animals stand in the lair ready to move out. The dragon's lair is the home of all the spirit animals. We all have a spirit animal already but it usually doesn't live in the dragon's lair. It is the thinking mind.

The average person's thinking mind does not like the emptiness of the lair. It wants to be in the midst of constant activity. Its footing is uncertain and it seeks stability in the form of fixed patterns of thought. It trades the vitality of the dragon's lair for rigidity. It searches about for absolute truths, which are fixed symbols of its identity. The mind hobbles about like an awkward vulture walking on the ground, searching for dead spirit animals to rip apart. Yet the thinking mind can certainly live in the dragon's lair and many do. Connected to BM and working as a team with the other spirit animals, the thinking mind becomes creative and joyful.

The Tai-chi exercise of Push Hands has a way of teaching you that your spirit animal may presently be living outside of the lair. An example is the technique of creating a "false floor" in the body of your Push Hands partner.

When someone pushes you, they are really pressing their legs into the ground and using that pressure to expand their arms forward, creating the push. What seems like pushing with the arms really depends on pressing down with the lower part of the body. If you push with your arms alone you will be disconnected from the hips and legs.

You can purposefully disconnect your partner from the lower half of his body. All you need to do is place a little pressure on his upper body, on the side of the ribs for example. Your partner will mistake this pressure for the "floor" and use your pressure as a base from which to push.

The mind in many people lives in just such a "false floor". It lives on the floor created by the pressure of our culture on our lives. The emphasis on making money, for example can take your attention away from the importance of human interaction. You start to look at situations, people and places as opportunities to make money rather than as opportunities for inner fulfillment. You may start using principles of accounting when dealing with human interaction.

Such a person would "use" people. To use them, he must manipulate them. To manipulate them, he must concentrate on their weaknesses, not to strengthen them, but to take advantage of them. He seeks and welcomes weakness in others. He contributes to the destruction of the human spirit. Yet, from his point of view, he is just looking out for himself. There is an attitude in business today that you can either be a predator or prey, so you might as well be a predator. To manipulate you, he must focus your attention away from the fact that he is destroying your spirit. Praise is the easiest way to do this. The desire to please this person, so he will praise you, becomes a false floor. You no longer act to "please" your spirit – to strengthen it – but to please this other person, even if it destroys your spirit.

It seems strange that simply by applying a little bit of pressure in the Push Hands exercise, your partner will disconnect from his legs and forget that he needs to stand firmly on the ground and push from the ground. He uses your pressure as a new floor. And all it takes is one pound or less of pressure. It is as if you chopped off the bottom half of his body.

This is because your partner's mind moves to the highest point where he feels pressure and works from there. A large part of the Push Hands dynamics is to get your partner's attention as high as possible so he has trouble connecting to the ground. If his attention is completely connected to his thinking mind, it will be easy to do. If his attention is distributed among several spirit animals, they will dance around your little pressure and laugh at it. Eventually the mind itself will become more alive and learn to participate with the other power animals.

When you rely on only one spirit animal (thinking) and it doesn't live in the dragon's lair, you are in sad shape. You wander without a home. The thinking mind jumps around on little twigs of ideas, hoping they don't snap from its weight.

The dragon's lair is your true home. Its stillness (Yin) is part of your identity and is the solid floor on which you can rest your haunches. Its readiness to act (Yang) is part of your identity and is a joyful yearning to join with the world. And the relationship between the two is the quality of your identity. The way Yin and Yang play together is the flavor of your creativity.

As you are pushing in Push Hands, your body needs to constantly re-align to maintain the most powerful position during the push. Most students have an idea of "a push" and their mechanics are fixed to conform to that idea until the push is over. All you have to do is change your body alignment as they push and you can neutralize their force. But a good Push Hands player keeps his attention alive and active during the push and adjusts to compensate for your neutralization.

The idea of the push (as opposed to the push itself) can be likened to a false floor. Your behavior is based on this idea rather than on the actual experience of the partner's balance, resistance and alignment. The Push Hands student is taught to use imagery to "find" spaces in the partner's alignment, which he can fill with his own force. These spaces are places where there is a disconnection along the length of the partner's body, separating him from the floor. You would "insert" your own force there, cutting his root and then uprooting him with your push. The mind in this case is used in a very dynamic and sensitive way, using imagery. It uses space (or emptiness) as its floor. I use the imagery of black and white blobs or spots representing the dead and live spaces in the partner. It is like a QR code (the square bar codes). The condition of my partner creates these images as feelings in me and I have learned how to respond according to the information they convey.

When some people do Push Hands, they flail their arms wildly around, hoping to knock the other person over or they wrestle like light weight sumo wrestlers (competition Push Hands.) But when your power animals are all working together, it takes very little movement. The slightest adjustments of posture and pressure keep you in a powerful, aligned position even while you are flowing with the other person to avoid resistance. This is how you can use the "four ounces" of pressure mentioned in the classical texts and still knock the partner across the room.

The spirit animals accomplish the constant re-alignment of each part of the body as they try to maintain their stand in the dragon's lair. They sense the other person's attempt to move into a more powerful position as an attempt to kick them out of the lair and they know how to work with the body to stay in their home. When a Zookinesis student does Push Hands, he is not concentrating so much on body mechanics as on letting the power animals do as they will to stay in the lair and to leap out at the proper times to push the partner over.

As soon as they leap out, they bounce back to the lair. When you watch a chameleon shoot out its tongue, it almost begins to relax as the tongue begins to shoot out. The relaxation is part of the explosion of power. The power animals shoot out of the lair like the thick rubber band on a slingshot. As soon as it shoots out the pebble, it bounces right back into a relaxed position. The emptiness of the dragon's lair is an important part of - it is the very source of - the power issuing forth from it.

When the force comes out (as in a push), you are not concentrating on the force, per se, but on maintaining the lair ready to receive the spirit animals when they return. This means that you concentrate on the steadiness of the body and its rooting into the ground and then let the power go.

If I were to shoot a bow and arrow, I would need to   keep the bow very steady. When the arrow is released the bow must not be let go of; it must remain steady. The steadiness of the bow allows the force to move out

Another important factor in shooting a bow is to let go of the string. This releases the force. When the force is released, one's body must compensate for the issuing force by adjusting its balance to keep the bow steady.

The steadiness of the bow is the guiding factor the body takes into consideration in minutely adjusting its balance. When you let go of the string it must be done in such a way as to cause the least instability in the body. So all the actions of shooting the bow are based on letting go, remaining balanced and centered - in other words on emptiness. Emptiness is the absence of imbalance - physically or mentally.

This Yin quality - emptiness, allows the Yang quality - force, to issue forth. Yet in order to shoot a bow one must pull back the string thereby creating the factors that tend to throw the body out of balance. The body tenses and must deal with the pull of the bow. The hands must keep the arrow in line and you must aim properly.

If you concentrate on the tension and anticipate the power, you will be a very poor archer. If you concentrate on the emptiness, you will greatly improve your abilities. That emptiness provides the "path" through which power can travel. Concentrating on the emptiness allows you to remain balanced through the whole process.

If you were to feel anger or aggression towards the target you would not be able to concentrate on emptiness. The target represents whatever you pay attention to in life. Each element of your being - mind, emotion, will, the body, creativity, is like the pressures and mechanics of the bow. If you can relate to each element as a good archer, you will remain centered.

Can you skillfully "disturb" a bow (pull it) and allow it to settle back into relaxed balance (spring back) in such a way as to release part of your spirit into the world? Do your arrows (writings, interactions with other people, your Tai-chi practice) contain the message of your spirit or just the message of the imbalance?

If your attention is focused on emptiness then the Yang force issuing from you will contain your spirit. If you concentrate on the imbalance (anger, jealousy, despair) then the Yang force will contain the imbalance.

Sending forth your inner spirit allows that spirit to cycle through the world around you and cycle back again - the very process of life. Your energy connects with the living energy around you, which further steadies and balances you. This connection also means that you are joined to the process of life - your spirit is no longer alone and healing is constantly taking place within you.

The dragon's lair is more than just a home for the spirit animals. It allows them to "interpenetrate" each other and evolve into one being - you. When we love another person, we seem to melt into each other.

We feel open to the other person and we feel welcome to fill that person with our spirit - an interpenetration of feeling. This provides a medium for love to grow into all its aspects - play, sex, building a family and sharing one's life (as a couple) with others.

If we do not have such space or medium for spirits to join, we deteriorate. Many aspects of Tai-chi training (such as "bone marrow washing") focus on maintaining these spaces.

When you regain the sense of chi and look at the physical world, it appears different. The physical world and spirit world interpenetrate. We *feel* the world as well as see it. There is less deadness. The spirit animals within us interact with the spirits within everything else - the rocks, the sky, the plants and animals. The whole earth then, becomes the dragon's lair. You see the emptiness in everything and therefore see the life, the spirit in everything.

Our spirits have become so integrated in the larger spirit world that even our physical death is seamless, as our spirits remain connected to the world around us. Our spirit animals then drift off, individually, no longer united as one "us", but still very much alive and active and can re-unite to form other individuals just as the molecules of your body form plants, worms and eventually other people.

When anthropologists move into a village to study a group of people, some will try to isolate themselves and have as little to do with the people as possible. They don't want to influence the people and change their behavior. In this way, they can observe their "natural" behavior.

But this is very difficult to do. The people wonder why this person has moved into their village and then is anti-social. They will try to bring the anthropologist into their activities. Their sociability is their natural behavior.

Another reason the anthropologists don't want to interact is that they often feel uncomfortable being with people who have a completely different culture. They may do things that bother or even disgust the anthropologist. He certainly can't lecture them and tell them to stop their customs. They may offer him a grub to eat. What does he do then - say he's full? That can only work for a short time.

Other anthropologists do become part of the community, participating in their activities. They find it easier to gain the peoples' confidence. But there are problems. Sometimes different factions of the people want the anthropologist to take sides. They may want him to settle in the village, marry and raise a family, forsaking his former life. Some anthropologists have agreed to this, falling in love with a simpler way of life.

Each of us is an anthropologist living for a time in a village. We are born into a culture and need to learn about it. There are some things about it which we don't like and we have to decide how much and in what way to participate in it. Luckily in this country there are a variety of cultures from which to choose. Probably every culture in the world is represented here and we can choose our friends. There is a common culture, an "American culture", if you will, but within that we are very free to live in our own way.

We are anthropologists looking around for a culture to hang out in for a while. A practice such as Zookinesis or Tai-chi allows us to live within a little community which appeals to us even while we must also live within the generic "American community" (or European Community etc.).

The space in time which you allow for your practice is like your dragon's lair. It is a place, empty of the generic culture, its ideas and assumptions, in which your own personal life can take place. The little garden you create in which to practice, is another form of dragon's lair, a special space set aside for you. Or you may live in an apartment building and create a little space in one of your rooms.

This is a place, wherever it is in the physical world, where your spirit animals can play, grow strong and healthy. This space and the time you spend there, steadies your life so that your power can issue forth. This space can help empty your internal dragon's lair. When that is truly empty, you can begin to detect other spirit animals entering the lair to play with your own spirit animals.

You will also be able to detect the spirit animals within other people you meet. You will appreciate the spirit animal community within them - a spirit community within each person. If you are a healer, you will diagnose and heal on that level.

Some people may wonder, how practical is this in the modern world? By practical, they mean can it improve their lives. What is it about our lives that needs improvement? For one, people are dying of heart attacks at an early age. Most of us lead very stressful lives. Tension can close off blood vessels, preventing our cells from receiving nutrients and oxygen. It also makes us feel miserable and ache all over.

Tai-chi and Zookinesis exercises reduce or eliminate excess tension, make you more aware of the health of your body and empower you to work in a tense environment without getting tense. By practicing these exercises, you are centered, focused, aware of what is going inside of other people so you know how to react to neutralize their aggression and their fears and you learn how to develop positive, enriching relationships. I think that's pretty good.

In business, you are more aware of the intricacies of a situation, you can react more subtly and can relate to your customers or boss with more awareness of their behavior and what lies behind it. I think the most important benefit is that Tai-chi and Zookinesis make your whole world come alive, it enlivens you and releases your creativity so you can enjoy every moment of life more.

The dragon's lair is the place from which to look at your life and try to understand what you really want from it. The dragon sits at the mouth of his cave, overlooking the nearby town. He sees people scurrying to and fro, frantically trying to get their work done before dinner. Then the televisions go on all over town and he sees the people sitting on their couches with a blank expression on their faces until it is time to go to bed.

Once in a while a knight in shining armor visits him and tries to kill him with his shiny sword (this is from Western mythology). He burns the knight a bit with his fiery breath and the knight is treated at the local hospital and released to go back to work.

The dragon wonders about all this and hopes for the day the knight will remove his armor and visit him as a friend (maybe when the knight retires). Each of us has a dragon waiting, in his lair, for us to stop running around, to stop trying to stab him and instead join him in soaring the spirit world. Would it hurt for you to visit your dragon before you retire? Let your healing begin now, even in the midst of your crazy life, by taking a little time each day to practice Tai-chi and Zookinesis. Consider it to be a little bit of retirement each day.

The modern idea of healing is to cure a disease or injury when it occurs. Tai-chi represents an older, more traditional approach to healing and that is to keep the body healthy so that it can resist disease and injury.

The *idea* that your body must deteriorate as you age can feed the deterioration itself. Those who practice Tai-chi know that you continue to strengthen as you have more years to practice. It is common to see people practicing extreme Tai-chi "Wushu" forms well into their '90s. We think our modern ideas such as inevitable deterioration, are superior to what we consider to be the mythologies of "olden times". But if those ancient ideas can free us from stress and sickness and can bring joy into our lives, why not spend a little time trying to understand them? Let's look a little deeper into the principles of "the elements" which form the basis of Tai-chi and Zookinesis.

Earth is the physical world. It represents how we need to make sense of the world around us by trying to create a coherent story of who we are and what is going on around us. Our society provides this story to us. Within that story we can find ideas that limit us and ideas that free us. The social movements throughout human history are an effort to change the story of the society about who we are and where we came from. They attempt to fashion a story that frees our creativity and allows us to fulfill our potential as human beings.

Earth also represents simplicity. We are encumbered by fears, patterns of habits and tensions, regrets, as well as by "stuff" (junk that we buy and don't need). By simplifying our lives, we can remove the ball and chains we are dragging behind us. We can also learn to let go of negative people who are pulling us down and have no intention of really helping themselves to heal.

Earth is also the food that we put inside of our bodies. That food is sacred. When we shovel pre-made, chemically infused who-knows-what into our bodies, we not only injure our health but break the bond between us and the earth. Simply growing some food that you eat repairs that bond. Eating organic, healthy food helps to repair your body.

Earth is the center, as our bodies are the center of our consciousness. It is knowing ourselves and our skills so well that we can speak with authority. This gives us a solid ground to stand on. We could go on much further about earth, but let us continue to metal.

Metal is transformation. It is creativity, the ability to allow yourself to change and to see things differently. We take base ore and melt it in heat to extract the metal. In the same way, you (base ore) go through the fire of life and of your training to become the shining pure gold that you are capable of becoming.

And then this metal is turned into useful implements, swords for example. Do you just live your life to take up space or is your life being used to help the world around you? To help heal our world, you must first become transformed in the smelting process and then become fashioned into a healer of some sort. Simply by having been healed, your presence, by example, can help to heal those around you.

Metal is also the element of "animal consciousness", or the natural "Body-Mind". This mind is contrasted to the "clever mind" of modern times. Not that there's anything wrong with the clever mind – it has produced technology. But the natural mind is the common sense and sensitivity to the natural world that lies at the base of our consciousness. It becomes aware of imbalances in our lives and pushes our behavior to correct those imbalances. In contrast, the "modern mind" seeks the extremes.

Yet metal can also represent the thinking mind when it is integrated with Body-Mind. Thinking can be like a sharp sword in the hands of a beginner, in which case it is dangerous to the student himself. But if that student has spent years honing his skill and understanding of the art of the sword, it is like thinking that is "sung" which is the connection to the consciousness of the body and the living world.

When you wake up in the forest and breathe in the beautiful scents, your natural awareness is awakened. Metal is associated with the lungs in Chinese medicine.

Wood is the element of life itself. It is the way nature unfolds and provides energy to all its creatures to promote the consciousness of metal. It is wood that provides the fuel to transform the metal ore.

Wood is the tree whose branches and leaves reach towards the sun to absorb energy and whose roots reach deep into the soil to absorb water and nutrients. It is an example of the balance of "heaven and earth".

If you are not rooted well, the events of your life will throw you over easily. To be rooted in an understanding of your personal history and the history of humankind is essential to really know who you are. To be rooted in a love of the natural world and therefore a love of your own health, will strengthen your body and soul. To be rooted in your family and community will balance and empower you.

"Heaven" does not refer to the mythological place we go to when we die (if we are good). It refers to yielding to the forces of nature around you so that your life can be lived in harmony with the promotion of the living world. It means accepting that you can become greater than you are now and yielding to teachings of all kinds so you can continue to grow (towards sources of "light" which means knowledge). Wood allows you to become transformed (metal) for the better while remaining rooted in the real world (earth) so you don't become an airhead.

A tree provides a home for birds, monkeys, insects plants and others. It provides food for everyone. It provides the raw material for homes and furniture. It holds the soil to prevent erosion. Wood takes care of the basic needs of life to make our lives easier. Is your life like a tree?

Fire is the energy of enthusiasm. When you let go of the encumbrances of life, the bitterness, resentments, self-righteousness and anger and learn to appreciate the simple, sacred beauty of the world around you (natural and human), then you can be enthusiastic about life. That enthusiasm goes a long way to healing you and can be considered to be the result of healing.

Fire is what gets you up in the morning because you love your life and want to live it. It is the heat in relationships that makes you want to interact with other people. Yet it is earth that moderates that heat so you don't become too aggressive. In this way the elements balance each other and the job of the healer is to find out which element is too strong or too weak. It is the balance that leads to health.

Fire gets you involved in practices like Tai-chi because you appreciate the beauty of the teaching. In this way it transforms you as fire transforms metal ore. It is the movement of the exercises, like the dancing flames of the campfire or fireplace.

Fire is the energy flowing through your body when you release the blockages to the flow of chi or when you let go of sorrow through tears. When your muscles let go of their tension through Tai-chi massage, you feel energy flowing through your body. While you feel very relaxed, you also feel cleansed and energized. Fire has burned up the fear stored in the muscles and released the energy.

Water connects. It is love and compassion. It is the end of the feeling of isolation so that your spirit can "enter the world" and become part of it. Yet it is balanced with earth, which establishes clear distinctions and boundaries, so that we don't lose our individual identity.

In any relationship there is the fear of losing oneself, yet the desire to lose oneself in the relationship. The balance of water and earth allows you to merge while not losing yourself for good.

Water cleanses. When you release sorrow or physical tension and feel a rush of energy through your body, the element of water then cleans out the debris. The body is mostly made of water. The lymph cleans out lactic acid and carbon dioxide from cellular metabolism. The intercellular fluid transfers nutrients and oxygen from the blood vessels to the cells.

Yet these fluids have no pump other than the movements of the body. Each muscle of the body must be used, in fluid movement, in order to move the lymph and intercellular fluid. Otherwise the nutrients and oxygen won't get to the cells to be metabolized and the cells will be bathed in waste. Your food will wind up as fat and you will be tired because your cells are not metabolizing well.

Water conforms to the shape of the container. It is what allows us to be "invisible" during push hands or fighting because we flow with the movements of our partner. It is the principle of not opposing force but flowing around it to continue to come in and accomplish our task.

Water is strategy as it is so adaptable. It allows us to "shed" our fixed patterns and become more creative. This is called "shape shifting" in some cultures. We identify more with our creativity than with our fixed patterns of behavior and thought.

This is just a hint of the levels of meaning of the elements, their interactions and use in Chinese traditional medical theory. It is a holistic approach in that it considers the body, mind and spirit and the relationship of all aspects of our lives. Each element is associated with a season, a direction, a color, an organ-system, etc.

And so, you can discuss the elements in diagnosing an ailment as well as how you live your life. It is a set of principles based on balance that is useful in every aspect of your life. The way that most people start to learn this system is through Tai-chi practice. The teacher instructs how the elements are used to explain aspects of the movements of your Tai-chi form, chi-gung exercises, Push Hands, massage and, if you go further, the self-defense.

This training strengthens each individual from the inside out. It strengthens not only their bodies but their lives as well, allowing them to live full, productive, long and fulfilling lives.

Body alignment and posture have a profound effect on your state of health and emotions. We maintain "attitudes" within our bodies, which then affect the posture. The slumped shoulders express the attitude that we are so troubled that we are "carrying the world on our shoulders". The prideful, arrogant attitude has the chest puffed out.

To many people, these attitudes are their identity. They are how we feel who we are. But they lock us into a set of behaviors that limit our ability to grow and be creative. Tai-chi frees us from being locked into attitudes. It allows the creative person, who you truly are, to become the core of your life.

When you are locked into a posture, energy cannot flow through the body. Blood cannot flow freely. The intercellular fluid and lymph cannot move. The body then deteriorates.

A body locked in attitude is a fearful body. It is afraid to let go of that attitude because that attitude is the only place it feels safe. Relaxing feels like jumping off a cliff. Yet if you take the chance and relax, you find that the cliff is only a few inches high.

I believe that most people are locked into these attitudes and that is destroying our health and our ability to enjoy our lives. Tai chi can be a lifesaver if you are willing to go beyond merely memorizing the movements of a form. Tai-chi practice, as an "investment in loss", means that you put time and effort into letting go of your locked attitudes. You stop investing in tightening up your muscles to express fear or "strength".

Invest in health and relaxation. Invest in making the rest of your life the most enjoyable life you can imagine.

Lessons from a student's cultural background can often be used to help teach Push Hands. The story of Jesus provides a great opportunity to explain the principles of Push Hands. Though I am not Christian I try to learn about my student's backgrounds and experiences to explain the training in terms they will understand.

The natural tendency in Push Hands is to use physical force – muscle tension. But the muscle tension makes the student even more vulnerable to a push. If he were soft and yielding, he could let the

190

partner's force flow by. When he is tense, he must take the full impact of his partner's push.

Most students have tense backs. There is a band of tension across their shoulders and another band of tension up and down their spines, including their necks. When their partner pushes them, this band tightens up, they lean forward as if to resist the push and this, of course, makes them more vulnerable.

I suggest that they imagine they are carrying a cross on their backs, like Jesus carrying the cross to his crucifixion. The cross is made of the horizontal tension across the shoulders and the vertical tension along the spine. Consider my pushes to be like the Romans, hammering Jesus to the cross with nails. As long as you carry the cross I will continue to "nail you". The only solution is to let go of your cross. Allow the back to relax so that I have nothing to nail you to.

In this way my force will simply move your body. You may turn, shift back or rotate your shoulder joint, allowing my force to flow by. While the students understand their situation, it is amazing how difficult it is to "let go of their cross". The cross of tension is the result of the attitude of meeting force with force.

In the days of Jesus, the Roman Empire occupied Israel, as it did most of the "known world". Rome made the roads safe, from China through India, Europe, Israel and Egypt. There was great commerce at that time because the trade people were not afraid of being robbed along the roads. They could travel from city to city safely. With this trade came the trade of ideas. Each culture shared its philosophy with the others and there was a flourishing of philosophies.

Many of the Jews believed that the Romans should be chased out of their country. These Jews (the Zealots) not only killed Romans but also Jews who felt comfortable with the idea of Romans running the municipal activities. There was civil war.

Jesus' view was that you could not win meeting force with force. Rome was a mighty empire. Rather, by elevating the spiritual awareness of each individual Jew, this would change the very nature of the relationship between the Jews and the Romans. Without this inner development, each power would conquer the other only to be re-conquered time and time again. But if an entire population is elevated to a higher state of consciousness, its relationships to other people would always be to its benefit.

191

Push Hands is based on a similar principle. When the partner pushes you, receive the force and transform it. You can dissipate it by letting it flow through your body into your "root" (into the ground). You can circle it around back to the partner. You can compress his force, add your own and bounce the combined force up, as if the partner were pushing against a trampoline. In this way you are creative with the force. You don't just fight against it. But to do so you need a great deal of awareness. You need to let go of ingrained patterns of behavior based on conflict. And you need to do all this in real time (within a fraction of a second).

In what ways do we carry a cross in everyday life and allow others to "nail" us? Can you feel that cross on your back, wearing you out?

When I practice Push Hands, I look for that cross on my partner's back, the resistance ready to fight with me. Although our eyes are closed during this exercise (at least in our school), I can easily feel that pattern of tension. My partner leans in towards me with his head hanging down. If I were to step away, he would fall down. He conducts himself only in relationship to my force and thus depends on my force to hold him up.

Can you notice any times during the day when your head hangs down and you lean forward? If you do, then let go of your cross. Stop resisting the world around you. This means that you stop interpreting life as a battle you must tense up against. When you drop the cross you also drop the feeling of battle. Then you can look forward instead of looking down.

In the story of Jesus, he was resurrected (some say physically, some say spiritually). He is heard from a few times by his disciples and then is never heard from again. Why? Once you are "resurrected" from the "dead" (when you stop living a story of battling your way through life) then the story is over. You just go on with your life.

At first, life may not seem as exciting if you are not fighting your way through it. But soon you discover other forms of excitement such as the very joy of being alive. You discover the fulfillment of joining with others rather than battling with them.

Push Hands can be such a joy. You can join the intricate world of consciousness within each part of your body with that of the partner's body. Your energies can unite. You still play the game of trying to push each other over but it is a joyful game. It is a game that teaches you how to unite with others by letting go of all the little "crosses" inside the body that resist connecting to others.

You learn that your real power is your awareness that allows you to transform the partner's push into your play. When you bring the element of play and creativity into your life you can create the story of your own life. Your life will be lived from that story rather than from the violence of the people and situations around you.

The key to progress in the internal martial arts is to recognize the three forces at work behind your techniques and your power. There are two "intelligent" forces at work that have power and one that depletes power. The depleting force is all the habits within the muscles and nerves which are based on fear. These habits have their own agenda that have nothing to do with your task at hand.

The powerful, intelligent forces are your intentions and the body's own consciousness. Internal training requires that you connect your intentions to the body's consciousness. For most people the body's consciousness has been so suppressed that their intentions are connected only to the forces of habit. In this case your intentions are side-tracked by the emotional agenda of your entire life.

A common example is that when we spar, we like to feel powerful. Most people feel powerful when they are tense. The tension makes them feel solid. Tension however, slows the body down and makes joint movement difficult. That person's sparring becomes awkward and based on emotional anger and fear. He is, in fact, countering his own power.

The body's natural intelligence (Body-Mind) is based on the biological structure and function of each part of the body. This intelligence can be felt as strongly as the fear-emotions that are usually lodged within each part of the body. When your intentions are connected to this natural intelligence your actions are "clean", smooth and effective. Yet you feel "empty". You feel as though you didn't do anything. This is a feeling I call, "nothing" ("wu" in Chinese). When I teach Phantom Kung-fu I emphasize that the students should seek that feeling of nothing at all times. At first, they don't trust that feeling because it doesn't feel "powerful". Yet when they are in that state, they are indeed powerful, fast and effective.

At this point they need to re-adjust what they consider to be the feeling of power. The feeling of "nothing" becomes their new feeling of power. They come to rely on using the experience of the Body-Mind as their reference point rather than relying on anger or other emotions.

People ask me, "How does the Body-Mind feel? How do you know when you are feeling it?" I explain that it is like smelling a hint of freshly baked bread as you walk down the street. You follow that smell because you know there is a bakery nearby. Your nose automatically aligns itself with that smell and your body automatically follows it. Where your nose points, your body follows.

As we approach the spring season the body naturally begins to stir. We emerge from the winter's hibernation. At this time of year, it is the easiest to "smell" the stirrings of the body's intelligence. This is called the "stirrings of the dragon" in Zookinesis mythology.

Imagine that you come upon a huge cave. You smell a dragon and even see its footprints around the cave. You peer into the cave's entrance, not daring to venture in. You can imagine the power within that empty cave. Then you begin to hear the rustlings of its waking even though you can't see anything. What do you do then? Do you run away or stay to watch it emerge? That depends on how connected your intentions are to your fears.

Most of us would quickly cement over the entrance to the cave and invest our energy adding layer after layer of cement to make sure the dragon doesn't escape. Yet that dragon is our own power. Why in the world would we hide our own power? The key to answering that question is to ask, "Who are we?" Are we indeed that dragon, our natural intelligence or are we the patterns of behavior based on fear? If we are the latter, then the emergence of the dragon would surely endanger us. Part of my work as a Zookinesis and Tai-chi teacher is to tell you that you are not your fears. You are the dragon. The dragon's actions are not based on fear and are therefore not destructive. When your intentions are connected to your natural power you are not destructive.

Yes, you punch or kick with great power but it is not power born of anger and fear. It is power born of competence. It is a relaxed, comfortable power, not an agitated power.

Once you understand these three parts of you – intentions, natural power (Body-Mind) and fear-based behavior patterns, you can start to differentiate them in each of your actions.

The reason the dragon's cave or "lair" seems empty is that most of us can't see our own power. We can only see representations of our power such as tension, large muscles, aggressive behavior and money. Our true power, by its very nature, is unseen.

It is like a Tai-chi form that is all about internal movement – the relationship of the center to the root, the relationship of each muscle and joint to each other, breathing mechanics and the fluidity and connection of attention. The external movements – those you can see, are just a reflection of the internal mechanics and should be as subtle as possible. A person not familiar with traditional Tai-chi wouldn't see the internal mechanics. It would be an empty cave. Yet that emptiness is where all the action really is. It is where your power resides.

Your intentions house your training. For example, if you want to avoid getting hit by the sparring partner's punch your intentions would be to block if you are in an external martial arts style and to evade if you are in an internal martial arts style. Your intentions tell you what situation you are in and how to respond. With the external styles an intruder is entering your space and you need to remove him from that space. With the internal styles force is flowing by you and you are naturally pushed aside by that force. You gently accommodate your alignment to allow the force to flow by while remaining in an advantageous position with regards to the sparring partner. In this case sparring is not a matter of conflict but of realignment to maintain harmony and balance. This is, in fact, the way the body is structured to behave.

When the dragon emerges from its cave, stretches and warms up in the sun, you can then ride it into the clouds. Your intentions are clear and connected to your inner power. You can do anything.

This is the training of Tai-chi and Zookinesis. Take advantage of the spring season when the dragon begins to stir. Avoid cementing the entrance to the cave and in fact, break down the old cement (the body's tensions). Release your tight grasp of your fears and let them go on their way. Give each fear a piece of cement to carry away with him. Remain at the entrance of the cave to greet the dragon.

The sun is used as a symbol of the energy of consciousness that flows through all living things. It unites all life on earth. When you feel the warmth of the spring sun it is easy to allow your fears to melt and to allow the dragon to emerge. All the natural parts of you become united. Then you realize that the feeling of "nothing" is really everything in your training.

Most of our lives are dedicated to just getting through the day so we often forget about play as we grow older. Play is not only children practicing to be adults. It is the joy of life. And by "play" I don't mean competitive sports. I'm talking about playing with what your life is all about.

It's easy to feel that because the bills keep coming in it's important to be serious all the time. My father was very serious and considered play to be a waste of good time that could be put to better use. It took me many years to be able to let go of that programming, yet I still feel its tug.

We have arranged our culture to "feed the economic machine" rather than to maximize the enjoyment of life. Do you really need all the new gadgets? Or would your money best be spent living simply and having fewer bills? What is it that leads to a more joyful life and what is it that takes joy away?

These are questions you ask if you want to be creative with your identity. Create a beautiful myth about who you are and what you are doing with your life. Gradually move in that direction, while of course, taking care of practical matters. Don't let a day go by without spending at least a few minutes remembering your myth and asking yourself, "How could I have become that myth a little bit more today?"

When our identity is the result of our creativity rather than our past patterns of behavior, we then gain power in our lives. We have to be willing to let go of elements of our old identity to gain new, brighter elements. We have to be willing to release our rear foot from the ground in order to take a step forward.

Your myth is similar to that barge mentioned before, attached to a sunken boat, that lifts the boat when the tide comes in. While your life may seem to be buried under bills and problems, the myth can just sit there. As the tide of time washes in, that myth can lift you up into a new life.

You are not being "false" by living a myth. A myth does not mean that your new identity is not true. It means that your identity is now part of your creative nature. It is alive and adds to your vitality. When your identity is alive and vital you feel energized and ready for life. Who would you really like to be?

196

We have culturally evolved away from animals. But our nature, as this human animal, is to develop both our thinking and our biological health.

In the primal state for our species there is a balance between the scientist or religious purist part of us, who knows everything as absolute fact, and the storyteller who understands that the way we see the world is a reflection of the stories we believe in.

For a primal state human, stories can change and he seeks those stories that empower his life and the lives of those around him. He is not afraid of the stories of other people.

But everything starts with re-experiencing the primal state. From this state of balance, the fixed ideas of the mind and the story telling of creativity can play with each other. Facts are still facts yet you can still live your life creatively.

Once you see the world through "primal eyes" then you truly comprehend what a huge part of our lives we have lost. You understand that many of our emotional problems and bad feelings are just a reflection of our deep inner loss of the primal state.

With the primal state returns, we become more creative, adventurous and willing to create a grand, powerful story of who we can become.

Fortunately, it is not difficult to achieve this state. With proper training, progress is steady and new worlds constantly open up before you. In my classes I have to be careful not to let the students spend too much time telling me about the new experiences they have had that week. Although I love to hear about these things, I feel that I am being paid to teach them and want to spend as much time actually training them as possible.

Yet it is wonderful to hear about their increasing joy for life and the great improvements in their lives. They now seem "fully human". Instead of battling against the world, they now can see that their life situation is a result of their internal dynamics. By gaining creative control over those dynamics they gain control over their lives. Tai-chi and Zookinesis give them the nuts and bolts of how to do that.

You may get angry when someone tries to control you. But what is it that is controlling your pattern of thinking, physical movement, emotions, etc.? Are you angry at whatever that is? Or do you just assume that is "you"? Are "you" what controls you? Do you organize

197

your memories in terms of success and defeat? On what basis do you judge yourself? Do you beat yourself up emotionally?

In Tai-chi you identify negative feelings and learn how they trap you. Then you learn to let them go. At first your identity is a battleground of feelings; you are the battleground. Then you realize you are not a battleground and that the antagonists of the battleground don't really exist. They are phantoms of your imbalance. Then the work is to balance yourself physically and energetically, so that the body, attention and creativity merge together and work together.

The use of imagery in doing the form such as moving like a wisp of smoke or like a tiger stirs the internal dynamics. If your self-image or your habits hold you back from moving like a tiger, for example, the image of a tiger can lift you out of your habits. So the image you use in the form is the barge that lifts the sunken boat.

The self-image can become alive rather than a portrait on a wall. It can be the principles of movement and interaction of Tai-chi rather than a static picture. It can be the "gatekeeper", influencing the interactions between the "inside and the outside", the dynamics of "interpenetration" as you interact with other people. It can be the process of continuous realignment of all your joints as you move. This is known as "Taoist Alchemy", the perception of yourself and the world around you as dynamic energy. Tai-chi practice sustains this way of living. It is a way of lifting life up out of the mud of the deadness of the modern world. As you interact with people now, you can judge if the relationship helps to sustain your aliveness or promotes your deadness.

The way a con artist works is to act in a very self-assured manner and cast self-doubt in others. People seek assurance in order to be grounded and sometimes don't much care what the assurance is about. Self-assurance is perceived as strength.

Your assurance in life shouldn't come from others. It should come from the success of your own transformation based on your understanding of what path you are on. What you have let go of is as important as what you gained. At a certain point your path becomes so clear to you and its effects so positive that you don't need the assurance of others.

The beginning Tai-chi student is like a dog that has wound his leash around a tree. The teacher tries to show him his predicament so he can understand how to unwind himself. But he howls and howls, runs about frantically and just can't understand. It takes a while before the student understands that the words you are saying about learning Tai-chi have something to do with what is going on inside of him. They tell him how to unwind himself from the tree by just removing the leash. The leash is the insistence that you attach your spirit to the turmoil inside of other people. Release your leash from that conflict.

When an aggressive person confronts you, sink each muscle and joint into the root while maintaining your structure. Allow your eyes to be like waterfalls, receiving the aggression into the pool in the belly. Make sure you don't stop the flow of chi either within you or between you and the arguer. Be happy. And then only respond to the things he says, not to the emotions behind them. In most cases the aggression will dissolve because the arguer only understands his own behavior through your reaction to him.

His response may be to harden because he feels more comfortable being disconnected. If you remain connected within yourself and to him, his hardening won't affect you. His ability to respond both mentally and physically becomes more restricted and so he weakens himself.

When a Push Hands partner grabs your arms, it is because he has run out of ways to respond and grabbing is his only option. Hardening or grabbing shuts off Body-Mind and is a statement that his attention has died. Don't let his dying cause your dying. Respond to the dying of his attention by maintaining aliveness of your attention.

What we are looking for in the Push Hands partner or when we are doing healing work is, "What is he doing with the flow of chi?" He may intend to stop the flow of chi or increase its flow. What he wants to do with the flow of chi expresses the mythology of his culture and reveals his understanding of who he is within the context of his culture. He will probably not understand his behavior in these terms. But when we are trained to look for this dynamic it allows us to respond more effectively.

For example: Something very bad may happen and you wish it hadn't happened. A common response to this is to hold your breath for a moment draw up your shoulders and tighten your jaw. What are you trying to do? Your breathing has stopped. The body has tightened and stopped its movement. It is as if you want to stop time itself because you don't want this bad event to have happened. Perhaps if you freeze you can stop time. And so, you freeze the flow of chi. This disconnects you from your environment, as if to say that if you can't stop time, you want to disconnect yourself from this reality.

There is an underlying mythology here. You can disconnect yourself from the world you see before you. You are a separate individual who can retreat from the world by cutting off the flow of chi to and from the world. If you become hard and stiff and stop your feelings, the harshness of the world will affect you less.

In this mythology extreme tension and the cessation of breathing can separate you from life. (Hey! Maybe you've got something there!) Is it any wonder people die of heart attacks at such an early age?

The point is to understand what you are trying to really do (in Zookinesis terms) by examining the relationship between your breathing and behavior, and feeling how that affects the flow of chi. Chi is that intelligent life energy which must flow through you to keep you part of life.

On the other hand, have you ever felt so angry that you were about to "burst"? You feel that if only your anger could jump out and strangle the person who is angering you, your emotions themselves could revenge the wrong that was done to you. You are trying to use your anger as a weapon. Notice your breath now. You are trying to increase the flow of chi, make it deadly and send it out to your victim.

In the old days people believed that this was possible (as do some people now). I believe that you are merely pumping up the flow of chi (not to mention adrenalin and the increase in blood pressure) in a body not designed to handle that much chi (or blood pressure). Your body will give out long before your victim begins to feel any effects.

The mythology here is you are in a battle with the world (or at least one part of it). When we spar, we must develop the feeling of uniting with our sparring partner. If we feel angry, our body slows down, and we get hit. The more anger we feel, the more we get hit. When my wife Jean started to learn sparring, she would get so frustrated that she once took off her gloves and threw them at me. Eventually the body gets the message to relax and flow between the partner's punches and kicks. We are far more effective in sparring when we are relaxed and don't really feel we are battling the world.

Anyone basing their feeling of self-worth on the pressures of others who want to control them, is "building their house on sand" which we actually do here on Long Island. That's why the wealthy homes on Dune Road here on Long Island get washed into the sea every few years. When those homeowners expect the taxpayer to rebuild their homes for them or to re-build Dune Road, they are not following the principles of Tai-chi.

Sparring is like dealing with people in business by transforming negative feelings about your product or service into positive feelings. It is well known that you should not argue with a customer. Instead of arguing that your product is indeed a good one, you ask the customer how you could improve your product. You not only make him feel that you care, but you may actually get some good advice. Customer complaints are the best source of good ideas.

If you are competing with other companies producing similar products, you could throw more money into advertising and spend more hours in the day promoting the product. Or you could ask yourself, "What real needs of people are the competing products not meeting? How can I adjust my product so that it will fill those needs?" In other words, you can compete in a "Yin" area, in a niche market that the other products are not reaching. It would wear you out to meet head on with large companies with big advertising budgets.

To be "nimble" in business in this way, the self-image of the business must be flexible. You think of your business as providing a product to the customer. Now you switch your viewpoint and think of your business as fulfilling a need of the customer. It's not the same and that switch changes the way you do business.

When I began producing the "Zookinesis" exercise series of DVDs, I approached the series as providing exercises to keep you strong, flexible and energized. I noticed a great change in my older students through the years. They looked, acted and felt much younger. In fact, these exercises are supposed to keep you young, but I never explained that in my advertising. Now I call Zookinesis "Age Reversal Exercises" and market them to seniors. I knew all along that they are supposed to reverse aging but never thought to promote that aspect.

Looking back, I realized that I thought that since most of my students were not seniors, I wanted to promote the fact that Zookinesis keeps you vigorous, athletic and toned. I didn't think age was an issue for non-seniors. But it seems that no one wants to feel that they are getting older, whatever age they are now, if by older you mean that the body deteriorates. I didn't change the exercises at all but just got better at explaining what they are in a way the students could appreciate.

Perhaps there was yet another factor. If I were teaching people to reverse the aging process, perhaps that means that I, myself, was getting old and that age reversal was an issue I needed to address myself. Not wanting to think of myself as getting old, I avoided using "age reversal" as an advertising point for Zookinesis. My vanity interfered with my business. Yet I, of all people, knew that age is not a matter of years but of health and attitude. This is an example of how issues of self-image can interfere with business as it can interfere with everyday life.

When I first started to learn to spar with Grandmaster William C. C. Chen, I couldn't help but concentrate on his fists and feet. Which one would hit me next? My attention hardened with each hit. After gaining some skill I found that I was more interested in the spaces between our body parts. Which space could I use to deliver my own strikes? I found that emptiness (space) was equally as important as form (the body, the strikes). I needed to know where I could move into to avoid his strikes. My attention needed to soften to allow my body to soften so I could move into the spaces.

I realized that sparring was not about maximizing hardness but rather maximizing balance. When you are not willing to change and when you invest all your hopes in one particular outcome, that is like hardness. When you invest in developing your attention to follow and adjust to change, when you accept change as part of life and when you learn the strategies of change to always look for opportunity, then your life is based on balance.

You maximize hardness when you try to defeat hardness by blocking rather than ducking. If you think of winning and losing you are already defeated. In Tai-chi sparring, you concentrate on the details of the aggressor's body mechanics and the pattern of his attention. You are so connected to him that you feel that he is part of you. Your ability to remain connected to him in this way is essential to how you spar. You don't think of defeating an "enemy" but of finding a weakness and striking that weakness. It is the weakness you discover at any one moment that you are sparring against, not the person. The aggressor and you are one unit. The weakness is the target.

The world around you is no longer your "enemy". Defeats are just changes. The only real defeat is when your attention becomes rigid and you can no longer adapt to change. You are defeated when you let yourself become old, no matter how many years you have lived. When you are no longer able to adapt to change, you are old. Flexible in body, flexible in mind – you stay young.

Tai-chi-Chuan students make their movements subtle. This leads them to ask, "Why wasn't I subtle in the first place?" Why do I make such exaggerated movements?"

It is because we like to "make statements" with our bodies – what is known as "body language", or "telegraphing" (announcing your intentions). It makes you feel tough, but it is extraneous and unnecessary for fighting well.

The students try to find out how they are tensing their muscles to make such statements as, "I am going to hit you now". With many martial artists, the whole body will be raised, especially the shoulder of the arm which is about to punch. The center of gravity of the body will be raised. The body will tense up.

Now the body has broken its connection to the ground. The tense, raised shoulder has pulled the arm back, which shortens the arm reach. The raised shoulder ensures that the returning force of the punch (each action has an equal and opposite reaction) will go to the puncher's shoulder, pushing him backward as well as injuring the shoulder. The body's tension slows down the punch.

Tai-chi training allows you to catch yourself in the act and say to your body, "Hey, why am I doing that?" You realize you have come to rely on tension to falsely feel secure. Simply being aware of it can help the student let go of the behavior.

When they finally let go of their tensions, they feel a great emptiness – the loss of a behavior pattern. Beneath that emptiness lies that which they sought to protect – their true selves. This means that all those behaviors were an act to hide who they really are.

Many people are afraid to be themselves. They put on an act they hope will be approved of. But in martial arts as in life, the act does no good. It robs you of power. It doesn't allow you to act in your own best self-interest. You act to appear a certain way but know, on a certain level, that you are acting. You feel like an imposter. This is especially true in the workplace when people are promoted beyond their abilities.

But in class, the teacher may just teach the exercises as they are, without discussing the deeper goal of healing this problem. That discussion might be too challenging for the student. Once you strengthen the body, increase range of motion of the joints and calm the mind and emotions, the teacher can then discuss the relationship between mind and body. Sometimes the principles of Tai-chi can be more challenging to a student than the exercises.

The body may be "set" in its alignment to express an attitude. If you relax one part of the body, another part will tense up to maintain that alignment. When the student can accept the underlying principles, it is time for them to notice this compensatory tensing of the body to maintain an attitude. This teaches her to concentrate on several parts of the body at the same time and their relationship with each other. The relationship between mind and body is really the relationship among all the "parts" of the person including memories, trauma, other emotions, muscles, nerves, etc. It is about the "culture" of the body and mind.

The key to allow the body to do its job is to stay relaxed while sparring; to keep yourself empty. When we spar in class, there is a lot of laughter. If someone gets hit hard, she laughs and says, "Good!" She feels good that a great technique was performed (even though she wound up on the wrong end of that technique). She is empty of anger and competitiveness. Anger is not the path to awareness. Laughter is!

Fear and anger are often what blocks the flow of attention through the body. Some martial arts teachers encourage the students to use fear and anger to energize their fighting. We dissolve the fear and anger to release blocked energy. Fear is like dry earth that can't grow anything. Attention is like water. The dry earth just needs water.

When you really know something, when you can pay attention to it, you don't fear it anymore. You see it for what it is and deal with it appropriately. If you were to know all your opponent's moves before she executed them, you wouldn't fear her. You would be confident that you would act appropriately to each of her moves. Push Hands teaches you to be aware of what is going on inside the opponent and you then bring that awareness into sparring.

Tai-chi-Chuan derives its greatest power from ending the battles inside the student. Fear, trauma and anger are dissolved and melt away. The student's attention flows through every cell allowing his body to regain its natural, instinctual power. And, like a tiger in the jungle, it is a mass of power that is hidden until it is too late.

Tai-chi-Chuan is not just a question of memorizing a series of punches, kicks and blocks. It is a complete transformation of the student that allows him to access the power of billions of years of biological evolution that is his heritage as a living being.

Chapter 5
Animals Can Heal

For many years I spent most of my time among wild animals, whether in the wild or in captivity. When you are dealing with a wild animal your whole body senses that animal and its whole body senses you. Every cell of its body is poised to deal with you. It stares at you with the intent of penetrating every part of your body with its full attention. Its attention is like a steel sword slicing through to your heart.

Yet its attention is not necessarily menacing. It penetrates to be ready to deal with you but if you mean it no harm, it has no reason to do you any harm. It's just that the attention of wild animals is powerful and they have only that moment to deal with. They invest the entire power of their attention into that one moment. If they recognize you as their friend, the intense power of their attention serves to connect you in a powerful bond.

You can sense that connection and either choose to let its entire force into you even though it is different from you, or to harden yourself up against it.

To be willing to let it in unconditionally, you must be very secure. You, too, must be a powerful animal.

I remember the first time I had to work with a very large monitor (dragon) lizard. It was a Southeast Asian water monitor (Varanus salvator) about eight feet long and about sixty pounds. As soon as I saw it, he ran up towards me and without hesitation. I picked him up and started to hug it. It rubbed its head onto my head and hissed

206

loudly. I couldn't pick it up completely off the floor but just enough to hug its body onto mine. After a while the lizard got bored and walked away.

This was a completely wild animal that I had just imported. Lizards are not known to be social animals yet I found that most responded very positively to being touched and held and massaged. This was also true with reptiles I found in the wild and picked up right off a tree or from under a rock.

There is a whole-body communication that takes place with an animal. Once you are aware of that you can work with them very well. But there is a problem.

Most people do not have that whole-body communication. This mechanism is dead. I found that I didn't feel comfortable among people because they had lost this mode of communication. I understood why wild animals don't feel comfortable among people.

Through my training I discovered that the way to interact with an animal is to let its personality, its basic nature, into your heart. Let its pattern of consciousness penetrate every pore of your being and so become that animal. Now when you interact - you and the animal are essentially the same on the level of whole-body communication.

It is like you and the animal are first oil and water and now you are water and water. We humans have such plasticity to our state of consciousness that we can mimic the states of other species. In this way we can interact with them very directly.

The reason we do this in Zookinesis training is to understand the full range of the dynamics of attention and to understand healing from that point of view. When we do Tai-chi massage for example, we sense the person with our whole-body awareness to understand his physical ailments and correct them. When we do Push Hands or self-defense, we are using this same awareness.

My original goal was simply to learn more about animals. As a zoologist I was curious about more than what I could get out of a textbook. While I memorized all the scientific names and the skeletal differences among many species, I knew there was more to understanding animals than those intellectual listings of facts. I sensed that when I interacted with an animal that it knew something that I didn't. Through Zookinesis and Tai-chi training I discovered the whole-body awareness.

Animals Can Heal

After regaining this awareness, it is as if you had been sleeping all your life and then suddenly woke up. I have seen Public Television programs about people who are paralyzed and cannot speak but are fully conscious or about people who are autistic and are fully aware but cannot communicate. They feel trapped in their own bodies.

When you regain whole-body awareness, you realize that you have been in that trapped state most of your life. You feel freed from your own jail. Some people have experienced sleep paralysis, in which you can't move for a short while after you wake up. It reminds me of beginning students struggling to move gracefully.

You don't need to get involved in any training to gain this awareness. You need to spend a lot of time with wild animals, as opposed to dogs and cats. And when you spend time with these animals, you need to feel that you are not superior to them. Remember that you are trapped in a limited awareness and they are not. You are seeking *their* help. You are not trying to turn them human. You are trying to learn to become an animal. You are, in fact, an animal, but one who is pretending not to be one. We are apes in designer fashions.

Let's admit it, we humans are very silly. We are self-destructive and pretentious. If we can give up our feelings of superiority and admire the beauty of animals and admire the power of their consciousness, then we can begin to understand our place in that beauty.

When I used to encounter an animal with a particularly nasty attitude, I would sit down near it, usually without any barrier, and just wait for it to calm down. I remember a six-foot Bengal monitor lizard which stood high up on its legs, puffed itself up, hissing very loudly and constantly whipping its tail. I sat down near it (but not too close to its tail) and just rested in a meditative position. It gradually calmed down but grumbled (by hissing) once in a while, eyeing me suspiciously.

After a long while the lizard sat down and curled up near me. I was surprised at this because it could have sat down at the other end of the cage. It gradually pressed its body up against mine because lizards like the warmth of a warm-blooded animal. I never had any trouble with it again. In fact, it became very friendly.

During the time I sat down near it and the lizard was upset, I could feel a real tug of war with the whole-body communication. I knew how to remain centered and relaxed with that awareness. There was a world of interaction on that level and yet from the visual point of view, I just sat there.

This is the way it is in quality martial arts. The opponents seem very calm and relaxed and yet they are completely connected to each other, searching for the slightest advantage. Their attentions tug at each other. There is much more sparring on that level than on the physical level.

Many people have seen the samurai movies in which the two opponents just stand there for a long time, not moving even the slightest bit. Suddenly one man makes a small, quick move and kills the other. You understand that there is a great deal of interaction of attention on the part of both men. The final physical action was just the end result of all the interaction of attention while the two bodies were not moving.

There are stories of traditional Tai-chi masters who got into position for Push Hands and a few seconds later one walked away admitting defeat. He sensed that the body awareness of his partner was much greater than his so there was no point in the competition.

We humans have lost something very important. We have lost the awareness that connects us to the rest of life – the awareness that allows us to really heal. Just as we search for cures for disease in the chemical makeup of wild plants, we can search for our lost awareness in the consciousness of animals.

I spent twenty years presenting live animal programs in schools. As children came up to the front to hold animals or have the big python draped around their necks, the radiant glow of joy and delight in their faces was my reward. They understood that there is something about interacting directly with a live wild animal that restores something inside you that is essential for happiness. It is our connection to the wild – to our original home – to our original consciousness. We have all been away from home for a long time.

I had a ten-foot Burmese python that was very nasty. Rather than try to take it out to clean the cage, I cleaned the cage with the python inside. It continuously struck at me but I got used to it and just ducked quickly. This was when I was learning Tai-chi-Chuan from Grandmaster William C. C. Chen. In this way I became good at ducking. But I also got good at punching because I became aware of the whole-body dynamics of the snake's strike. I learned to punch using the same dynamics the snake used for striking. As I sparred with other students in my class I could easily switch to that snake's pattern of attention and my body actions followed that attention pattern.

The python never stopped striking me as I cleaned its cage but we both got used to each other and it became more like a game between us. Yet it was a serious game because it struck for the face and I never wore any face protection.

When you practice in sparring class it is a serious game. You are punching or kicking with the intention of a powerful strike yet you like your fellow students. There is no anger involved. You respect the skill of your partner and understand that your actions are meant to enhance that skill. When you do connect with him or he with you, it hurts. Yet it would hurt even more, once knowing how you could develop your awareness, to choose not to do so. Martial arts are one means of developing that awareness and the people involved are willing to get hurt in every class rather than let that awareness become dull and dead.

Working with wild animals is similar. They don't always calm down. And they are usually a lot stronger and faster than you. People who work with wild animals must be willing to have much of their bodies covered with the scars of bites and scratches. You really have to know what you're doing, so if you plan to work with wild animals, make sure you are working with a zoologist. Tapping into the rich treasure of animal consciousness is so important to zoologists that they feel scars are a small price to pay.

Consciousness is a treasure that is laid out before us. We can develop it within ourselves and we can participate in the variety of consciousness of the world's many species. Yet it is a treasure that is not highly valued. We value a lump of gold or a tiny diamond more than the great treasure of consciousness in each wild animal.

I love and respect the training of Zookinesis because it is a path back to this understanding, a path back to our animal awareness, a path back to our home.

This system involves a large series of animal-like movements. The tiger movements, for example, based on the sequential rotation of all the joints of the body, have become an essential part of the way I do Push Hands and fighting.

I worked for an animal importing company when I was in high school. That place was my second home. Many of the animals had been there for a long time and I knew them well: they were my second family.

There were five other large animal importers at that time in the New York City area. Most Saturdays I visited one or two of them to see what new species they brought in. The owners of these animal compounds would discuss their new animals with me. If I found the animal especially interesting, I would get a few to work with them.

During the 1960's I went to Cornell to study zoology and spent several summers canoeing my way through the jungles of Central America to study animals in the wild and to learn from the local people.

I then returned to studying chi-gung and began learning Tai-chi-Chuan first from Herb Ray (a student of Grandmaster William C. C. Chen) and then from the Grandmaster himself. Grandmaster Chen's main interest is in fighting and I was more interested in healing. But he insisted that I take at least a few months of fighting class. One day one of his instructors started beating me up, at least from my point of view. He backed me against the wall and wouldn't stop hitting me.

I hid my face in my arms and peaked out at Grandmaster Chen hoping he saw this and would help me. He was indeed watching but was also laughing. My only hope was to swing my arms wildly and the instructor backed away (he was being kind). Something clicked inside of me and I suddenly liked fighting. I continued with Grandmaster Chen for many years thereafter.

To earn a living, I put on the live animal programs in schools throughout New York, New Jersey and Connecticut, ("The Animal Man" Programs), teaching about the importance of protecting the environment. The program was presented to over one and a half million students and teachers.

After my last day of teaching, I was walking out of the school and some of the students were playing on a "jungle gym" in the school yard. A little girl on top of the "jungle gym" called to me as I walked to my car, saying "Goodbye Animal Man". It felt like the universe telling me it was all right to retire from that career.

The yearning of children to connect with animals is the same yearning for each of us to be connected to our own bodies. We have become strangers to our own bodies. The body seems to us like some big, awkward thing down there that carries our head around. With Tai-chi and Zookinesis we learn to feel each part of our bodies and to understand how to use the body properly. Through these exercises each part of the body feels alive and awake. You can feel healing taking place as the body becomes more conscious.

I continued the animal importing company I had worked for, but this time on my own, bringing animals in from habitats that were being destroyed and selling them to zoos and individuals who were setting up breeding programs to save these species. I also developed my own breeding programs for reptiles.

I soon realized that I could use my chi-gung training as well as my experience with thousands of live animals to add to my Tai-chi-Chuan self-defense training. I called the resultant combination "Phantom Kung-fu" and it is the type of fighting I now teach. The name comes from the principle of moving within areas where the opponent's attention is weak, as if you are a phantom.

The interactions with each species of animal revealed a deeper set of mechanics. I realized that they were manipulating my energy within their bodies, and their energy within my body to control me. We became in essence, a single energetic system and their attention was at the center of that system. Mine was not. It was only on my side. Furthermore, they could place the fulcrum of interaction at any point that was most beneficial for them. The fulcrum in this case, refers to the reference point their joints use to pivot around. For example, I can move my body pivoting around my Tai-tien or around my sternum. Just by placing my concentration at such a point, the joints function with that point as their reference.

As I fought or played with the animal (depending on its disposition), it could constantly change that fulcrum point which confused the heck out of me. Tayras and grisons were my favorite. These Central and South American weasel-like mammals are about five to fifteen pounds. They are like little wolverines. There were many species of cats, monkeys, honey bears, coati-mundis, anteaters, as well as pythons up to thirteen feet, monitor (dragon) lizards up to eight feet long, many birds and others. Each had its own way of using energy and I had to learn them all.

When I practiced Push Hands with the other students, I would use these methods of using energy, and Push Hands became more fun than competition. Many of the animals could throw me off just by expanding their bodies with their breath and I brought this dynamic into Tai-chi class. When I learned something in class, I brought it back to the animals. Eventually, the animals all learned to do Push Hands with me and their moods were always good.

So now when I teach Push Hands to my students, I substitute for the animals, using one dynamic in one class and another dynamic another day. When I still had the animal-importing set-up, I used to bring the animals themselves into class. Now I just bring in the energy so my students can get a similar experience.

I found dozens of energy dynamics in the many species and integrated them into what Grandmaster Chen taught me. Today my Push Hands is not so much about how many times a student can push over another student to get points. It is about learning these energy dynamics, which can then be used in everyday life. These dynamics don't necessarily require physical contact. They can be done even in a verbal interaction, because there are always energy dynamics going on underneath.

My students regularly tell me how they used a particular dynamic in an interaction, often at work. Translating Push Hands dynamics into everyday life is the greatest benefit of this exercise. It is also humbling to realize that animals are so much smarter in certain ways, than people.

It was exciting to introduce new students to the animals. They had never seen these species before in person. The black, rough necked monitor lizard sat in its own huge cage. At six feet long, thirty inches tall (when straightening out its legs) and about two feet wide (when puffed up), it was an impressive animal, especially when hissing and whipping its tail. Its long neck, covered with large spiked scales and long, narrow head and nose gave it a bizarre appearance. It was as black and intimidating as Darth Vader.

The students had to enter the cage and, while the dragon lizard hissed and whipped its tail, the student had to pet it to calm it down. Soon the lizard's hiss changed to what was obviously a hiss of ecstasy. The ability to walk right over to what seemed like a live, angry dragon changed the perspective of the student. It allowed him to overcome his fears and spar better.

I found that each encounter served to alter the state of consciousness of the student, gradually allowing him or her to be able to connect better with the animals, and with each other. It allowed the student to be able to perceive the consciousness of the animal and understand how he could control his own behavior to control the behavior of the animal so it would calm down. This is an essential skill in sparring.

The pine and bull snakes were great teachers. Their hiss was so loud it seemed like you were standing right next to a steam locomotive. You would walk near the cage and the incredible hiss would suddenly be upon you. It was very hard not to jump into the air with fright even though you knew it was just a harmless snake. The student would pick it up and the snake dug the tip of its tail (which was fairly sharp) into his arm as it stared at him. It looked like it was saying, "Now take that!"

The students soon realized that as frightening as the animals seemed at first, they were very gentle when handled correctly. I once bought a thirteen-foot reticulated python from someone because it was too vicious for her to handle. I thought this would make a great animal for my students to handle. But when I brought it into the Tai-chi studio, the snake became very tame. We couldn't get it to misbehave if we wanted to. I had played up this snake as being very tough to handle. I guess it sensed the peaceful atmosphere and felt safe.

I used to have a very large African python. This species is very active and very intelligent. As you hold it, the snake brings its face right next to yours to see you (snakes' eyesight isn't very good). Its movements are sudden. It will quickly turn around, come right up to your face and then just stare at you without moving (just sticking out its tongue). I have found that there are some people who don't like that (though I can't imagine why.) If you can get used to the African python, you can get used to the intensity of sparring.

I used to import many species of monkeys and to keep them from getting bored, we would play fight with each other. I got into the cages and just started mixing it up. The monkeys loved it so much that each time I stopped fighting they would complain loudly to keep playing. So many hours were spent fighting with the monkeys that it was easy

214

for me to spar in their "style". Raccoon-like animals like the coati-mundi were also a lot of fun. I probably spent two hours a day fighting with various animals to keep them amused.

Sparring with people then became easy. No person was as quick or had as much endurance as the animals. The animals were my real sparring partners. It would be impossible to duplicate the training you get when working directly with animals. Yet few people have this opportunity. These days I have too much work to maintain a collection of animals and so my students don't receive that kind of training anymore. I hope one day to create a training center where people can learn directly from animals as well as from human teachers, as I did many years ago. Wouldn't it be a great experience to learn martial arts and healing exercises from both a human and from animal teachers?

My students and I used to have long talks about what we learned from our experiences with animals and how to apply them to sparring or to healing. I could tell which animal the student had been concentrating on from how he sparred that day.

You always have to respect the animal's power, though. I remember working in the Bronx Zoo one summer. I worked with the small mammals, the monkeys and the apes. I opened the shift cage for a gorilla. This allows the gorilla to move to this separate cage so you can clean its main cage. After he entered the shift cage, he sat down. I then began to close the large iron door. It weighed five hundred pounds and was closed by pushing an iron bar. It took all my might to almost push it closed. The head keeper warned me to close the door very quickly because the gorilla would wait until the door was almost closed and then flip it completely open with his fingers. The door would come crashing open, throwing a keeper against the back wall. It showed us who is boss!

When I spent two months in Nicaragua, we had to catch our own food. The townspeople were going on a caiman hunt (caimans are a type of alligator) and I was invited. At night you can only see their eyes reflecting back from your flashlight. The head caiman wrangler used a forked stick to catch the caiman's neck and he and another man flung it into the canoe. He turned to me and said, "Grab its head and close its mouth". Now, this eight-foot caiman was snapping its jaws and thrashing its tail. I wasn't prepared to move towards the snapping jaws let alone to grab them. But the alternative was for us all to just stand there with a snapping caiman in the canoe. So I jumped on top of its head and bear hugged its jaws. The head wrangler then tied the mouth with a rope. We ate well that night.

If you can jump towards the snapping jaws of a caiman, you won't fear sparring or for that matter, doing anything else in life.

The animal forms of Kung-fu give you a taste of fighting like wild animals. I believe that a teacher of animal styles should have extensive experience with the animals of those styles. Otherwise you are just doing "empty" movements with no real experience of what is behind the movements. When the student spars with the teacher, the student should really feel that he is sparring with an animal because the animal spirit is indeed, in the teacher.

As our civilization moves further away from nature, the Kung-fu forms can help us keep a feeling for the wild so that at least our bodies can remain natural.

My days as a zoologist, canoeing through the jungles of Central America, gave me a unique perspective of how living in a wild area affects the perspectives and perceptions of people. Living in my canoe or in a small tent set up by the edge of a river made me feel like just another animal among many. The villages I visited were just a few huts clustered together every few miles at the river's edge. The human presence was small compared to the overwhelming intensity of the jungle – its colors and shapes, its humidity, smells and rhythms of life. As soon as I arrived in the jungle, it "grabbed" me. There was an instant transformation in the way my mind perceived and understood my relationship to the surroundings. By traveling back and forth from New York to Central America, I could feel the effect of each environment on me. I could also see and understand how the people in each area were very different because of their respective environments. It was like my experience during my first six years as a child, spending half the year in North Branch, a tiny one-block long town in the Catskill Mountains of New York, and half the year in Brooklyn.

These experiences, plus my life-time of training in several types of traditional healing, has led me to several conclusions. The first is that the natural tendency of our attention is to expand into the environment and connect with it. This means more than looking at something. It means that each of our minds, in order to operate properly, cannot be locked up inside of us. The mind is not just a by-product of brain activity. It is the biological glue that connects us to the environment. One of the effects of modern life is to "lock up" our minds into our thinking process. In this way, mind is no longer connected to the body. The body seems to be "down there". The mind is no longer biologically connected to the environment, except in the sense that we think about our environment. I have found a fundamental difference in human nature in those societies in which the mind is "locked up" as compared to those in which the mind is not locked up. Stress levels, for example, are higher when the mind is locked up, as if it were soda in a bottle that was shaken. Warmth and humidity have the effect of making the mind more fluid so that it is like watercolor ink dropped onto the wet rice paper. Notice how you feel inside your home in the winter as compared to lying in an open area on a warm summer day.

We have designed our environment to be disconnected. Our shoes and our floors disconnect us from the ground. Our cell phones and computers disconnect us from other people, even as we try to communicate with them. Our packaged, prepared foods disconnect us from picking food from trees and plants. Our single celled ancestors gathered together in colonies and eventually formed multi-cellular animals that are now considered to be a single animal. Each cell became more and more disconnected from the environment external to the colony. In the same way, we are now creating super-organisms, disconnected from the natural environment.

But there are many people who don't feel comfortable giving up their individual, biological identity, in a sense handing over their very minds to the "hive". These people require a direct connection to nature, balancing their membership in society with their membership in the living earth.

One of the things I have noticed is that the more removed you are from nature, the more you are addicted to the "drama of life". The people living at the edge of the jungle certainly had their interpersonal dramas, but their joy of life came mostly from simpler things. On my first trip to Panama, my hosts sat at the edge of the river every evening, staring at the river. They weren't looking at anything in particular; they were just participating in the world around them. They listened to the howler monkeys and tree frogs. Then someone upriver began singing a song and someone downriver sang the next part. My hosts then joined in. The human voices joined with the animal voices in a bizarre choir.

When I was young, people would sit in chairs in front of their houses in Brooklyn, "participating" in life. Things have changed drastically since then. Now we have our televisions and computers to look at. Our activities are less communal. While our society is becoming more isolated from nature, we are becoming more isolated from each other, even as our society as a whole is becoming more condensed and interdependent. When single celled animals formed into multi-cellular animals, each cell lost much of its function and became specialized (muscle cell, gland cell, etc.). They were no longer whole organisms within themselves.

I am reminded of our educational system, no longer emphasizing a "classical education", but just teaching students to pass tests. It certainly seems like we are witnessing the birth of a new type of organism that requires a new type of "mind". This new mind is not whole and balanced. It is not aware of the whole history of humankind, to serve as the backdrop to understand what is going on now. It is designed to be only a piece of a person that is useful for one particular function of the society.

This is similar to what happened at the beginning of the industrial revolution. Company towns grew up around a factory and each worker learned only one skill, which he repeated over and over. Creativity in one's work was not appreciated.

The goal of many philosophies and religions is to acquire a natural type of mind. When Buddhists speak of Buddha, they aren't only referring to the person, but to the state of mind that he attained and that we can also attain: The same is true for Christians who use the term "Christ", really meaning the Christ type of mind. When Taoists speak of "no-mind", they mean a mind not filled with excess of any kind. I consider each to be a rebellion against re-shaping the natural human mind for use in the new societal "machine" of each time period.

With the natural mind, each person is a whole human, directly connected to the living earth. Relationships are between two whole people rather than between two parts of a machine. If we believe in developing whole people, connected to nature, then I believe that a well-rounded education is the place to start, an education that emphasizes creative thinking rather than memorizing answers to tests.

Growing your own food is another place to start so that your food is healthy and nutritious and so that you have a feeling for where your food came from.

I cut and split wood for my wood heating stove. If I figured out the amount of labor involved in getting wood and taking care of the heating stove, I'm sure it would be a lot cheaper just to use the furnace. But heating the house by my own efforts keeps me connected to nature, especially in winter. On the one hand, I could just consider how to be the most efficient to amass wealth. On the other hand, I could consider how to be the most efficient to maintain the natural mind. I try to balance the two, willing to sacrifice some wealth in order to hold onto the wholeness of my life. What is the balance of these two factors in your life?

It is especially hard to maintain this balance in tough economic times. Putting food on the table – any food – is pretty important. But let's remember that if we put off the health of our bodies and minds, we are more prone to disease and we feel miserable. If you can find one thing to do that re-connects you to nature, such as cooking your own food, or growing it, that will go a long way to keeping you healthy and happy. Meet someone face to face, rather than texting. Sit in the back yard, or at a sunny window, and watch the sun set. Doing one natural thing each day can help us to maintain our humanity in the face of a more and more machine-like world.

Never forget that we are an animal species though we have covered the earth with concrete cities. We still breathe air and drink water as animals do. And, no matter how wise and respected we may become, we must still go to the bathroom just as any other creature goes to its "bathroom".

The snake reminds us that we are creatures of nature. This legless being slithers along the earth and hides under rocks and pieces of wood. Though we cover the land with lawns and flowerbeds, reforming it to our artistic tastes, there may be a snake lurking under that marigold or behind that bed of tulips.

There is another piece of nature that we have covered over and that is our own selves. We are civilized and our behavior must conform to the standards of a particular culture. If we don't, we would be punished as a snake who wandered into the kitchen of a lady holding a rolling pin who tries to smash the snake with her "weapon" (personal recollection).

Imagine a hunter in the wild searching for an elusive deer or bird. His senses must be very sharp. The slightest sound, smell or sight will reveal his prey. After a life of hunting he just "knows" where his prey will be found. He knows what the weather will be the next day and how that will affect each animal. The rhythms of nature are his life – night and day, winter and summer, the cycles of the moon. He doesn't eat just because it is a certain time but because nature reveals the proper time to eat. The food he eats is a direct result of his own efforts whether vegetables he has grown or meat he has hunted.

A natural person is healthy and energetic. There is a life force, an energy that flows through nature, through the trees, the lakes, the mountains. This force fills and energizes each creature, each "child of the forest". That energy is called, "chi" and is represented by the snake.

But we are not hunters in the middle of the forest. How is the life force of nature to fill us? How is our snake to uncoil and reveal its power? The first lesson of the snake is that we are still children of the forest. Concrete and lawns cannot keep the snake from our cities and towns. It cannot keep the energy of nature from flowing through us.

Our power comes from the sun, from the moon, from every bit of exposed earth and from every blade of grass. Feel this power. It is real. Believe in this power because you must. When you believe in the power of nature you add to her power, for that power – the snake – is within you, and you will become stronger.

Taoists say that there is a great energy that flows from the earth to the sky and from the sky to the earth. The snake within you will feel it and will uncoil to align itself with that pathway of energy. Your snake loves to bathe in the "earth-sky energy" as a snake loves to sit on a rock and absorb the warmth of the sun. If the snake fails to bathe in the sun it will weaken. The Kundalini energy of Yoga is also represented by a snake.

Feel the energy of flowing water, a stream, river or beach. Allow your snake to swim in this water energy, to drink it in. You will find different energies in each natural area – the forest, a pond, the desert. Allow your internal snake to become a hunter of the energies of nature, to absorb them and become healthy.

The snake confronts each new situation with suspicion. It rears and gets ready to protect itself. Once it is held and feels the gentleness of its captor it calms down and is trusting. If we were to act roughly to the snake, it would bite us. We are creating the reality of the interaction. Creativity can take the place of fear. To understand your creative role in every encounter is the antidote to complaining. Some people use their creativity to turn any situation into an excuse to complain, and that complaining is their drug. What do you use your creativity for in your encounters with people and situations?

In my travels through the jungles of Central America I would park my canoe at a house or small town alongside the river. I found that the first thing I needed to do was explain why I was there. The suspicion was that I was from the government investigating something and that wasn't what they wanted to hear. Being a zoologist searching for reptiles to study wasn't threatening and was entertaining. Establishing the grounds of the interaction was always the first step.

When you expand this idea to your life (what am I doing here?) the answer empowers you. This is the "vision quest" of Native Americans. When you live your life from your vision, life doesn't bite you as much.

If you believe that the world is composed of dead and unconscious molecules acting automatically and that the only consciousness is within human brains, that will lead you to living your life according to that belief. It will then be easy to regard other species as operating by instinct alone and not conscious. You may regard other groups of people in the same way.

When you meet someone do you start by respecting that they are conscious? Do you respect that they are intelligent? Do you respect that they are well meaning? The way you establish the grounds of the interaction, even just within your own mind, will determine the outcome of the interaction.

When practicing the form do you respect that your body is conscious? Do you respect that it is intelligent? Do you respect that it is well meaning? If you do not, then how do you expect to grow the relationship between the mind and body in mutual respect? You might ask, "But what if the body is not conscious, then aren't I just wasting time on an illusion?"

Animals Can Heal

This is the dilemma ethologists (the evolution of animal behavior) faced early in the development of that science. I remember when I was in college during a biology class when this topic was discussed. Are animals conscious? Someone brought in a recent issue of Time Magazine with full-page photos of lions in Africa. The love of a pair of lions for each other was absolutely clear from the photo. Photographers started spending days and weeks, sometimes years, living among animals to get to know them. Behaviors showing deep emotions and creative skills revealed themselves once the photographers really became part of a group of animals.

This was a threat to those who considered humans to be the only conscious or intelligent beings on the planet and it took years until these new findings were accepted. As Tai-chi students we need to do the same with our bodies. We need to "live within" our bodies. This means that our attention needs to seat itself quietly within the body and watch its behavior.

Ethologists and photographers used to use a "blind" to observe animals. They hid within a camouflaged area so the animals wouldn't see them. Lately, people simply stay with a group of animals, not necessarily interacting with them but just letting the animals get used to their presence. This is the same process we use in Tai-chi. Observe the body but don't interfere, so you can witness its intelligence.

As you practice your form, allow your body to play with the momentum. This will challenge your balance and root. If each joint has full range of motion and if you have full awareness of the actions of each muscle you can be challenged more and still stay balanced and rooted. The degree of your body's creativity depends on its health. A healthy body filled with awareness needs very little input from the thinking mind. Let the body get used to the presence of your mind by not interfering with the body's creativity.

In a natural environment many animals coexist peacefully and don't interfere with each other. But if a predator enters the scene, the animals scatter. Don't allow your thinking mind to be a predator of the body. Let it coexist peacefully. Don't confront the body as you practice or judge it – just notice it as if you were a scientist taking notes.

If you come upon a group of animals and you look around for food the animals won't get startled. But if you look right at them, they will think you are looking at them as food. Allow your thinking mind to be affected by the creativity of the body so that it becomes the student – not the teacher. You are not trying to teach the body how to be natural. You are listening to the body so you can stop being artificial.

The thinking mind is a member of a diverse community. The other members are not lesser nor are they the slaves of the thinking mind. When you arrive at a peaceful interaction among the members of the community you become a member of a larger "self". It is that journey to learn how to peacefully interact within yourself that teaches you how to peacefully interact with others and become a member in good standing of an even larger "self". The goal is to enlarge the definition of "self", not to pit one self against another. In all cases the key is to "listen" with a quiet mind, for each to really know the other and respect each other's creativity, so that you can create the reality of your relationship. That relationship is then a living myth, a story that is constantly being written.

Many modern people have entered into such a relationship with nature. At first there were just a few. They wrote about nature. They photographed nature. They spent most of their lives in natural areas. Largely due to the force of their personalities, the power of their writing and the strength of their beliefs, others joined them. Those who followed felt the same joy, the same power in nature. They created the "ecology movement".

Each person joined this movement not to be part of some exclusive club but because they felt a voice calling to them. Their internal "snake" awakened to the energies of nature. In this way modern ecology is similar to ancient Taoism.

An old Taoist once lived in an area where few people shared his beliefs. He loved to lecture about nature and since no people would listen, he spoke to the rocks. It was said that his speeches were so convincing, so full of his love for nature that the rocks nodded in agreement.

A student of Zen was walking with his teacher. The student said, "I have been studying here for a long time. Why don't you reveal your secrets to me?"

"Do you hear the sound of the stream?" asked his teacher.

"Yes, I do," replied the student.

"Do you smell the blossoming flowers?" asked his teacher.

"Yes, I do."

"There!" replied his teacher. "I have hidden nothing from you."

You will find out about many religions and philosophies as you go through life. The Zen teacher didn't give his student yet another philosophy. He told the student to hear and to smell, to be part of the living world, just like the Gnostic saying, "The fragrance of God comes not through the ears but through the nose."

To see the larger self is the path to wisdom. To see that the qualities we value in ourselves are a result of our common connection to nature is the path to peace. To believe in and eventually to experience the life force that joins us to this living community is the path to health.

When your attention lives within your body and the larger body of nature, the thinking mind and the social identity seem smaller – yet you feel healthier. When you are awed by seeing majestic mountains, it doesn't make you sad to feel so small. It brings peacefulness inside you to understand how you are part of something grand.

There is a grandness of the body. Its trillions of cells, each with its own organs ("organelles") and all the molecules within each cell working in concert, combine to form a grand internal world. The grandness of the body can only be appreciated by an attention with a fine resolution that can perceive intricately and that can be absorbed into each part of the body individually.

When you begin your Tai-chi training you are clunky because your attention is clunky and your body is not used to fine, coordinated movement. With practice, your body becomes more liquid and seems to ooze from place to place. Every joint moves in relation to the others.

You learn that there is another mind that can keep track of all this intricate activity. You can watch it act. You spent your youth filling your thinking mind with all sorts of subjects and were taught that with enough information; you could know all there is about any subject. If you became a doctor you were taught about all the systems of the body. Think of all the knowledge of all the doctors in the world put together. Even that much knowledge would not be enough to run the body, for doctors don't yet know all of the ways our bodies function.

Yet you yourself have a mind within you that does have all of this knowledge – the Body-Mind. It knows how to heal and repair itself. It knows how we must grow and change through the years. It knows how to turn "dead matter" into a living being.

We think of young children as being "ignorant" because they haven't yet developed their thinking minds. But their Body-Minds are already well developed. It is what created them. It was in the parts that joined together to create them. Even within the stupidest person, the Body-Mind still functions with knowledge greater than all the doctors of the world.

Wouldn't it be worth something to be able to "see" this knowledge directly and to access this type of mind? The goal would not be to write down information but to include this "world" as part of our senses. If we see a chair in front of us, we intuitively know to walk around it and not trip over it. If we could see inside of us with high resolution we would know how to live in a healthier way.

The body works in a similar way as a human community. Roads allow products to be transported across the country just as the circulatory system transports food and oxygen. White blood cells and antibodies, both of which fight disease, travel these inner roads to protect us, acting like police. Glands, whose secretions control the function of the organs, flow through the blood. These secretions are like a vast postal system or the Internet, sending vital information to every house (cell) in the body.

We secrete our waste outside of the body and receive our nutrients and oxygen from outside the body. Each community collects the waste of its citizens and deposits these outside of the community. At a certain point there is no more outside because one community's outside is another community's inside. Toxic chemicals now pervade the entire planet including the air and the process of evolution is not quick enough to adjust. The earth is a single organism that is being poisoned. It has nowhere "outside" to look for help or to dump its wastes.

When the waste of your body empties into the cesspool, all of the chemicals and drugs you ingested now enter the ground and the ground water. That water then gets pumped back into our sinks to be used to cook our food or as drinking water. When the waste empties into a sewage system, the processed product is pumped into some waterway such as the ocean, there to be ingested by fish and then by people. There is really no "outside".

We are at a similar point as when single celled animals formed into multi-celled animals. Each could no longer function on its own but were part of an intricately balanced system. Our culture at the present time is based on imbalance – maximum consumption, maximum profit, and maximum power. If the entire planet functions as a single organism we no longer have other organisms over which to exert power. We need balance within this one community. That begins with each individual seeking balance within himself.

The nexus of the solution to the imbalance in our world and within our bodies is our creative consciousness – our identity on a whole person level. The decisions we make determine our health and the survival of the earth. It's all on you!

You are like the cell wall that determines which chemicals to allow in and out. The cell's survival depends on this job. Your job also includes which thoughts and attitudes to allow through. These decisions grow from your vision – the vision for your life and for the future of your community. When we release and really let go of "chemicals" (attitudes, fears, anger) through our cell wall to the outside, it is not directed at anyone just as waste from a cell is not directed at another cell. That waste is picked up by the lymphatic system and sent out of the body. Nature can recycle that waste.

When we let go of fear, for example, it can no longer create anger and direct it toward anyone. It is simply released. Somehow, we know that the released energy will be recycled, perhaps giving us more energy to do useful things. It is no longer anger that propels us but such things as a sense of justice and our vision for a better world. We can be calm and still work as hard for the changes we seek. Let the air recycle your shouts and the ground your tears and then get on with your vision.

This transformation then gives us a different perspective when faced with another person releasing their anger. We understand its origin as their fear and that it does not need to enter us if we remain relaxed and centered. Their waste does not need to go back into our drinking water.

The carbon dioxide we breathe out of our lungs is just waste to us. But the plants use it and release their own waste, oxygen that we need to breathe. Nature is based on this kind of cyclic giving and taking. The sea gives its water to the sky where it forms clouds. The clouds rain down onto the earth and sea completing the cycle.

Releasing old behavior patterns and ideas and allowing you to be transformed is the cycle of growth. You don't have the same ideas you had as a child. You aren't the same person. But just as nature itself continues to flourish even with all the changes that take place over millions of years, there is a creative thread inside of you that continues to grow even as your personality changes. Its strength and growth depend on your ability to release wastes and not to hoard and defend those wastes. To let go of your anger or old ideas is not betraying who you are; it is realizing that letting go is part of a cycle that is also you. When the snake sheds its old skin, it is not betraying itself. Another newer, larger skin has taken its place. Tai-chi provides exercises that test what is useful and what needs to be sent to the recycling bin.

I know someone who thought she had to pay attention to her heart at all times or it would stop beating. She had trouble sleeping. When I told her she didn't have to pay attention to her heart, she thought I was trying to trick her to hurt her. She thought everyone paid attention to their hearts all the time. Finally, her therapist gave her a stethoscope to listen to her heart and suggested that she stop paying attention to it. If it stopped, she would know it by hearing it. She was able to get over this habit, got a lot better sleep and had more energy. You never know what odd ideas people have that are interfering with their lives. When you go through Tai-chi training these ideas are exposed and challenged, freeing you from their grasp.

The journey of Tai-chi is the realization of how many bizarre ideas you have that control your life. If you root your life in those ideas you are like a vegetable grown with hydroponics. Many vegetables today are grown in water with chemicals added for nutrients. To most organic farmers the soil is most important. Soil is a community of living organisms whose vitality is the basis of the value of the crop it produces. The vegetable grown from a healthy, living soil absorbs and stores the life of the soil and transmits that to us when we eat it. Plants and trees growing from this soil communicate with each other in many ways to strengthen each other and create balance in the soil ecology.

If the soil were deficient in some way the plants and trees would suffer and the farmer would remedy this problem by improving the soil, not by spraying chemicals on the plants. In the same way much of our illness is caused by where our roots get their nutrients. If the thinking mind is disconnected and acts like a demiurge, it is like hydroponics. The body, connected by internal energy to the rest of the natural world, is like the earth. To promote our health, Tai-chi not only gives us exercises to strengthen the body, but roots our consciousness in the body and restores its communication system. Our bodies become a living community of living beings full of vitality rather than just a machine. This transformation itself is the healing.

Much of modern agriculture considers the soil to be a neutral medium in which chemical fertilizers are mixed to provide "nutrients" for crops. The soil is no longer living and the crops roots just absorb the chemicals that are provided. They are not part of a living community of soil nor do they participate in that vitality.

Has the culture we live in also become a "neutral medium" into which the agendas of political groups, religions and corporations and poured for us to absorb? At this point where are minds are so plugged into the digital world, I feel we need to pull our roots out of the neutral medium and place it into a living soil i.e. the ancient teachings such as Tai-chi. The living soil is our living bodies and the living world around us. The roots are made of our attention.

Why do you think there is a lot of depression and drug addiction? We are increasingly disconnected from the living soil that is the basis of our real lives and so we feel less and less real. Many people are no longer able to feel joy, not because they are sad due to some misfortune, but because they are disconnected. Their roots are no longer in living soil and they mistake the experience of drugs for that soil.

Like Hansel and Gretel, we are lost and the breadcrumbs marking our path back have been eaten. They have been eaten by the erasure of the history of the aboriginal cultures' methods of maintaining our relationship to nature. They have been eaten by the erasure of labor history, women's history, cultural history, art history, etc. so that we don't know how we got here. We are the demiurge, created by the seeking for wisdom, which looks around seeing only himself. We feel that all knowledge that has come before is irrelevant.

There are two types of Zookinesis teachers – human and animal. The human teachers teach you how to learn from the animals. The influence of these animals has created the "personality" of my healing and way of teaching Tai-chi. While we may think of animals as inferior to humans, you can appreciate that the animals don't necessarily share the same view.

My Madagascan chameleon peered down at me from one of the rafters of the greenhouse. This group of lizards inhabit Africa, and Madagascar with one species in India and one in southern Europe. The Oustalet's chameleon is one of the largest, around two feet from nose to tail tip. They feel most comfortable being above you, looking down at you.

From this lofty perch, my friend rolled his independently rotating eyes in a pattern that communicated his feelings towards me. After looking me up and down, he said, "You're no big deal".

My experiences have led me to believe that the chameleon's assessment of me is appropriate. In their degree of awareness, most animals are vastly superior to most humans. Students of Tai-chi, or of any training that requires fine-tuned awareness, feel very awkward at first. After a few years of training, they can appreciate how far their awareness has grown when they help to instruct a new, beginning student.

We should be able to coordinate the movements of every joint and muscle of the body at the same time, just as the animals do. It often takes three years or more to be able to coordinate the left and right sides of the body at the same time in Push Hands. Few people have much awareness of their bodies, of the dynamics of attention, of the dynamics of internal energy, of the dynamics of breathing or much else that comes very naturally to any animal. And yet we feel superior to animals!

As any student wishes to clearly and precisely reflect the training of his teacher, I wish to reflect the teachings of mine – the animals.

There is a tendency, when meeting a foreigner, to judge his intelligence by his skills in speaking your own language. If he has trouble communicating, you might assume he is dumb.

The chameleon feels the same way. I have learned to communicate with him through the movement of my eyes. I can sense its intelligence. It is something you must learn to do and to perceive. Otherwise, you would look at a lizard moving its eyes and think, "Dumb animal".

My ability to move my eyes is not as great as that of the chameleon and so I will never be able to be as "smart" as he (from his point of view). Yet, he cannot talk so he will never be as smart as I (from my point of view). His color changes are also a form of communication

229

and I will never be able to do that (and I don't have much of a fashion sense.) We are equals, though, when it comes to the use of our hands in expression. Chameleons have many ways of holding their arms and hands.

All things considered; we are equals. What we must do is to find means of communication we can both do and appreciate – eye and hand movements in this case. As I communicate with my scaly friend, I cannot help but talk because I am so talk oriented. My talking may not help him understand unless, over time, he gains some understanding of the tones and volumes of my voice.

Similarly, I may not understand his color changes right away but may come to appreciate the subtleties over time. So we may actually learn new ways of communicating from each other.

The process of becoming acquainted with our communication systems, in itself, is very fulfilling. The information one receives is even more fulfilling.

Logical thoughts may not be the way information is stored or conveyed in a lizard, but his type of information is still valuable and is still a reflection of the intelligence that flows through him. If we humans limit our expression of intelligence to logical thinking, we will truly show our stupidity among all the species in the animal world.

Logical thinking is a wonderful expression of intelligence, but it is only one small part of it. When we become too enamored with logic, it can turn against us. Violent religious fanatics explain their violence in logical terms. The rest of us can see the faults within their logic and use our own counter-logic.

Logic can be misused when it is not balanced with other forms of intelligence. It can allow us to perceive enemies where there are none, to doubt our power to achieve great things and it can even ruin our health. In other words, we can be convinced of anything, if ideas are repeated often enough.

With all the power our technology has achieved, we have robbed ourselves of basic happiness and understanding the ability to perceive our connection to the rest of nature. When I would tire of paddling through the jungle rivers, I would pull the canoe to the shore and tie it up at a spot that allowed me to walk through the dense growth at the river's edge. I was walking on someone else's land – a tribe of monkeys, a flock of macaws or perhaps, a solitary sloth. I became very aware this was their land because they would look at me as I neared them. Their look was always the same, "What are you and what are you doing here?" Anyone would look the same if he found someone on his property.

Their stare would make me stop and wonder, "What indeed, am I and what, indeed, am I doing here?" At first, I returned the stare as if to say, "I'm a human and I came here to look at you." Later on, it became, "I'm not really sure what I am and what I'm doing here." Finally, I understood better and it became, "I am human and I'm here because I love being here and I belong here. How are you today?"

Consider the process of healing. You are really "intruding" on the territory of the body. It wants to know what you are doing – what are your intentions. That initial response of the body to your presence (to your pressures) can tell you a lot about its condition.

Then you must gather information from the patient's mind before you can figure out the cause of the problem. You can ask the patient questions. "Where do you hurt? What kind of pain is it? When do you have this pain?" You can ask lifestyle questions. "What is your diet like? What is your occupation? How much sleep do you get at night?"

But you need a lot more information. You need to diagnose by getting readings from the patient. You might take a pulse, either in the modern medical sense or the Chinese medical sense. You can do blood analysis (modern medicine) or check the skin texture (Chinese medicine).

Some methods of "reading" a patient may seem bizarre or even fraudulent (and sometimes are.) These readings require the use of additional senses. By explaining how these senses are used I hope to make their identity clear to you.

When we focus several senses on something, we can understand it more clearly. If you heard a crunching noise and smelled an apple, you would guess that someone was eating an apple even without seeing him.

The sense of internal energy gives you another angle by which to judge what is going on. This sense is based on how the Body-Mind of two individuals interact, or how your Body-Mind interacts with your environment. This is what you are using when the patient's body first "sees you on its property".

You must establish why you are there by how you interact with the body. You are not there to plunder (to impose your clever techniques on the body) but to cooperate in its healing. The body and you develop a means of communication.

I remember the first time I lifted the screen top off a tank with a female Oustalet's chameleon. She was flabbergasted. Her expression (facial, color, eyes and hand movements) was one of total astonishment. She looked at the open top, then at me. Back and forth she looked, as if to try to figure out some explanation.

When she had grown used to this amazing phenomenon of opening and closing the cage top, she would look back and forth from me to the screen top, when the top was still on the tank. I knew this to mean, "Please take the top off so I can get out and walk around the rafters of the greenhouse." When the top came off, she waved her little arms around, again looking back and forth from me to the now open top, to be picked up and freed. These are not stupid animals.

In this case, she was really saying to me, "What is the connection between you, the open top, and me waving my arms around, huh?"

I have learned that the parts of the human body are also not dumb. They have a way of expressing themselves and trying to convey their needs to the healer. In the case of the chameleon, my regular senses were enough to understand her. But a healer needs to acquire a great deal of information from the patient's body and much of this can only be obtained through the sense of internal energy (chi) and the sense of attention.

I went to a friend's house and met his large Burmese python. As the python crawled over to me, he stopped, reared up and stared at me. I knew this meant he was unsure if it was all right to come over to me. I just softened my eyes and relaxed my body to let him know it was all right and he approached and crawled on my body. We humans also use these types of cues with each other to judge temperament, intention and emotional context, even when we are having a very logical discussion.

I once handed a boa to a woman student in Push Hands class to let her have her turn to experience its energy, and then walked off to teach other people. When I returned, fifteen minutes later, she told me that she was deathly afraid of snakes and didn't know I was going to hand it to her, let alone walk away. But in those fifteen minutes, she grew fond of it.

In each case the snake communicated in a way that is not easily observable. When my friend's snake looked at me, its slight head movements, the posture of its rearing, the sound of its hiss and the movement of its eyes all conveyed the question, "Can I approach?" The softening of my eyes was a language it could understand.

There was even another method of communication. Snakes do not see especially well. Part of the effect of softening the eyes is to change the quality of internal energy in my body. This is something a snake can sense better than sight. It is certainly not a scientifically accepted idea, but it is one that is well accepted among traditional healers. It is something I experience clearly.

When I handed the snake to my Push Hands student, its calm energy allowed her to calm down. Its gentleness was very apparent and she quickly realized it was no danger to her.

Awareness of "internal energy" is a common theme among healers of many cultures. It may be called by different names (e.g. prana) and may be represented by different symbols (the sun, a snake or dragon). It is something a healer feels vividly and uses daily so for him, it is absolutely real and is vital in his work.

Another related sense is the sense of attention. There is a pattern to our attention. What are we paying attention to? How strong is that attention? Can we pay attention to more than one thing at a time? Can we follow something that is quickly changing with our attention?

That sense can detect the pattern and quality of someone's else's attention. The relationship between attention and internal energy is as follows. Attention is the substance that binds all living things together. Internal energy is the dynamics of that substance.

You could relate it to electricity. Electricity is a wave of electrons. The electrons are there all the time. When they move in a wave, we call it electricity and this wave can be harnessed to do work.

There was a movement of attention between the snake and me, a closed circuit. This allowed information to flow between us just as the changes in the wave of electricity conveys information through a phone line.

The individual organs and muscles in the human body are also connected with internal energy. This is their communication system.

The healer observes how the parts of the body communicate with each other.

You can develop these senses by communicating with animals. These same senses can then be used to observe the dynamics of energy within a patient. When you first meet an animal, you both stare at each other. There is silence and stillness. You may each be watching for each other's next move. But there is something even more wonderful happening. You are trying to sense the pattern and quality of each other's attention.

This first moment is a great time to learn about these new senses. There is no movement, no sound. Try to detect any other type of information you are instinctually "listening" for. What do you see when you look into its eyes?

When I massage someone, I allow for this moment to take place whenever I place my hand on a new spot. I "listen" for information. I perceive that the muscle I'm working with is "connecting with me" or perhaps it is too weak and dull to connect with me. I have methods equivalent to shouting, "Hey! You there!" My first effort is to engage the muscle's attention, not to just start manipulating it.

The muscle may soften (as I softened my eyes to the snake), as if to say, "You may come in." Only then do I manipulate. I respect the muscle as I would respect you, walking up to your house. I would knock on the door first and enter only if you opened the door and allowed me in.

My purpose of entering would be to have a conversation with you, to exchange information and perhaps change your point of view (or have mine changed by you).

I approach healing in the same way. I converse with the muscle using finger and palm pressure, exchange of energy, passive stretching, etc.

Handling a python over ten feet long is done in a similar way. You can't overpower it. You can't let it overpower you. Each of you gives each other information about your balance, feelings of security, how much pressure you can take, how much the snake needs to feel secure, etc. You eventually blend together and react to each other automatically.

The snake expresses its comfort level by the sound of its hiss. You learn to interpret its hiss. A loud hiss may mean it feels very good. It depends on the sound of the hiss.

A person's body is composed of many muscles and other parts, each with its own ability to communicate. A healer must be able to perceive each part's qualities and the way they all relate to each other to form the whole.

It is like an ecologist's work to study each species in a habitat, the geology and climate and then learn to see the habitat as a whole with all its dynamics. Our body is an ecological system.

I once acquired a four-foot iguana. Someone found it sitting on a wall behind a library. I had to learn about its personality. It didn't like to eat from a bowl but preferred hand feeding. Someone had obviously kept it as a pet for a long time and had fed it by hand. Unfortunately, they hadn't fed it a varied diet because there were signs of calcium deficiency.

I approach each muscle in the body in the same way when I massage. What is it used to? What condition is it in?

The iguana was very happy to be paid attention to. Though they are usually loners in the wild, they come to crave human attention. Many animal species which are loners in the wild (house cats, for example), fit in very well with a family. Some zoologists say it is because we keep the animal at a baby stage of its development. I think the case is harder to make with snakes and lizards. Baby snakes are also loners.

When it comes to the human body, our muscles have learned to become loners too – to be disconnected from the rest of the body. Yet they, too, crave attention. A massage feels great, doesn't it, even if you touch just lightly. When you pay attention to the muscle, it lights up (with internal energy).

There is a difference between a body filled with lone parts and a family of parts. When there is a flow of communication among all of your parts, it is an easy step to extend your attention to other people or animals. When you extend your attention, it is still connected to all of the parts – to the whole system.

When you and an animal extend your attentions into each other, you can each instantly access the whole pattern of each other's attention and energy flow. The animal is not just waiting for your next move; it is accessing the deepest recesses of your being.

We fear that. We fear someone else going into places inside of us that even we can't get into. For those who do have access to all parts of themselves, there is no fear. They can follow the snake's attention as it enters into them and join it into every crevice. When you know yourself, you don't fear having others know you.

There is a technique in massage in which you pay attention to the part in your body, that you are massaging in your patient's body, connecting them together. Then you relax both at the same time. By connecting your bodies together via internal energy, you open up the patient's body to communication. It is as if the part in your body says, "See, this is how to relax" and the same part in the patient's body then knows how to do it.

There is a special feeling when you first communicate with an animal and you know it has communicated with you. You are accepted as a fellow snake or bird. I remember working with toucans. They watched people as a form of entertainment. If I was cleaning or doing paperwork, they looked at what I was doing, then back at me, back and forth. I could sense what was going on inside of them, "When does the exciting stuff start?".

Toucans are always up for fun. If I didn't entertain them, they did a little dance in which they squatted and then stood up repeatedly as if preparing to fly, as they stared into my eyes. So I had to come up with something – a song, a little dance or at least rubbing their heads. I thought of setting up a little television set in front of their enclosure, but I thought that would mess up their heads. I learned to understand each animal's personality to avoid dealing with them as just "an animal".

There is a similar feeling when you know that you have communicated with a muscle, "telling" it to relax, and it relaxes practically all by itself. You realize that a muscle is intelligent, or at least responsive, and that gives you a whole new respect for the human body. It also gives you a new respect for the human being as a whole. You know that a person is a community of intelligences.

Perhaps the schizophrenic with multiple personalities is tuned into some of these and imagines them as whole people. They may lack the ability to integrate them and to accept them as body parts. Certain other people may be sensitive to the intelligence that flows through all life. When they experience such intelligence, they also may lack the ability to perceive the whole network of intelligence and appreciate its unified nature. And so, they interpret such energy as coming from a dead person's spirit. They need to feel such intelligence comes from a specific source other than themselves, that has a personality. Their internal dynamics are projected onto the image of a separate person. It is as if they are shielding their "fashioned creature", their created personality, from the biological, creative intelligence that created that creature in the first place.

That Body-Mind uses the patterns of the world around you as an artist uses paints. Yet the patterns of the world also use you as paints. These two influences are like battling artists or musicians. The results can be beautiful art and music if you are willing to accept your identity as the art itself, that is constantly being created.

When you interact with an animal you can't rely on programmed responses that we humans have learned when we interact with each other. Due to the differences in behavior patterns, it is the creativity of each that is called forth to figure out how to interact. We can't pluck a pattern of behavior out of our repertoire. We really have to enter into a relationship with the animal and allow the energy of creativity to interact.

In order to allow energy to flow you must cultivate emptiness. It is the hollowness of a pipe that allows water to flow through. This emptiness is not the same as emotional sadness. These pipes are empty of emotions as well. When you relax a muscle that is tense because of fear, you are emptying that muscle.

When a person stares at a snake for the first time, it is its emptiness that makes him feel uncomfortable. The snake stares, yet it is very still. You can sense stillness within its body and it is this stillness that seems dangerous. You don't know what will come out of it.

Furthermore, your own energy is drawn into that stillness as air is sucked into a vacuum. As your attention moves into the snake's eyes, your own rigid pattern of attention is disturbed. It is moving in a direction and with a force not under your control. We are not used to the dynamic movement of attention and to its methods of connecting with other living things. Our attention is one-dimensional. We place it here and then there. We don't know much about in between here and there.

Tai-chi practice trains us to develop a "field" of attention. This field is like a large sphere all around us. Our attention penetrates our whole body and the surroundings. It is fluid, so that if it is drawn by the snake's stare, part of it flows to the snake but the rest is undisturbed. If there are multiple pulls on our attention, as in sparring, a part of our attention can flow to each of the pulls. The rest remains undisturbed.

There is less fear with this type of attention because you feel comfortable connecting with your surroundings, with all its complex dynamics.

When I was young, I went to the New York Herpetological Society every month at the Bronx Zoo. I was the Vice President of that group. Just outside the zoo was a reptile shop that always had a tank of Cook's tree boas. These are thin, bird eating snakes that have to bite very quickly to get their meal. They have unusually long teeth to penetrate the feathers.

After the "herp' meeting, some of us would visit the reptile shop. We would challenge each other to grab a Cook's boa out of the swarming mass of intertwined snakes at the bottom of the cage. One person would point to a specific snake that another person was to grab. That person had to reach in, untwine the snakes and take out that specific boa.

A skilled "herper" could grab the snake and receive no more than one or two bites on the arm. Your attention had to be everywhere at once. You had to know where each head was and how ready it was to bite. You had to know the quickest way to unwind the designated snake and, as you did that, to avoid the bites.

If you withdrew your hand before removing your snake, you were considered an amateur. By the time the arm was withdrawn it usually had at least three snakes hanging onto it by their teeth. I'm proud to say that I often got my snake without any bites.

The world of herpetologists can be a bit odd. I was in a New York City apartment of another member of the herp group. His living room was filled with huge fish tanks filled with alligators and crocs.

He told me that a nineteen-foot reticulated python had recently gotten loose. When he walked in the door, he heard his wife screaming. She had locked herself in the bathroom and shouted that the retic was loose. He looked around the room and found it draped around the molding of the entrance door. He tried to coax it down, but the enormous snake struck at him repeatedly. Calling to his wife to stay in the bathroom, he ran out the door and found the superintendent of the building. The two of them plus a friend found some metal garbage can covers they could use as shields and plungers they could use as weapons.

Running back into the apartment, they pushed the snake with the plungers (using the rubber end so as not to injure the snake). They protected themselves from the strikes with the metal covers. Each time the snake struck the cover, there was a loud "bong" sound. This battle went on for a couple of hours until the snake was finally subdued.

Unfortunately, the snake died a few days later as a result of the battle. Our friend loaded the corpse into the trunk of his car with the intention of dumping it into the East River. His wife called to him from the window because he had a call from a patient. (He was a psychiatrist). Somehow, beyond my understanding, he forgot about the snake after his phone call.

It was the middle of the summer. A few days later he noticed a smell coming from the trunk and finally remembered the snake.

My own worst snake experience was also with a retic. This species is very unpredictable and powerful. My retic was only thirteen feet long. I reached into its cage to retrieve the water tub. The snake assumed I was feeding it and the only object it could see was my body. It bit me several times on the arm. A python has a hundred long teeth. My arm was black, blue, purple and green for a few weeks after.

The snake gave one last bite but this time held on, coiling around and trapping my body, arms and legs. I managed to hold onto its neck to prevent further biting but after a while my strength was giving out. It was stupid of me to stick my hand into the cage. I should also not have opened the cage when I was tired. I thought of all these things as the coils got tighter. This would be a good time to test my Tai-chi abilities, I figured, as it may be my last chance.

I was finally able to extricate myself by using Push Hands. I pushed the snake back into the cage, closed the door tightly and took care of my arm.

It's not that we particularly enjoy the danger of working with large, powerful reptiles; we just love having them around. Most species are very docile. As for the less docile varieties, it's enjoyable to have pets with a little spunk. You just have to respect that to them, you may look like lunch.

In most cases, what appears to be aggression by a reptile is really a misunderstanding. You may have the smell of a mouse on your hand, for example. As you and your reptile get used to each other there are less mistakes. You are more tuned into its behavior and vice versa.

Herpers truly love their animals. Yet the human knows that his beloved reptile is a wild animal and easily capable of killing him. The animal might be in a bad mood or something may just trigger an aggressive behavior. So while you love a big python, for example, you must stay alert lest it try to devour you. Perhaps this seems familiar to relationships you have had with humans as well.

There is no anger about the aggressive potential of the snake; that is just its nature and you love the animal for what it is. You know that it is not a human, subject to the morals and standards of behavior of human culture. You love its wildness and you love the way you can connect with and appreciate each other.

If there were an intellectual snake, it might view us in a similar way. It could love an individual human, but as a group, we are destroying its native home and its "people." We are aggressive too in our own way. After all, we may have captured it from its native habitat, put it in a box, flown it across the world, placed it in a big glass tank, heaped upon numerous other snakes, then shipped to a store and bought by a herper. And now we expect it to be friends with us! It is amazing, after all that abuse, that they are indeed willing to be friends.

When I used to collect reptiles, I found them to be very tame when I first pick them up, as long as I held them gently. Reptiles and people seem to get along well.

I would canoe through jungle rivers in Central America, looking for reptiles sunning themselves on tree branches. When one was spotted, I brought the canoe near, pulled down the branch and waved my hand to call the snake forth. The other people on board were amazed to see the snake come right over to me. I simply picked it up and placed it into the snake bag (pillow case). The snake came over to me because it saw some vague movement (of my waving hand) and smelled something. I just took advantage of its behavior to amaze my friends.

A newcomer to the snake world will not understand their inner workings. If you ask them why they are afraid of a snake staring into their eyes, they will probably say it is because they think the snake will bite them.

Actually, the snake is just being friendly. But all this person knows is that this legless creature is sending its powerful attention into their inner recesses, shining a bright spotlight in areas the person himself dares not visit. It is all too sudden and too massive an exposure. The snake goes right in there, with its attention, as if those places were mouse burrows the snake was exploring.

We are not so much afraid of the snake as we are of those unknown, and now exposed places inside of us. Snakes can help you heal by making your inner world visible to you. Rather than projecting your inner fears onto the snake, you project your inner beauty onto the snake. You welcome its attention and explore your inner worlds together. You "soar". The spirit world is not sinister to those who know how to traverse it and the snake is skilled in that world. Of course, it is not a good idea to work with venomous snakes. Even with non-venomous snakes, it takes time to learn to work with them, just as it takes time to learn Tai-chi, so I am not advocating carelessness.

The snake's stare is like a knock on the door. It moves towards you and then stops and stares. She can tell by the way her attention moves into you whether you are prey, a creature to be ignored or one she can play with. The tongue darts in and out to gather additional information.

If you relax, allow her attention to seep into you and "greet" that attention with your own, the snake knows there is a human spirit inside you and it can play. It then moves over to you, coils around your body, pushes its nose into your hair, hisses with contentment and does all the things a snake does to play with you.

The moment the snake's attention meets yours is the subject of the training called, "The gatekeeper". The gate is where "external" attention meets your own attention. It is like a gate in the middle of a forest – meaningless in a way (you could just walk around the gate) and very meaningful in another way (it represents a boundary). The gatekeeper greets the newcomer, assesses his intentions and then either lets him in or not. The gatekeeper will be more likely to let the newcomer in if the "city" behind the gate is strong.

With most of us, the city is weak and there is no real gatekeeper – just a rusty, old, unguarded gate. That is why, when someone passes the gate, the whole army must come out to defend the city – just in case.

The snake respects the gate and that is why she stops first, to allow the gatekeeper time to look her over. The snake must be on her best behavior at that moment. If you look at her with understanding eyes, you can see her trying to look angelic. When the gatekeeper finally opens the gate, the snake can relax and crawl through. Imagine her surprise if that army came out to attack her when she was looking her most angelic. This is how a snake feels when someone gets frightened of her and starts screaming.

The gatekeeper is the mediating process to allow the merging of two attentions. It is important in all human relationships. It is the same gate that mediates the relationship among the mind, body, emotions and will. The spirit of the gatekeeper serves as the basis for the spirit of the person as a whole. The quality of the relationship between the parts of a person will be the same as the relationship between the person as a whole and the rest of his world, including other people.

It is easy to understand, then, how spending time with certain types of animals can influence everything about you. The "people" he meets affect the gatekeeper. He must judge if their qualities will have a good effect on yours. To do this, he must be a healer because he must fully understand the balance of all the parts of his city. He must know how they interact, what they need and if the qualities of the visitor will enhance that balance or not. If the gatekeeper is a healer, then the person as a whole must also be a healer. He must understand how to maintain balance and how to judge the internal state of others. The maturity, experience, sensitivity and kindness of the gatekeeper are the most important issues in healing.

Chapter 6
Spirit World & the Inner Senses

I saw an interview with Paul Simon in which someone accused him of stealing music from South Africa. Simon incorporated the South African musical sound into his songs and even toured with a backup band from there. It was not that he played a South African song and claimed it was his own; he simply allowed his music to be influenced by that sound.

Paul Simon explained that all musicians are influenced by other musicians. In order to truly incorporate that sound into yours, you have to really let it affect you so that you can hear with the ears of another group of people. Then you create your own music which arises out of your own inner transformation and greater awareness.

It is the same with learning Tai-chi. It is not just a question of memorizing movements that a Chinese person invented. The exercises are just a door that can be opened to a new vision of life, a way of connecting to the world around you. If you don't walk through that door, you will never do Tai-chi. It has to affect you right down to your cells – to your soul. Otherwise, you will indeed just be imitating or "stealing" something from another culture.

Many Native Americans reject the idea of deciding who is a member of their culture with a genetic test. It is the ability to see with their eyes, hear with their ears and live your life according to the principles of their culture that determines who is a Native American. This is especially the case because they have intermarried with people of other cultures.

When you are practicing a Tai-chi form, you are looking through the "eyes" of every part of your body and joining the "culture" of the biological evolution of the earth. To practice Tai-chi movements without such awareness seems to me as offensive as donning a Native American headdress and making believe you are an "Indian".

The thinking mind can also "look" through the eyes of nature; it can become a true citizen of that culture, just as someone who intermarries with a Native American can become a Native American. Yet we know that America's original people were slaughtered and the lands they lived on were robbed from them. Even practicing their own culture was illegal until recently.

An unbalanced mind engages in a struggle for control of the sensing systems so that what we sense conforms to our ideas. A balanced mind uses the world we experience as an artist to create ideas but doesn't damage the clarity of our senses.

The spirit – your creative identity - uses the senses to make better connections to the physical world. To the spirit - the body, the senses, the physical world and even the emotions and thoughts, form one whole reality and it is their union that is the goal. The unbalanced mind rips each apart and analyzes its components, mining their value to re-enforce its thought structure (which was created by our society). This is the way our culture rips the connection of our bodies, emotions, mind and physical world apart from each other. It creates this war and we are the victims. That war is then projected onto other people and to the physical world, based on intolerance for minds that are not also involved in that war.

Those who rip apart themselves and the world around them, live a different life from those who seek the connections among all their experiences of the world. In the movie, "Excalibur", the solution to the dead world King Arthur found himself in, was in understanding that "The land and the King are one".

Isn't union with our environment the basis of spirituality? It might not seem that two people squaring off and trying to push each other off balance is a spiritual practice, but Push Hands is ruthlessly spiritual. It turns conflict into union. Yet at the same time, each partner is genuinely trying to push the other off balance every chance he gets. So this is not a lazy spirituality, but fully active. When you spar (Tai-chi-Chuan), it is even more active yet the principles are the same. You need to connect and live within the sparring partner even though you are not in contact (except at the moment of the punch or kick or when you are grappling).

The way to progress in Tai-chi practice is not to acquire techniques, but to see clearly. To see clearly, we must understand what there is to see and at the same time, be open to experiencing things we don't yet know anything about. Once we understand that attention itself has qualities and dynamics that can be developed, we become aware of those qualities in ourselves. We also need to be open to the experience of new dynamics that we have never experienced before and know nothing about. These experiences seem like that whiff of smell from a distant bakery. It calls us to seek out the source but we have only hints of smell to go on. We trust that someone must be baking bread somewhere nearby and hope we can get some of it. Our nose leads us.

There is another type of nose within us, one that "smells" dynamics of energy, including the dynamics of attention itself. This is the sense of "chi". It opens up a whole new world of experience and therefore, the ability to respond to situations in new ways. It allows us to live differently. While chi is sometimes thought of as shooting out from the body to knock people down, this is a cartoon version. Healing the sense of chi allows you to "see" things from different points of view. If onlookers do not understand these new ways, it seems mysterious.

Letting the Push Hands partner control the top, including the head, helps detach emotions from the thoughts. Then what we call emotions and what we call physical feelings can be seen as the same thing because you are not labelling your emotions. When you release your attention, you allow the emotions to inhabit the world around you, including the Push Hands partner. Your emotions were prisoners of the thinking, labelling mind; now they are residents of the world, allowing you to see it in new ways. That new way is called, "the Spirit World". Love is experienced as entering the grandness of the universe. Your creative spirit is the grandness of the universe entering your individual life.

That two-way flow strengthens the internal energy. The practice of dragon breathing described previously is very important for then storing life energy in the body. It creates inertia to the flow of energy, like speeding up a heavy flywheel. The issue of storing inertia is vital for health. If you are operating at or near your maximum energy ability, your body and spirit can be easily damaged.

Many people do aerobics to increase their aerobic capacity for those times it will be needed. You can also store the inertia of life energy.

First you must experience this inertia so you will know what it is. When your body is cleared of tension and other blockages so that life energy can flow through it, you are now ready to create mechanisms that can store this energy. You can call these batteries instead of flywheels but I think the latter term is more descriptive. It is not a static reservoir of energy but very dynamic. It is the movement or flow that creates the storage of energy just like a steep mountain stream keeps a waterwheel moving.

The result of this practice is that you feel as if you are riding a tiger. The storage of dynamic energy creates a fueling of potential power inside of you like a tiger ready to spring. This feeling penetrates every fiber of your body so there is an army of tigers ready to spring. You will build your attention's aerobic capacity.

Yet this does not result in anxiety or aggressiveness because there is an overall calm feeling as well. When you are operating well within your maximum power level the "engines" aren't straining. They can relax even as they are working. The resultant feeling is self-confidence to the finest depths of your being.

A key to this training is to "strengthen" the Yin channels of energy flow. I previously described how Yang energy flows through Yin parts of the body (and Yin energy travels through Yang parts). Generally, the Yin parts of the body are the front of the torso and the inside of the legs and arms.

If you ask someone to show you how strong they are or to act as if they are tough, they will generally expand their back and outside of the arms and legs. They strengthen the Yang parts of their body. When we want a powerful storage of energy, we must strengthen the Yin areas.

Some people may think that "Yin" means empty of attention. The Yin parts of the body need as much attention as the Yang parts. Yielding is full of attention. You learn to let go with skill.

One way to do this is to simply stretch a Yin spot or area and breathe in. In this case the spot may be all the Yin areas of the body, or the inside of one arm for example (upper and lower arm). You send energy out of the skin as described above (dragon breath) and your attention follows and is released. You will be "spinning the flywheel" of that area to store energy and strengthen it.

Yang energy is outgoing energy. Yin energy moves in through the body and into the ground. As the Yang energy moves out through the Yin areas there must be a corresponding "sinking" or relaxing of the Yang parts of the body, allowing Yin energy to move through those parts and ground through the legs. This relaxing also helps Yang force to be released into the Yin parts of the body so it can expand upward (on the in-breath). In the example above (the inside of an arm), you might relax the shoulder blades, then the upper back, low back, glutes, hamstrings and then calves and feet, as you are releasing energy out the inside of the arm. When the pace of the movement of Yin and Yang energy is even you get maximum spinning of the flywheel and maximum storage of energy.

The goal is to do this with the body as a whole. This requires physically relaxing your back and outsides and back of the arms and legs while energizing the front of the body and inside of the arms and legs (on the inbreath). Your attention must divide up in this way so that you can organize the relationship between Yin and Yang areas, between energizing and relaxing.

Between these two areas there are parts of the body where the energy circles between Yin and Yang energies. These are like whirlpools between the outgoing and incoming energies. The simplest such place to work with is the Tan-tien - the area just below the navel in the middle of the body. These areas actually feel like flywheels. Another area is the solar plexus at the base of the sternum. The sternum area also rotates energetically in this way.

When you are doing a Tai-chi form and you transition between an inbreath and outbreath or vice versa, your attention must circle around these whirlpools. The joints in the areas of the whirlpools must also circle. In fact, each joint of the body should have a whirlpool or flywheel within it. The more joints with well-developed flywheels, the more smoothly your body will move, meaning that energy circles there. This allows your movements to be smooth and continuous.

This brings up an issue that seems to be important to my students. (To me, everything seems important but my students tell me that some issues need more careful explanation).

The flywheel is continuously turning and the Yin and Yang energies are always connected from your root through the body and into the world around you (earth and heaven connected). Yet when a joint moves, it can only be at one point of its rotation at any time. The movement of a joint, while it may be smooth, is not at all points of the circle at all times. For example, the hips rotate under and forward as you move forward, up and back as you move back – like using a shovel to dig up earth.

So the part of your attention which keeps track of energy flow and the part keeping track of joint movement are in two different kinds of modes - one a continuous flow of energy and the other at only one point in the circle at any one time. The relationship between these two ways of using the attention is an important issue and lies at the heart of many issues of internal power and healing as well as spiritual growth. The proper mechanics of the joints allows for the continuity of flow of momentum.

Part of your attention is working linearly and part is working in what might be called a three dimensional or holistic way. The attention can work in different ways at the same time. We are used to a linear mode - paying attention to one thing at a time and jumping from one thing to another.

The ability of your attention to work in many modes at the same time gives depth to your presence in the world, allows you to experience yourself and your world more fully and allows you to use all your senses, integrating them together.

If, at each point in the form, you know where within the circles each joint should be, the form becomes fluid yet crisp and the energies flowing through your body are continuous. You can think of "energy" as momentum to keep it simple. If you also can release the momentum at the end of each sinking and rising, you can avoid popping up and down. The momentum doesn't pull your body out of your root as you breathe in and expand and doesn't pull you down as you breathe out and sink. Rather, the movement of energy in the body stretches and releases the muscles and connective tissue, and the organs including the skin. The body becomes dynamic within itself and the releases connect it energetically to the surroundings.

This is called, "Not cutting the stem of the flower". Each mode of attention takes practice to develop. You do not abandon one for the

248

other but learn to use all of the modes. You don't cut yourself off from the earlier modes you learned.

In a similar way, as our civilization learns new technologies, it is not a good idea to cut ourselves off from earlier knowledge, such as Taoism, or we will be like a cut flower that eventually dies and dries up.

Getting back to the joints, the mind has a tendency, when operating in the linear mode (such as when thinking) to shut down its three-dimensional modes of attention, allowing the flywheels to slow down and disconnecting the body and mind from them.

It is important when using the mind in a linear way, to continue to move those flywheels. The linear mode plays off of the three-dimensional mode and returns to it.

Any activity such as thinking, pushing (as in Push hands), punching (as in sparring) or just walking, may seem linear in its mechanics but it must remain connected to a closed circle of energy generation and storage to have any power. If at any point (such as sparring) you freeze and disconnect from the circular source of power, you short circuit yourself.

This is why it is important to work on developing your flywheels of energy storage. Sometimes in life there are forces or situations that may cause us to freeze and disconnect. If our flywheels are strong enough, their force will break through our tendency to freeze and will connect us right back to their circular power. They may even prevent our freezing in the first place.

In this way we will never feel worn out, fearful or emotionally frazzled. We will have a reserve of power that can be transformed into physical, emotional or mental energy.

As an exercise, imagine your breath moving in a circle up along the front of your body and then, as you breathe out, the breath goes forward from your body and down, in a circle. Imagine that the breath travels around the rim of a wheel that is perpendicular to the front of your body.

Then conduct your activities while maintaining this image as you breathe. You will get an idea of remaining connected to your flywheel. At first it may be distracting or even annoying. But if you stick with it you will find it energizing, centering and relaxing. You can even do this exercise while watching T.V.

When a magnet spins within a coil of wire, electricity is created. In the same way, when attention circles around parts of the body, internal energy is created.

You might try the above exercise and ask a friend to stand near you. Ask them what they feel. Then stop doing the exercise and ask them again. People can feel a difference, though they may not be able to express what they are feeling.

Feel the skin of someone doing this exercise and then feel their skin when they stop. Just touch lightly. You will probably feel a difference. The skin becomes active, connected to the flow of energy, when you spin the flywheels. Look into the eyes of a person doing and not doing the exercise. Look at an animal while doing it. Notice its reaction.

Now let's connect this exercise of energizing the flywheels to dragon breathing. Specifically, the dragon breath moving outward occurs at the same time as your attention finishes circling up the front of your body (as you breathe in) and then moves out at a tangent to the circle up and forward (after which you breathe out). In this case you are not circling back down again, but "throw" the breath out as if it were a stone thrown out of a sling. The sling stores circular energy, then releases it linearly. The dragon breath does the same.

Yet even though the energy moves out and forward, the flywheel continues to spin. When you breathe in again its spinning "gathers the breath together" and draws energy in towards your body from the ground.

The above process is very important. Its dynamics express the principles of Zookinesis very clearly.

The circling energy is empowered by the breathing process and in turn, empowers the breathing. This is not a perpetual motion machine because it, in turn, is empowered by the body's physical/chemical activity.

The world experienced as dynamics of energy and the world experienced as a collection of objects are mutually dependent because they are the same world. The awareness and competent use of energy strengthens the body and emotions. You know this. How do you feel if you have to get up to do something you enjoy doing as opposed to something you dread? How long does it take you in the morning to get those flywheels turning? I have found that the difference of

250

dreading and looking forward to the day depends to a large extent on how much energy I have.

The flywheels greatly influence the connection and merging of the spirit and physical worlds. They are called "chakras" in Yoga and while Yoga describes a specific number of chakras at specific locations, Zookinesis recognizes the flywheels as a quality of the connection of the physical and spirit worlds and so, are not limited to specific locations.

The ability to use the flywheels and how they are connected to your body determines how well you can release the momentum and your attention. These "forces" want to be released, as an eagle wants to fly. When released they should indeed feel like an eagle that continues its voyage under its own power. They are your "spirit eagle".

And when it reaches the heights, it cries out like an eagle, to say, "Look at how high I'm flying." And you sit at the center of your flywheels, see the eagle and call out to it, "Good show old boy!"

The flight of the eagle lifts your spirit while the tortoise in some cultures, or among North American Indians the buffalo, represents the grounding of your spirit. The flywheel has both a soaring and grounding aspect and there are exercises to develop both. The height to which you can soar depends on how well you can ground. The flying and grounding aspects of energy allow you to do practical work in your life.

The series of techniques of animal gazing use energy moving into and out of the eyes. Each pattern of this movement of energy creates an effect in the other person.

When another person is draining your energy or trying to control your behavior for their benefit, they are generally using such a flow of energy through the eyes. It is a simple matter to use another pattern to neutralize theirs. They will usually be stuck with one pattern that they have learned to be effective. They may not be aware that this is what they are doing; it is usually subconscious.

Your advantage is that you are aware of the process and are skilled at many patterns. Each pattern is likened to an animal that seems to use that pattern. The patterns differ in the angles of the energy, how much they come out the front as opposed to the rear or the sides, how they are or aren't grounded, how wide the beam of energy, etc. The gaze of a rhino, for example differs from that of a deer.

By understanding the pattern of an animal's gaze and experiencing how you feel when one gazes at you, you can develop your animal gazing abilities. While it is easy to know how you feel when a wild rhino looks at you, it may not be so easy to analyze the pattern of its energy, of its attention, nor how to duplicate it within yourself. But with practice you can create the same feeling in another person even though you yourself may not be a huge wild beast. You can seem to be one in the feelings of another person. Remember that even a person who is not attuned to the sense of chi still is affected by that sense.

These are all defensive techniques but in the wrong hands they can be used for coercion. We need at least, to be aware of this type of interaction, how it can affect us and how to avoid it, or we will have a hard time succeeding in life.

We need to be aware of and understand the spirit world. There you will find the path to your power before others find it and take your power away from you.

We are amazed by the complex interactions of many species and habitats. If we look out at the cosmos, we see great precision and complexity in the interaction of planets, stars and galaxies. And yet, as individuals, struggling to get through life, understand its complexities and even move with a minimum of grace, we feel as though we are the only intelligent globs of matter in the universe.

Many ancient cultures, though, believe that consciousness is a natural force, part of every animal, plant, rock and habitat. We now call them "animists". They feel that the force of intelligence is the unseen mover in all the activity of the universe. It is not a "God" based perspective but simply includes the force of consciousness along with what we now would call the four forces of the universe (gravity, electro-magnetic and strong and weak nuclear forces). They search for the forces of intelligence and creativity in their surroundings and so feel a bond with every animal, plant and rock. They search for the forces of creativity and intelligence within their bodies to keep these forces strong so they will remain healthy. To them, consciousness is as much part of their world as matter. Matter did not create consciousness.

If the inside and the outside are made of the same "flesh" (as in the Zen saying) and you look at the world outside of you as if it was dead, then you tend to become dead inside as well. When the science of

252

physics looks at the world as dead objects moving about, then the science of medicine looks at the body as unconscious organs and cells, functioning automatically. By removing the possibility of consciousness from everything in the world but our brains, the world and our bodies become dead to us.

This is not a religious perspective. What would be the point of praying to something? You are conscious and everything else is conscious. What is praying to what? It is simply a way of bringing life back to our world, including to ourselves. Realize that you are not separate from the rest of life, either as a glob of matter, or as a center of consciousness.

The thinking mind can reach into the consciousness of another person by reading a book. Our emotions can do so by viewing someone's art. When we do Push Hands, we are reaching into the consciousness of our partner's body by "watching" or "reading" their responses to our actions. We challenge that consciousness to see further into ours.

If you can detect the intent of your Push Hands partner to act, you can respond to that action earlier than if you wait for the action itself. If you can detect how he "sees" the situation, you can respond to the intent earlier than if you waited for the intent itself. We try to detect the behavior of our partner at its earliest inception. How he understands what is going on will determine how he responds.

You can feel how he "sees" the situation by his body's responses to deal with your movements. Are his movements excessive or appropriate to your movements? Does he respond to every nuance of your movements? To what degree are his responses in direct relation to your actions, to what degree are they emotional and to what degree are they techniques he has learned? Can he change his actions as conditions change or does he need to follow through on everything he starts? You are evaluating his state at every moment and, of course, trying to confuse him so he can't respond. You can confuse him by being so subtle that you give him little to work with or provide so much intricacy of mechanics that he is overwhelmed.

This familiarity with behavior of your partner can help you with your own. It allows you to see the origins of your behavior and emotions so you can deal with their root causes. This requires stillness of attention. Your emotions and programmed behavior agitate the attention, making it difficult to see within you as the disturbed water on the surface of a lake makes it difficult to see through to the bottom.

You learn to keep the attention still and even, so the emotions and behavior patterns stand out clearly against the stillness. If you stay still enough, you can see what is tugging at your attention with great clarity. You can also discover your creative process as it bursts through the webs of emotions and behavior patterns. "Be still and know that I am God". This means that stillness of your attention is the key to knowing the creative process inside of you.

You will know the composition of an intent – how much is creative and how much patterned or based on emotions like fear. You will be able to "clean up" the intent so your partner won't detect it. It is easy for your partner to see, if it is carrying a load of patterns and fear. Such intents leave an obvious trail. The goal is not to be sneaky in life but to not carry a load of patterns and fear.

When we peer into the universe with a telescope we are actually peering back in time. Light takes time to reach us so the light we see now was created a long time ago. In a similar way, we can peer back into the origins of our intents and see the whole process. We can see that a behavior now is the end result of a whole process of intending. If we can concentrate on the issues that interact and give rise to the behavior, we will understand our behavior in general.

Push Hands tells us if that process of our behavior is working well for us. Is it dealing with the present situation accurately? If not, then which parts of the process are at fault? We break down our reaction to the mechanics of the movements and ask, what was it that caused us to choose a particular reaction. At every moment we are working with segments of time during which decisions are made, often unconsciously. Push Hands brings those decisions to conscious awareness.

Many people scurry to and fro in a frantic way. Their attention jumps from one thing to another, without a center or a root. Their viewing platform is at the end of the process, where intents are already blooming into actions. They stand at the point on the shore where the waves are breaking and are thereby tossed about.

Other people are calmer. They are aware of each moment in the context of the whole process. Rather than scurrying about, they know where to go. They see the path within the overall pattern. Their viewing platform is at the origin of intent and they can change the course of the process to more accurately follow the preferred path of their lives.

When we are closer to the origin of intent, we are closer to creativity. We play a more active role in the nature of our consciousness. We make ourselves, rather than being made by the forces around us.

If your viewing platform is "earlier" than your partner's, you can veer his path off to your advantage and he will think this change was his own intent. You are planting intent in his body and consciousness that is at an earlier stage than his own viewing platform. Those involved in the advertising industry will be familiar with this idea.

You can bring this skill into your massage. In this case you are aware of the client's muscles reacting to your pressures, even though the client, as a whole, is not moving. If a muscle releases or resists you also pay attention to how other parts of the body adjust to that change. This builds up a picture of the relationship of tensions in the body and how they reinforce each other. It is a relationship that has built up over time and involves the client's emotional history. You are healing that relationship so that the body can respond to current events accurately, without the burden of the emotional history, and can respond more positively. You are teaching the body to respond with joy rather than fear.

Push Hands gives you a more vivid version of massage in that the partner is actively trying to thwart your efforts. The massage client's resistances are at an earlier "viewing platform" on a more subconscious level and the interaction is at a finer level.

The process of intent growing like a seed and expanding into an action is represented in Tai-chi practice by starting each movement from your center. You then allow that "seed" (the dynamics created at the center) to flow outward through the rest of the body and be released.

As the movements of the center move out, the attention also expands into the rest of the body. This is true whether you are expanding out from the center or if you are sinking into the center. When you sink, that action starts from the center as well. This means that, while your attention expands outward on the expansion, it still remains "seated" in the center so that it can direct the subsequent sinking. The attention that moves out on the expansion is like a searchlight that lights up the dark scene in front of you, but the person holding the flashlight remains where he is. Attention expands outward like a spherical searchlight so that it is like a wave that is let go at the end.

In this way you can think of attention like the energy of light in physics that can be thought of as both a particle and a wave because it acts in both those ways. Attention can be condensed and focused on one spot or it can be like a spider's web, filling your whole body and the surroundings.

If one part of the attention is affected by an outside force as in Push Hands, that affects the rest of the attention as well because all of attention is really one cohesive energy. Affecting one part of it affects all of it and affects the body, emotions, thinking mind, intentions, etc. The body should respond by adjusting to remain centered and its energy even. Affecting one part of one "element" affects all the elements because they are also one cohesive whole. In this way, a previous experience can have such an impact on you that part of your attention becomes permanently focused, like a particle, distorting the physical body and other elements in a particular way. Your Tai-chi practice reveals and releases these distortions so that each release realigns the entire complex of elements. The relaxation of one muscle can have a powerful emotional effect.

Developing "inertia" in the attention is a healing practice in this sense: If it is hard to "yank" attention from its natural flow, then the cohesive elemental system (which is us) will also not be disturbed as easily. That inertia is developed by practicing the form with the dynamics of attention as in the "flywheel" exercises. A form without such practice is not Tai-chi in my opinion.

If the thinking mind, the misalignment of the body, the unbalanced emotions, ingrained habits and other factors constantly "yank" the attention, the student will not progress. That is why I suggest concentrating on what it is that is being "yanked" so the student will gain the experience of attention itself and its dynamics. At least then, the student will understand that "substance", that energy of life and know what he is trying to heal. This will lead him to understand who is the healer, which of course, is himself. He will understand that the interaction of attention and creativity is the basis of his identity. When they can play together "nicely" his life will become easier and more joyful.

Healing the dynamics of attention and the movement of his body is the beginning of that process. The Yang aspect of interacting with attention is to send that wave out from the center. The Yin aspect is to release your control of the wave so that it can seamlessly blend with the physical movements and be affected by them. If the movements are "off" because of poor posture or other factors, the Yin attention will be disturbed and that will be apparent to the student. He will not feel a smooth release of attention – a smooth wave.

When practicing Push Hands, the aggression of the partner is received into the student's center, with his sinking attention leading the force of the partner. When the student's own energy moves outward, it incorporates the energy absorbed from the partner, releasing it back with the outward wave. He avoids "locking" his attention with the "idea of pushing". The exercise should really be called, "Receiving and Returning".

This skill then allows you to perceive these same dynamics in the partner. What is his relationship between creativity and attention or is attention completely locked by habits and thinking patterns? Are you doing Push Hands with his genuine skills or with his fears (of losing)? If the partner genuinely wants to learn Tai-chi, then you can help him "see" these factors inside of himself and he can help you in this way as well. If not, then the Push Hands is just annoying.

At a certain point it is the two attentions that are doing Push Hands. They blend together and separate in an intricate internal dance of creativity. Sometimes it is hard to know who initiated what at moments when the two become one. It is a dance of spirits, spiraling into and out of the centers, healing both.

The key to healing is - what you are are looking for. If you look at the beauty of things, then beauty will grow inside of you. If you are looking for the weakness in others to take advantage of that, weakness will grow inside of you. If you look at others from the viewpoint of healing, then healing will take place inside of you.

Some people feel the purpose of the body is to carry around the mind. But carrying around the self-righteousness, anger, drama and resentments of the mind is too heavy a burden to bear. If you want the body to carry around the mind, make the mind light. A heavy mind blocks the beauty of the world from affecting you and lifting you. It blocks your spirit from joining the world by always trying to win against the world. The spirit then sits in a dungeon and dies.

To lighten the mind requires trusting the flow of intelligence through the body. It requires trusting the skill and creativity of the body. You seek answers within your connection to the world around you rather than in cleverness. Those connections are your professors.

In Push Hands practice, our responses come from our connection to the partner and in knowing his internal state through your touch. You are seeking intelligence in touch. The touch is not a grab because a grab would close the flow of information into you. The lighter the touch that you can use to provide you with information, the less you "give yourself away".

Students often wonder if the teacher is keeping the deeper training a secret. It is not the teacher who keeps secrets; it's the student who keeps secrets from himself. If the student learns to be open to information from the teacher, and allow that information to affect his body and spirit, then there would be no secrets. The system of Tai-chi is a kind of beauty that one must see and be open to.

Some people carry around with them an image of how they think others see them. Their behavior is controlled by maximizing what they feel will be a positive impression of that image in the eyes of others. When you practice Tai-chi, the beauty of how the body works, how your attention is connected to the entirety of attention of nature and the beauty of all aspects of nature takes the place of that self-image. Your behavior stems from maximizing that beauty. The image of beauty sets you on a different path.

In the second case the body feels enthusiastic and its actions are joyful. You try to connect to and be part of each moment. You look forward to the world around you. In the first case the body feels fearful and its actions tense. You try to capture and contain each moment. You look back at yourself. The enthusiasm is like a stream flowing through you. The fear is like a dam.

Song writers can take two approaches. The first is to write a song they think will be a hit. The second is to write a song that comes directly from their creativity and sense of beauty. In the second case, they are producing the song to bring joy to themselves and share it with others. Songwriting is their way of connecting to similar spirits.

In the first approach, songwriting is just a way to earn a living. The intention determines the resulting quality of music.

The subject of intention is vital to understand in Tai-chi practice. When practicing a form, for example, where does the intention to do each movement originate? Is the mind ordering the body around like a boss ordering around his workers? In this case, the form will be contrived and stiff. If the movements arise just from creativity then the form will be completely different each time.

How can the form be precise and creative at the same time, like a musician who can play the same song, but no two performances are exactly alike? It is more than a question of practicing a lot so you are familiar with the song or the Tai-chi form? If the relationship between your mind and body is one of boss and worker then the form will never express the Tai-chi principles.

In fact, the main purpose of practicing any form is to establish a different relationship between mind and body. Most of us are only familiar with mental intention but Tai-chi teaches us about "body intention". As each part of the body gains skill, it develops muscle memory but also a "desire" to maintain its alignment with the rest of the body and with the flow of motion. This "desire" or intention is gradually coaxed out of each part of the body, encouraged to express itself and to take over the role of "boss" to some extent.

The mind's job is to remember the precision of the form but it is the body's job to translate that into motion. If the mind suddenly wants to take over, you can see the form lose its fluidity and connection to the ground.

Gradually the intentions of the parts of the body and of the mind enter into a cooperative and creative relationship where each learns to yield to the other and exert just enough intention to do the job. This relationship can be destroyed by fear and other distractions and again the form suffers. The fear is based on the thinking mind not wanting to lose any of its authority or worrying about your body's degree of competence.

We are taught to examine this feeling of fear and recognize it as just a set of feelings that are allowed to flow through you as your Tai-chi form flows through the air. There is another "mind" inside of you, residing in every muscle, organ and cell of the body. When the form turns into an expression of the creative cooperation of all these "minds", then you are really doing Tai-chi, not just a set of movements.

The connection between attention and your physical body is a vital issue in Zookinesis as well. On a simple level this just means being aware of your body - each joint, muscle, nerve, concentration of salts, oxygen and nutrients in the blood etc., at each moment. You are designed to be aware of all this. Most of us have forgotten how to feel the consciousness of the body. The memory of those feelings can be deeply buried.

We work with the quality of the connection of attention to the body and with the pattern of distribution of attention within the body. Further we examine how far attention projects out of the body and the pattern of that projection. What is the quality of attention at the skin and beyond the skin? This is what some people refer to as an aura.

When attention projects outside the body does it do so in a cycle, connected to the breath? Do you allow some to be released and "picked up" by the environment? How much is released and how much retained?

The answers to these questions are a very important diagnostic tool. They are at the heart of many physical, emotional and mental ailments.

Each quality of attention we try to develop, may be described as an animal or some natural phenomenon. For example, the connection of attention to the physical body may be described as a tree frog. The tree frog merges onto a leaf or even a pane of glass. If you ever had one merge onto your hand (or face - as I've experienced many times), you know that connected yet soft feeling. If it is disturbed the tree frog will instantly separate and jump away.

Many frogs develop a waterproof coating around their bodies to avoid drying out. This coating can keep a frog safe for a year if needed. As soon as it rains again, the coating softens; the frog eats it and emerges fresh as new.

This is similar to the internal memories that seem to have developed an impenetrable coating. It's hard to get back in touch with them. But when you dissolve their coatings through Zookinesis, the memories emerge fresh as new.

While we humans don't "eat" the coatings, we do something similar. We use a very important technique called, "breathing in". When you feel the resistance to getting in touch with a Body-Mind memory, you "breathe in" the resistance. This consists of being as aware of the nature of the resistance as possible and breathing in as if you were drawing your breath from the resistance and then breathe out as usual. This softens and dissolves the resistant coating. You should take a normal breath in between each of these special breaths, to allow the softening effect to settle into the resistance.

You develop this ability by learning to "breathe in through the feet" as the Taoists would say. This means that, before the in-breath, your attention first sinks into your root, and as you breathe in, your attention rises through the body and is released out of the head. This is the "heaven and earth breathing" of the Taoists. In the case of dissolving resistance to a biological (Body-Mind) memory, your root is in the resistance. You "root" your attention within the resistance and breathe in to dissolve it.

A simpler way of saying this is that as you breathe in and out smoothly, you pay attention to the "hint" of that memory. Whether you have actively repressed the memory or it has just gotten lost due to neglect, the details of that memory will stand out against the smoothness of your breathing.

Such memories are encoded in patterns of tension in the muscles. An external stimulus can trigger these tension patterns. Attitudes can also trigger them and, in turn, are reinforced by them. This repetitive loop of tension patterns can cause you to keep making the same mistakes in life.

There was a Star Trek episode in which the Starship Enterprise and another Starship were trapped in a repetitive loop of time. The officers were playing a poker game and after a few repetitions of the game began to realize that they kept reenacting the same poker hands. They also kept repeating the experience of a head-on collision with the other ship. The android named "Data" was able to install a program in his android brain that led to a solution of the collision that eventually allowed both ships to escape the time-loop.

I mention this because we are all caught in such time-loops. Tension patterns installed in us in the past keep getting triggered and that tension reinforces the programming. We need to install a new program to escape our own collisions. That program is the exercises of Tai-chi.

The tension patterns are a screen that hides the living consciousness of the body and the earth. By refocusing your attention on the creativity of the body, the tension-loops which previously controlled your life, now have less power.

When you search for frogs during the breeding season you may hear many frog songs emanating from bushes, tree branches and from the swamp water. Each type of frog sits at a different height. The night is black so you can't see them. You find them through their sounds. Simply by listening and comparing that to the little you can see, you get a pretty good idea of where the frogs are and of which species.

This is similar to becoming aware of the various "forms of life" inside of you. You are like an environment, a swamp for example. Each form of life calls out and if you "listen" carefully enough you can "hear" them. Instead of listening with our ears, though, we use the sense of chi.

If you "listen" too forcefully, you won't hear anything. Using the sense of chi requires finesse. It requires a Yin, quiet attention.

If you were to visit the swamp on a full moon, the frogs would be gone. They shun the light because they become too visible to predators. The life inside you shuns too strong a "light" of attention. Instead, just allow your attention to "sink" into the body rather than pushing it into the body.

"Be still and know that you are alive". Stillness allows attention to settle into the body.

Be satisfied with hearing the frogs even though you can't see them. Be satisfied with listening to your body through the sense of chi even though your other senses can't come into play. Gradually this sense will become clearer - as clear as the sense of sight. Your attention will wander through the nighttime forests and swamps of your body and soul.

As you search through the swamp you are tempted to shine your flashlight into the darkness to see the frogs. As soon as you do, all the singing ceases. The frogs are frightened.

It is better to train your eyes to see in the darkness than to eliminate the darkness. Develop your senses - don't alter the environment to suit your poor vision. Developing the sense of chi in this way reveals another type of "light".

In the same way, you want to observe your own body "in vivo" - in the act of behaving and functioning. If you use Yang attention, you will stop your inner frogs from singing. You may see something but

262

all you will see is a bunch of frogs with surprised looks on their faces, frozen in fear.

What we do instead is to allow our still attention to gradually sink down and be "disturbed" by the activity of our internal "frogs". This stirs up the chi. The disturbance of our chi tells us about our bodies.

This is what happens with any other sense. The disturbance of air is what we call sound. The way light is absorbed, reflected and refracted is what we call sight and the way in which life energy is affected by the natural world is what we call chi.

Projecting chi out of the body works the same way. We allow it to slowly evaporate - as if a mist - and watch how the "winds of life" catch the mist and swirl it around. In this way we can "see" things that are invisible to our other senses. Each sense opens up another world. We don't actually see air but when we see branches swaying or dead leaves swirling around, we know there is a wind.

We consider our bones and teeth to be part of our living body even though they are hard, like rocks. In the same way we realize, with the sense of chi, that the entire planet is alive, including its rocks.

Gradually our understanding of our goals in life shifts. We now see the enhancement of life as our goal, life with a big "L" - the life of the planet. We can see how our actions directly affect all life around us. And even more importantly - the degree of our awareness of life energy is what really improves our lives and contributes to the health of the life around us. This is the same as saying that by strengthening our heart, we heal our entire body.

Each of us can magnify the life force flowing through us. We can keep the connection open so that this force doesn't get "stuck" inside of us.

Imagine if, in a synchrotron, one of the electromagnets were not functioning. A synchrotron works by sequentially turning electromagnets on and off to propel a subatomic particle forward. There are hundreds of these magnets and they must be timed exactly. If but one was to malfunction, the entire operation would stop working. In fact, calibrating the magnets is a lot of the work of maintaining a synchrotron.

In the same way each person who clears up the flow of chi inside him, calibrates his magnet in a sense. Relaxing a tense muscle and allowing energy to flow is an important contribution to life on earth.

It may seem trivial but when you can see with chi you realize it is not trivial.

If you were a Zookinesis student back in the "old days" you might be required to spend time in a swamp listening to the frogs to get a sense of all this. In these "new" days it is no less important to do that. Certainly, there is somewhere you can go in the spring to listen to frogs sing at night. Spend time in nature to "read the living book" as the Gnostics would say.

The snake has long been used as a metaphor for these principles. One of the most intriguing things about snakes is the shedding of their old skin. The outer layer of dead skin comes off in one piece, while ours is shed cell by cell over the course of several months so we don't notice it.

A snake will soak its body in water for a few days to get the old skin soft and then rub the skin off, nose first, actually crawling out of its old skin. The new skin is shiny and beautiful. Shedding skin is used as a metaphor for being able to shed any set pattern of behavior or pattern of identity. In Tai-chi it is called, "letting go".

This identity, one's impression of oneself, is very important to get by in the social world. But often it is not under our control. Your identity is an important tool for other people. Haven't you heard people say, "If you were really my friend, you would...."? Your identity is the battleground of the marketing industry. Once your identity becomes connected to your body and its biological feelings, you win and the manufacturers, religions and politicians lose. The body can be satisfied with a good meal, sex with someone you love and warm, dry clothes. The advertising industry must shape your self-image to be satisfied only with their products (deodorant, God or a political party).

This is why it's important to shape your own identity and to shed useless parts of it. When you shape your own identity, you remember the creative process that went into shaping it and realize that there is a deeper, more real part of yourself - the creator. I don't mean that in a cosmic sense; I mean the part of you that shapes and creates your world. If you identify with that part, you have power. If you identify with the pattern (which is usually formed by outside influences), you don't have power. "Shed the dead" (skin) to gain power.

Tai-chi animal forms allow you to replace your identity with that of an animal to help you see the creative process of your identity. This is known as "shape shifting" in some cultures. You change the shape of your identity. The strange thing is that every person can see your self-image. Others can see how we seem to ourselves because that image is projected outward. We are really all connected through chi. We can become more aware of how we are connected by working on our self-image and observing how that affects others around us. If we are working on tiger form and have allowed the tiger to "live" inside of us a few minutes a day, how does that affect our friends' view of us?

We begin to see that there is, indeed, a great affect. The tiger is being used as a spirit animal. It gives us power by giving us creative control of our identity.

But how shall we alter our identity? What are the guidelines? There are three. One is the reality of dealing with your world. If you become obnoxious, you won't be effective in dealing with people. The second guideline is being aware of your body and the life energy around you. Your identity must make you effective here as well. The third guideline is your "vision", your yearnings, and your goals in life.

The forked tongue of the snake is also used as a metaphor for freeing your spirit from set patterns. For example, when you talk to yourself there seems to be two people there - the talker and the listener. When we must understand with words, we divide ourselves into these two parts. The initial idea that pops into your head is an entire concept encapsulated in a single point. Words unroll that idea into a linear series of thoughts. The original "jolt of thought" is a collage of images and feelings in which the entire body participates. It is alive. Word-thoughts isolate the process into the thinking mind, leaving behind much of the potent content.

We take the experience of talking to others and project that back into ourselves so we are talking to ourselves. There is nothing wrong with that, if you are trying to figure something out. But it leads us to forget the original experience of thought as a holistic living process.

In a life lived from thinking, much of the potency of life is missing. This potency lurks behind our every moment of life, emerging in dreams or mythical stories. Have you ever woken up from a dream and remembered an incredible insight, only to find out once you awoke, that the insight makes no sense? While you were dreaming, the original potency of experience remained intact. Then you labeled it with words you wrote down on a piece of paper. When you awoke, you switched into the thinking mode. The label of your sleeping experience is not the experience itself. It merely points to the experience. To a large extent we are a people looking for pointers back to the spirit world. Yet we get trapped in the maze of the thinking mind assuming that the spirit world lies somewhere in there.

The potency of life is not found in the labels. If you have such an experience in dreams, don't worry about the idea you remembered; remember the experience that gave rise to the idea. Bring that with you into your waking world and you will have power!

The snake's tongue is used as a metaphor for the divergence of our original unified selves into these two parts - Body Mind and thinking mind. The thinking mind tries to find its way to the potency of life through thinking that only serves to lengthen that half of the snake's tongue. The result is that it gets tongue-tied and comes up with nonsense. To regain that potency, we need to understand the situation (using thinking mind), unravel the nonsense (letting go) and remember BM (our original creative selves). Zookinesis exercises and Tai-chi massage do this.

So *feel* thought. When a thought arises, resist the temptation to unravel it into words. Just feel that original jolt of thought. You will feel potency surging back into you. Eventually you will be able to think with the jolts. It is quicker, contains more information and keeps you vital.

Furthermore, it is less susceptible to being distorted. When we translate the jolt into thoughts, those thoughts contain a lot of extraneous patterns. Usually entire patterns of words come together in chunks. This is a similar situation to the "mosaic" effect in video production. The screen is divided into a certain number of little squares. Each square is colored with a single color - the predominant color of the original scene in its area.

The result is an approximation of the original scene with none of the details. This is what happens in the thinking process. Our thoughts are arranged into little squares. When a jolt comes up, the thoughts produce a mosaic.

My brother's field was writing computer code. He explained that early programs were short and "clean". Now, few people actually write code; they use programs to write code. These programs contain whole segments of code, much of which may not be necessary for the program you want to create. So the modern code writers create huge programs (in terms of size of memory) and much of it is unnecessary. My first word processing program was 30 kilobytes. In a similar way, we have a lot of clutter in our bodies and minds that is unnecessary.

We long for the detail and potency of the original experience of life. This is the gift of Zookinesis. The snake reminds us that by letting go of the boxes (identity boxes) and re-unifying mind and body we can be as close to the earth as a snake that rests its whole body on the earth.

The term, "identity boxes" refers to the way in which our thoughts are patterned together. The style of this patterning is the framework of our identity. I remember a Turkish visitor to an AAAS meeting (American Association for the Advancement of Science). The President of Yale University was speaking. The speech was full of pomp and hot air and said nothing (in my opinion). The audience loudly applauded the president and then this Turkish man raised his hand and said, in his thick accent, "Sir, the style of your speech greatly exceeds its content." He could barely speak English yet he had captured the idea eloquently.

I'm afraid that the same comment can be applied to many of our conversations. The way we string words together is an expression of our identities rather than an effective means of conveying ideas and experiences. When our identities congeal into these patterns, our speech congeals into patterns filled with style but little content.

In jazz improvisation you don't really know where the piece is going. It can go anywhere. It is free. It is creative. Yet it holds together. You sense the underlying progression of notes. But that progression turns you around and upside down. It makes your insides dance.

When your insides dance, you can appreciate the creativity of others. That is part of the potency of life as well. Sometimes we may feel bad when faced with the creativity of others. We are jealous of them as I used to be when very young. We may feel competitive towards their creativity.

This is because we are not connected to the potency, the creativity of our own lives. We can appreciate the creativity of others only to the extent that we are connected to our own. When we are connected to our creativity, we understand that creativity is not so individualistic. It is like a force flowing through all of us and is part of the life force - chi. There is no need for competition - just understand who you are. You *are* creativity. You *are* life.

Create patterns of thought by all means, but remember that you created them. Remember the Yin (letting go of patterns) and the Yang (creating new ones). To be congealed into patterns and depend on the creativity of others for your joy is "half a smile, half a tear". Let their creativity lead you to your own and then to the source of creativity, the life force of the earth.

One more thing about snakes. In nature they are loners (except during hibernation when they join together for heat preservation). Yet when you pick them up and handle them gently, they love to be handled. They become used to being handled and look forward to it, hissing with delight. And it is delightful to play with them. They are happy, you are happy and nothing needs to be said. Two species, totally unrelated, find pleasure in giving each other pleasure and simply being with each other, two united into one through the experience of chi. It is said that the individual chi of snakes and humans blend perfectly and thus snakes were the symbols of many early religions and cultures.

The early concept of God or "the Gods" was expressed as, "Without the gods we cannot be and without us, the Gods cannot be". This changed to a disembodied overlord terrorizing *his* people into "willful" submission. The Gods and people were originally two sides of the same coin, and then they were split. God or Gods were the expression of the creative aspect of our world, of us. We shifted our identity to the products of our creativity. The creativity itself was projected into the disembodied God; it was no longer our true selves or even part of ourselves.

When we are connected within ourselves, we can connect to others. We can experience the chi flowing through ourselves and snakes and other people. Snakes are not evil, nature is not the enemy and our creativity is not a mad tyrant. The world seems different when you practice Zookinesis - nicer.

When people were still living in natural conditions, they were awed by the animals around them. Some of the animals were powerful, some very fast, others were very graceful or tricky. They reasoned

268

that if they could take the powers of all these animals and combine them into us, we would be the most powerful animals in the world.

They studied the animals carefully, copied their movements and behaviors. These early people discovered something important. The abilities of each animal were the direct result of the quality of their attention. Each animal paid attention to its surrounding in a unique way. Its body's movements and reactions were a reflection of the movements of their attention.

Aboriginal people called the attention of the animals, "spirit". They tried to learn the spirit of each animal they wished to copy. They felt that the human "spirit" needs to be nourished by its connection to the spirit of other species.

This study of nourishing the human spirit with animal spirits developed into a complex training system. Certain types of breathing combined with attention exercises formed the basis of this training. In China, it was called chi-gung (or Qigong).

In the ensuing millennia, civilization developed. The idea of developing the qualities and power of each individual changed to altering the environment so that we would not need such qualities. The thinking mind was used to "free us" from the "limitations" of nature so that we could live apart from the biological world and even wage war against it. We are now reaping the results in climate change, habitat destruction and mass extinction.

The thinking mind is not inherently destructive; it is part of our biological heritage. It is the split of that "element" from the rest of us that damages the "glue" that holds our whole being together. That glue is attention, rooted in the body and natural world. With that grounding, the thinking mind is healthy; without it, it is a ship unmoored, drifting out to sea.

Tai-chi slow forms teach the body to move like water. The joints open and close sequentially so that you look as though you were floating in water. You are told to follow the flow of momentum of the body with your attention. This loosens the attention, allowing it to flow. Then you are told to follow the momentum as it flows out the feet into the ground (into your "root") and as you expand upward, to follow the momentum out the hands and the top of the head. This trains your attention to flow in and out of the body.

This is very difficult for most people. We are trained that our attention is contained within the confines of the body. We can pay attention to something out there by looking at it or hearing it but our attention doesn't "flow out" towards the object and meet with it. It is just a question of looking at something. This is why people can listen and not really hear, look and not really see. Looking at something doesn't necessarily mean you are paying attention to it. When your attention flows out to an object, meets with it and blends with it, you experience the object in a very different way – you join with it. It is the difference between knowing about someone and hanging out with them.

It is surprising how many people don't really feel part of the world they are in. They feel there is a wall between them and the world or between them and other people. When I teach Phantom Kung-fu I see people punching and at the same time pulling away from their own punch (to avoid getting hit back). This limits the range and power of their own punch. I tell them not to worry about getting hit. Protect yourself with your awareness. Put your whole self into the punch but keep watching what the opponent is doing.

People also tell me that they guard themselves against other people as if they were wearing armor. They rehearse what they will say instead of being spontaneous. This is a hell of a way to live. They say they don't trust other people, but they really don't trust themselves; they don't trust their own power or that they are likeable. Tai chi strengthens your attention so you will feel part of this world and be able to function in it effectively. Then you won't need to armor yourself.

That armor is just a way of preventing your attention from flowing out of your body and preventing other peoples' attention from flowing into your body. It is an attempt to disconnect yourself from the flow of attention throughout the earth.

The next stage of learning the Tai chi form is to realize that each part of the body (each arm, leg, the torso and head) has its own momentum. You divide your attention so that you can follow the flow of momentum of each part of the body. You soon discover that the momentum of one part sometimes flows into the momentum of another part. The various momentums create a complex interference pattern and you learn to pay attention to that complexity. In this way your attention gets more intricate.

This complexity overlays a basic pattern in the flow of attention. Attention expands spherically as you breathe in and expand the body, and contracts spherically as you breathe out and relax the body. Your physical expansion and expansion of attention thus moves up and down, to the right and left and front and back.

On the relaxing phase, your attention moves into the Tan-tien (the center of the body just below the navel) and then through the legs into the ground. After you have breathed in and are about to breathe out, some of your attention has expanded out of the body into the environment and some is still within the body. As you breathe out, the attention that has left the body continues to flow outward and evaporates into the environment. The result of that evaporation (letting go of attention) is a relaxation of the body and an inward flow of attention energy from the environment.

The result is that on both inbreath and outbreath, energy is dynamically moving into the surroundings and also into you. The specific movements of your Tai-chi form overlay this basic dynamic. While the spherical dynamics serve as a basis for your form movements, they are also affected by those movements. The result is an intricate symphony of dynamics of momentum, attention and chi that you are completely aware of at each moment. You "bathe" in that complexity. It is your spa.

Your own individuality (movements of the form for example) and the ebb and flow of nature must constantly interact to keep you healthy and happy. Knowing this, you are no longer interested in building stronger armor.

During Push Hands, you must pay attention to all the dynamics of force, your and your partner's balance, the readiness of each of his muscles to respond to your push, the pattern of his attention, the alignment of each of his joints and many other factors that are constantly changing. Your push must flow evenly out of the flow of movement and not be abrupt, not be separate from what is already going on.

The speed of movement and the amount of force of one arm against the other or the hand against the body vary constantly. Each partner fakes being off balance or having a dull attention in order to lead the other person in. So there is a lot to pay attention to here as well.

After each "round" or "volley" the partners discuss what happened on the level of body movement and the dynamics of attention. This helps the students "see" attention. It helps you to sort out the factor of attention among all the other factors involved in Push Hands. You can use words like "soft" (I felt that your attention was "soft" here but very firm over there"), "stiff" ("I changed speed and your attention was too stiff to change and follow"). The attempt to describe attention in everyday words helps to understand it and to perceive it.

Seeing attention opens up a whole new world. It is the world based on perceiving how everything is connected to each other, how all life is filled with intelligence and vitality. It is also important to use the sense of sight to understand how everything is separate from each other. In order to understand the sense of sight we need an intellectual framework – guideposts and categories so we know what's what. The intellectual framework for the sense of sight is called, "The Physical World". It is composed of matter, space and movement.

The sense of attention also needs an intellectual framework in order for us to understand it. This framework is called, "The Spirit World". If we can perceive both the spirit world and the physical world then all our senses are working. If we can understand the connections between the "things" of the spirit world and the physical world, then we can be effective in our lives.

This is why I feel it is important to approach developing the sense of attention from a physical point of view (forms, push hands, sparring, working with animals, massage, etc.). I see too many people "getting into" spirituality but it's all mental. It's the same old "living in the mind" but talking about spirituality rather than about politics or religion. You still need to chop wood for the fire when you can perceive attention.

Most people are interested in this training for a particular purpose – to reduce stress, to heal a particular ailment, to improve their self-defense abilities, to improve some form of artistic endeavor or sports, etc. The teacher needs to gear the training for each particular purpose.

While the student's original purpose may be to develop one particular skill, the basic principles of Zookinesis and Tai-chi will affect all aspects of his life. When you "live in the Spirit world" as well as living in the physical world, your personal life is affected. You can see the dynamics of attention in other people and this gives you a greater appreciation of their situation and their limitations. Relationships of two people both involved with this practice take place on a much deeper level.

An entire nation or culture can vary in its awareness of the spirit world over time. I believe that modern culture is becoming more aware of the spirit world. This is largely due to the science of ecology that has made us realize that all living things are interconnected. Those interconnections may be described physically (the water cycle, genetics and the process of evolution, etc.) but many ecologists have evolved a deeper awareness through their involvement in their work. It would be difficult not to become aware of the true nature of attention if you spend a great deal of time in nature. The nature programs on television can bring a little bit of that awareness to the rest of us.

The transformation of nature programming followed the transformation that takes place in a person who becomes aware of the spirit world. First there was Wild Kingdom. Our heroes went around the world capturing animals. Next, Lorne Greene's Last of the Wild brought us into the wilderness to watch the animals going about their daily business with extensive commentary. Now such shows as George Page's Nature and other series cut down on the commentary and give us longer moments with the animals and plants – time to just be with them. The quality of the photography eliminates the need for a lot of talking. This follows our own attitudes of conquering, explaining and then just being part of nature. The next step would be to stop watching television and spend time outside.

Animals are no longer "things" to be subdued and caught. They are now part of an environment and the environment is part of you. You can look into the jaguar's eyes as some squawking birds disrupt its hunt. You can relate to its annoyance and can translate its thoughts into words you know wouldn't be allowed on T.V.

For you it was a competitor interfering with your sale or your car blowing a tire. As you watch the jaguar's eyes, you relate to it as you would relate to your buddies complaining about their missed opportunities. You almost want to invite the jaguar to a few drinks after work.

In the same way programs about our own bodies give us an appreciation of the worlds within us. We find ourselves at one particular point of a series of worlds within worlds, all very active, very intricate and filled with biological intelligence. If there is a continuum of life, what are *we* then as individuals? This is the search for individuality.

Once while watching "Nature" I noticed that the show had an unusual amount of commentary. Every scene was described in detail, even though it was obvious what was going on. Then I realized that the commentary was for blind people. I had pressed the wrong button on the remote by mistake. How appropriate an analogy! Aren't most of us blind to the spirit world? If we are blind to this living energy of nature, the energy that is its substance, do we need an extensive commentary explaining it to us?

I feel that religion has become the extensive commentary provided for blind people who cannot see the program. Luckily our blindness can be easily reversed. Rather than having someone tell us what God has to say, we can directly see the intelligent dynamic of living energy and participate in it.

The term, "subtle body" refers to a person who, having let go of habits, tensions and trauma, now experiences what is left of himself. For each habit or attitude released, he gains an experience of himself that is his connection to the world around him. The habits can no longer claim him as their own.

Devoid of his isolation from the world, he melts into it, returning to his original state. For a while, he is disoriented, not seeing the source of his intentions. That source is "relationship" – the relationship of each part of himself to the other, in which the term, "himself" is his total experience of his existence. His intentions arise from his biological state, trying to maintain health and balance. It is at this point that the principles of the teaching in which he is involved, must be re-enforced, to keep him from going adrift and losing energy.

The student then, lives in two worlds – 1. The world of separation and a battle of programmed behavior – 2. The natural world. He must be able to live in both because, practically speaking, we need to be able to function in the world most people live in. Yet those habits cannot be allowed to control him. He is in the world but not *of* the world.

Zen Koan: "Give your flesh to your mother and your bones to your father and show me your original face". You can think of the bones as the habits and conditioning. The flesh would be the way these habits affect how you actually see things. The world looks, sounds, smells and feels different each time you let go of some habit. The world, including your experience of yourself, becomes fluid.

That fluidity is the living quality of the world. Most people try to stop the fluidity as if we were preparing a slice of muscle tissue on a slide so we can view it through a microscope. They want the world to stay in place so they don't have to deal with its complexity. The Zookinesis teacher (or teacher of any similar training) convinces the student that the fluidity is extremely beautiful and is life itself. "Fixing" each moment in time (as you would "fix" a tissue slide with a stain) is not as fulfilling and not an effective way to live your life. In fact, it is really the "living dead".

The result of proper training is that the student feels very "light", free, energized, aware, creative and connected to the rest of life. The "spirit world" we then enter is not a different world; it is just a world that is not warped by our habits, attitudes, programming and fears.

When I had my animal importing company, I would walk down the row of cages, looking at the expressions of the animals (mostly reptiles). I could tell if one snake's water dish was dry or if it was dirty, if the snake was hungry or if it had mites - just from its expression. Most people don't realize that snakes have expressions. If you asked me to describe what a snake does with its face to change its expression, I couldn't answer you. I don't know. But after working with them all my life, all I need is a quick glance. The snake can tell me a whole story.

Perhaps you can accept that a snake has an expression but how about a plant? People who work with plants all their lives feel the same about them as I do about snakes. Their plants tell them how they feel.

What about a whole ecosystem? Again, just talk to someone who lives in a swamp or a desert and they will tell you about their land's moods and about how their ecosystem "talks" to them. Nature talks. She talks through chi. As a culture we have turned a deaf ear to the way nature talks. Perhaps we don't want to know what she is saying.

There is a point in Zookinesis practice when you do hear that voice. You realize you are surrounded by this communication, that it penetrates you and you penetrate it.

A teacher will wait for the "inversion". This is when your identity turns inside out. Your identity depended on your isolation from all life; now it depends on your connection to it. Frankly, with most students, the inversion never happens.

It sounds like a simple change but your whole life changes with it. You are no longer the isolated individual but now you are the larger life within which all this communication bounces around. As you feel the mood of the swamp, you are the swamp. Your mood, your identity depends on the swamp. It is hard to tell where you end and the swamp begins. Sight gives us that information but not chi.

Koko the gorilla used sign language in her last message before her death. ""I am gorilla… I am flowers, animals. I am nature. Man, Koko love. Earth, Koko love. But man stupid… Stupid! Koko sorry. Koko cry. Time hurry! Fix Earth! Help Earth! Hurry! Protect Earth… Nature see you. Thank you." Some critics may doubt the accuracy of her conversation – that a gorilla could think in such complex terms. Yet her message is very simple, so simple that most humans, mired in their complexity, are not capable of understanding "I am nature".

Why have we lost the sense of chi? The answer to that question may now be obvious. If the world around us is composed of living, intelligent energy as much as it is of matter then how could we destroy it? Do we use the same psychology as we use for hunting? (I am killing an animal but I need it for food and I respect its spirit).

How do developers respect the spirit of the land they plow under? Certainly, some try to maintain the natural beauty and in some areas are required to do so by law. A person who has lived in a forest, for example, who identifies with it and with all its creatures and moods, would certainly die inwardly if that forest were plowed under. As a plundering culture, we have had to "die to the spirit world" to be comfortable for the plundering to take place.

Even our memory that there is a spirit world is forgotten. We are soothed by our inventions, including the invention of our identity.

I remember as a child, understanding that people forgot and that my ability to maintain my awareness of the spirit world was challenged at every turn. I reminded myself constantly not to forget, even though I didn't yet have the words to say what it is I shouldn't forget. I could only say to myself, "Don't ever forget" and I knew what I meant.

Now as a healer, I tend to diagnose the people around me in terms of how much they have forgotten. Are they still connected to some extent to the life energy? When I do massage, that is how I diagnose. Has the invented identity completely taken over? Is it battling the memory of the spirit world as if its existence depends on forgetting the real self?

Your invented identity can exist side by side with your true, spirit identity. But sometimes the invented identity becomes defensive and tries to gain full power like some politicians. The created pattern now wants to shut off the force that created it. It is cutting off the source of its existence ("cutting the stem of the flower"). The invention is battling the inventor. This battle is common in many people and gives rise to many physical and emotional ailments. The cure for this battle is merely to remember the spirit world and for the invented identity to maintain its connection to it.

The inversion simply puts your life back into perspective. It can't bring back the forests of course, not immediately, so you may feel bad when your memory returns and you realize how much has been lost. But by healing each of us, the inversion process can eventually heal the planet.

A personal identification with a natural area is very important. That area can be your back yard, some place you actually can spend time in. In the past it was a place you could be buried in. (As you can now as well, if you are cremated). It is a place you can love.

The inversion itself has been called the "little death", that is, the death of your invented identity. It doesn't die of course. It just gives up absolute power. By going through the little death, you are reborn into a larger perspective. Your invented identity is what holds you back from moving in the spirit world.

You can use that identity as a focal point from which to re-enter the world most of us know. Then you can roam the spirit world again. The invented identity is useful in this way, as a door to our usual world. This is why in some cultures, another identity is developed specifically as a door to the spirit world. The new identity can propel you into the spirit world as easily as your old identify held you fast to this one.

I belonged to a group practicing an ancient European tradition. They used this alternate identity, along with an alternate name and alternate mode of dress. It is just a device to help you remember that the identity we carry around with us every day allows us to function in the world we have all invented. As we go through the day, we may have several identities, as parent, student, worker, boss, customer, etc. We may act differently in each situation. That doesn't mean we are crazy. It just means that we see ourselves differently in different situations and act appropriately for the situation.

Yet we feel inside that we are still the same person. We balance the flexibility of our personality with certain basic qualities that remain the same, perhaps our opinions or moral principles. When we get to these basics, we think we have discovered ourselves. Yet opinions may change. Moral understanding may change as we experience life. Our identity may be challenged and when it is, we often become interested in God and religion, to give us a firmer footing. But religions vary. One preacher may say, "God says this," another, "God says that". Wars are fought over what God says.

Zookinesis leads you to a firmer foundation, the dynamic experience of life itself. Can you see how most religions promote, not the "one God", but the one, isolated individual? Monotheism can be as much a symbol of this individual isolation as it can be a symbol of the union of all life.

When we undergo the inversion, we realize that this search for individuality is, in reality, a search for creativity. This means that we are no longer satisfied with feeling the world as a bunch of isolated objects, of which we are one. We experience the world's vitality, connectedness and flow. We now want to be that world, to feel that world and to appreciate that world. I call it, "be yourself, see yourself, and appreciate yourself." The inversion simply makes us interested in a different pursuit in life. It is expansive, inclusive and non-destructive.

Our culture has poked its head out of the spirit world and gotten it stuck. All we see is a bunch of heads poking up from the ground. We can't see want connects them together. If you were to look at a forest underground, you would see a world of roots and fungi interconnecting all the plants and trees. Yet above ground they all seem as isolated individuals. We now know there are forms of communication among the trees and plants through these roots and fungi. Our roots are in the spirit world. Our roots are the creative intelligence that interconnects all life.

You don't need a priest to tell you what this intelligence has to say. You can feel it for yourself. You *must* feel it for yourself to heal yourself and the planet. You can listen to priests all your life and it won't do you as much good as listening to nature for one minute. Nature doesn't need interpreters. Feel your body. Feel your environment. Bring the two feelings together. Breathe. The spirit world will open to you.

Look back on your childhood and the way you understood things back then. Certainly, your understanding was only partial at best, if not erroneous. You didn't have the background to know what was reasonable and what was not. Notwithstanding all our scientific knowledge we are really in a similar situation. As children we thought we knew it all. But we didn't know how much we didn't know.

When you go through Zookinesis training, that is what hits you the most - how much we didn't know. Our "knowledge" gave us a false sense of superiority. As we thought our parents were "stupid" when we were teenagers, we think our "parent cultures" are stupid. After all, look at all we know. Aren't we smarter than our parents? It is a process that repeats itself every generation and every generation of cultures as well.

How can you tell your children that they aren't smarter than you? They know better. There is also no way to "tell" a culture that it isn't as all-knowing as it may think. All you can do is help it mature and gain wisdom through experience.

Zookinesis is based on experience - being able to experience life energy. When you do - then you will know, then you will understand.

During the winter months, I used to take the goldfish from my outdoor pond and bring them to a large fish tank in the basement. I didn't dig the pond deep enough at that time to be able to leave them out over the winter. As I watched them swim around, I wondered if they are aware of the medium of water they are swimming in. The water supports them, protects them and allows them to move.

We are also moving within a dense medium – air. While we can't see it, the pressure of the air around us is over 14.7 pounds per square inch at sea level. Several miles of air above us press down on the air around us, making the air at sea level very dense.

Yet we are not usually aware of air unless it is a windy day. Then we can feel the air on our skins and can see dead leaves and trash flying around. We are aware of the effects of air even if we are not directly aware of the air itself.

Without an atmosphere, life could not exist. Without water, fish would suffocate, dry out and die. There is another medium that is equally as vital to life as air and water and equally as hard to see. This is the medium of consciousness. While most people can't perceive consciousness directly, we can see its effects. In fact, everything we are aware of is the effect of the medium of consciousness.

Many people have told me that they are seeking spiritual development or self-awareness or some kind of inner training. There is a tendency in modern times to think that there is some trick or secret to be learned that will immediately lead to enlightenment or spiritual awareness. So they repeat phrases to themselves or listen to motivational speakers repeat various clichés. If they only hear the right phrase or repeat the right magical spell, they will be transformed.

My take on this is that any kind of training must begin with the awareness of the medium you exist in, the mechanism that you are as a human being and how this mechanism has been designed to work in the medium. Fish have fins so that they can swim in water. They are not just decorations someone placed on them. Animals have muscles and joints so they can use leverage to work with the force of gravity, which is another medium. Reptiles developed a thick-scaled skin to avoid drying out in the medium of air.

We can understand how our bodies have evolved to work within various mediums. To understand our minds, emotions and other inner aspects of being human, we need to understand the other mediums in which we exist.

We can know consciousness by the dynamics of our attention. I believe that there is no secret phrase or idea we can think about that will lead to a significant transformation of our lives. But awareness of how our minds, emotions and other "inner" parts are designed to work in the medium of consciousness can't help but to restore our full potential and vitality.

One of the Chinese Zen (Chan) masters witnessed a group of Buddhists arguing about a waving flag. Some of the Buddhists said that the flag was waving. Others said that it was actually the wind that was waving. The Zen master told them that it was their minds that were waving.

The wind and the flag show how you can perceive an invisible force by watching a visible object's reaction to that force. The force was the movement of the air. In the same way, the movement of the flag created an effect on the minds of the Buddhists. The thinking mind and the consciousness are in the same relationship as the flag and the wind.

If you were to see a flag moving but didn't know about the wind you would wonder, "Why is the flag moving?" In the same way, my first koan (Zen question) as a child was, "Why does one thought follow another in a particular pattern?" To understand this, you need to understand the relationship between thinking and consciousness. They are not the same.

The movement of consciousness does not necessarily have to result in thinking. It can lead to the movement of chi (internal energy). It is said that consciousness leads, the internal energy follows and the body then follows that. The saying actually is translated as "mind leads" but this mind does not mean thinking. It refers to attention itself. Our attention is often ripped and pulled this way and that by the influences around us, like the wind waving the flag. When we are seeking spiritual development, or whatever glorious phrase is used, we are usually trying to bring our attention more under our creative control. We want our creativity to be more of an influence over our attention than the external forces such as advertisers or peer pressure.

So spiritual development is really about perfecting the relationship of creativity (Yang) and attention (Yin). Creativity is active; it is the shaper. Attention is passive; it is the substance, the medium that is shaped.

What we are trying to discover in our training, is: to what extent is what we perceive a result of what is actually there and to what extent is it a result of how our attention is shaped and affected by the forces around us. We are trying to get a clear picture of our lives and the world around us.

Telescopes are placed high on mountaintops because the atmosphere interferes with the light coming into the telescopes. This light is distorted by the miles of compacted air that is usually in a state of turbulence. The higher up you go, the less air and the less distortion. Orbiting telescopes are free of this problem.

That is why silent meditation is part of any spiritual practice. The thinking mind is like the miles of air. It is usually in a state of movement that distorts your perception of the world around you. The key is to see things as they really are.

Then you can work on your forms, your Push Hands or, in other systems, on your rituals and really know what you are doing. You can do your healing such as Tai-chi Massage and really see the problems within your patient about how his creativity and attention interact and how that interaction affects the body. When these factors become clearly visible, then you can easily see how to use the techniques you have learned to correct those problems.

There is another saying that if you put a frog into hot water it will jump out. But if you put it into room temperature water then slowly heat the water up, the frog will not notice the slow increase and will eventually get boiled. We are in a similar situation. We cannot see how the influences around us control our thinking minds, how this affects or interferes with the dynamics of our attention and how that degrades the body. Our whole system gradually degrades until we are in a sorry mess. The solution is to become aware of this whole process.

One of the reasons I love Tai-chi and Zookinesis so much is that it so clearly explains this whole process and gives you a clearly defined, step by step method to use for your training. There is no mystery. Yet there is an appreciation for the process and an awe of the process. It is similar to a car fanatic who loves his cars and knows every detail about how they work. He will spend an enormous amount of time repairing and improving his cars while people like me would rather just send it to a mechanic and only if it really needs fixing.

During the spring the daylight increases. As the moon enters its "full" stage the amount of light at night increases. This is considered by ancient people to be the best time to work on any practice that gives you greater awareness (light). While it seems simplistic it points to a greater principle. Our inner world should be in harmony with the dynamics of nature around us. If we can see, understand and predict the patterns of nature, we will then know when to plant, when to harvest, etc.

If we can see and understand the forces "inside" of us, then our training will be more effective. Rather than just making the mind more "windy" by repeating clichés to ourselves or trying to discover the "correct" ideas, we can quiet down the wind, perceive our basic nature and how our nature is designed to work in the medium of consciousness.

There is a fear that if we perceive fully, if we can see the spirit world and function within it, then our thinking abilities will weaken. There is a deep-seated illusion that full awareness competes with full ability to think clearly.

The root of that illusion is our weak attention. This is the root of all the problems. Our attention is just not strong enough to think and to have our bodies function well at the same time. If we do not maintain an animal awareness in which attention is distributed evenly throughout the body, then attention weakens. When the attention is so concentrated on thinking as it is today, then the rest of you suffers.

Attention then becomes like a lake, usually fed by a stream that suddenly is cut off from the stream. It then turns into a smelly swamp (not that there's anything wrong with a smelly swamp).

Attention that is not connected to the rest of nature decays. Just see what happens when our political leaders think they know so much that they don't listen to people who disagree with them. They don't consider all views and facts. The result is poor leadership.

Martial arts training requires you to pay attention quickly and accurately and provides an incentive (not getting hit). The martial arts are a personal path, much like a religion or a philosophy. The fact that you are learning to punch and kick people is just the method of teaching the path. You are actually learning about your own desire to be violent, about its roots and about how to resolve those issues. You are also learning how to see inside the opponent and understand him on an internal level. While effectively defending yourself, you can still remain calm and not have the violent emotions of the opponent duplicate themselves inside of you. If the opponent has transferred his pattern of violence inside of you then you lose, even if you have won that particular fight.

And that's how it is in everyday life. There are many angry people walking around. Many of my students are doctors. One told me that many doctors nowadays are "practicing angry". This means that patient's relatives are angry with doctors and ready to sue them. Medical insurance companies look for every excuse not to pay the doctor because perhaps, the patient's name was misspelled on one of the papers. This makes the doctors angry.

I remember as a child watching situation comedies on television. They seemed to all be based on the same premise. The husband and wives conspire against each other to get what they want. I wondered, "Is this what a relationship should really be about?"

Have we become a culture of fearful people conspiring against each other to get what we want? I guess it's silly to even ask the question. But is this what you want for yourself?

The martial arts seem to be so much about fearful people conspiring to hit each other, to "win over" each other. Yet, whether an internal or external martial art, this training is supposed to be about self-awareness and the ability to live in harmony with other people. It is really about becoming a fully developed human being. Your thinking mind must be involved in learning martial arts but when you spar you use the animal attention.

In Push Hands practice, you begin to neutralize the partner's incoming force at the exact same time as the force begins to come in to you. You saw the origins of that force in the preparation of the partner and know what to expect. Push Hands then takes place in real time. Yet as a beginner you didn't realize the force was coming in until it was right on top of you and then it was too late to neutralize it.

Imagine if you could see things coming at you much earlier and prepare for them. Many people can do this economically. They study the economic trends and know that a recession or that good times are around the corner. They can then prepare for the future. They use their thinking minds to see into the future. We can do this with our animal attention as well.

Just for a moment, consider the trends of how the behaviors of people are changing. Then look into the future. Are you happy with what you see? All we can do as individuals is to develop ourselves. Our nature as individuals can then affect those around us. Each interaction with another person is a chance to decide the future of our culture.

I always ask myself, "Am I in the spirit world right now?" Have I let the angers and conflicts of the world around me program my own behavior or do I have some say over my behavior? The concept of the spirit world helps me to maintain my direction in life.

Why is Tai-chi spiritual? As a child, you may have opened the back of a watch (when they were made with gears and mainsprings) and were amazed at what you saw. You gradually came to understand how the watch worked and may have even embarked on a career as a mechanic or engineer.

When you understand the mechanisms that control how you behave as a person you can be more creative with yourself. In a music band, one member may play part of the song a little differently and the other band members, hearing this change, go along with it and support it. In the same way, part of your body may want to move differently and the other parts are consciously aware of this and support that creative change.

The result is a consciousness or feeling of self, which is evenly distributed throughout the body and not just located in the head. In some disciplines you are taught to eliminate the ego or feeling of self. In the Tai-chi approach you just share this feeling of self with every cell, organ, muscle and bone in the body. You become a cooperative community of living individuals who all feel they are part of the same "tribe" (which is you as a whole person).

How would this world be if all people felt they were part of the same tribe? In Taoist theory, the way you relate to other people is based on how you relate to your own body. If a whole culture is taught to believe that we live in our heads and in our thoughts and our bodies are just a dumb machine, then that affects how that culture relates to other cultures. If the head just orders the rest of the body around and doesn't care how the body feels that also affects your relationships with other people. When we practice Push Hands, we quickly learn that if we forcefully try to push the other person over, this locks us up and actually allows the other person to push us more easily.

If you use force, you have the attitude of force in your mind and your opponent can use that attitude to defeat you. In a similar way, if you are the type of person who is always trying to get away with something, to take more than you give, then you are actually more susceptible to get scammed. The Internet scam emails only work if you think you are getting something for nothing.

That is why, in our practice, we always try to have even exchanges with people, to not cheat them and to not be cheated by them. In Push Hands, where the other person comes in to push, we yield. But we move into the part of their body that is inactive. The balance of Yin and Yang is maintained but the result is that we always feel empty to the other person and we can always move into them to push.

The other person learns that if he is tense and has an aggressive attitude, then his body is really dead. It is dead to awareness. It is locked. The attitude of balance always leads to maximum awareness. The attitude of maximum aggressiveness (or passivity) leads to a deadening of awareness.

While Tai-chi is not a religion, there is a morality – the morality of balance. There is empathy of understanding of the torture many people live with because you yourself extricated yourself from that internal torture. In this way, you see that there is a spiritual path in life. It is not the path of maximum power of one part of you over another or of one person over another. It is not about thinking this as opposed to that. It is the path of discovering, understanding and then releasing useless behaviors and allowing the body, mind and emotions to function naturally and in harmony with each other and with the community of life. You are allowed to laugh at your useless behaviors and be entertained by your own ridiculousness.

The key is to let go. If your attention is now mainly caught up in your thoughts and emotions, let your attention move into the body as water moves into dry earth. If you feel your attention ready to combat another person, first let it flow into that person and learn how that feels. You may think that if you connect with another person in this way you are being too "new-age". People say, "We must be tough to live in this world."

Remember that Tai-chi is also a martial art. The full name is Tai-chi-Chuan (The Grand Ultimate Martial Art). One of the most important parts of the skills of Tai-chi fighting is for your attention to remain connected to the "opponent" and to flow with him. Flow away from his strikes and into his open areas. If your attention disconnects from his body you are in trouble.

There is an old Chinese story. A famous calligrapher was asked to make a scroll for someone's living room, summarizing the essence of Zen or Taoist philosophy. He presented them with a large scroll with a tiny character of "attention" in the center. The purchaser liked the scroll but asked the calligrapher to draw something larger and giving more of an explanation. The calligrapher returned with another scroll, this time with a larger character of "attention". The purchaser asked one more time for something appropriate for a large living room, something that would really explain the principles of his philosophy. The calligrapher then returned with a very large scroll with a very large character "attention" drawn on it.

Within your own body the attention of each organ and each cell has its own unique pattern and is its individual Body-Mind. The attention of each person, of each habitat and of the earth as a whole, has its own unique pattern and is its individual Body-Mind. The alignment of these levels of Body-Mind is an issue at each stage of a student's development. I call it the "spiral staircase". If you stand at the center of this staircase, you can see all the way up and down. Each floor represents a level of Body-Mind. A goal of the student is to be able to travel up and down that staircase, exploring each floor. This is the approach of Zookinesis.

We begin by having the student follow the flow of momentum in the form. When this momentum flows down into the ground or out the head or fingers, the student follows it out of his body with his attention. When the momentum circles around under the foot and then back up into the foot, his attention follows that as well. The teacher will explain how the momentum should flow and the student adjusts his posture and movements to get it to flow that way.

As an example, the momentum should flow down the inside of the legs and back up the inside of the legs. The legs form an arch and the weight on top of the arch must always move towards the inside of the arch. This means that every point on the torso of his body must move towards the inside of the thigh of the forward leg (if you are shifting forward). When you rise up from that leg, the force should move up from the foot to the inside of that thigh, to your Tan-tien and then out to wherever it is going.

The student gets used to following momentum with his attention. He then divides his attention so he can follow the individual momentum of each part of the body as described before. This is like colliding galaxies. When they merge, it is extremely rare for one solar system to hit another solar system, because the distances between solar systems are so vast. Yet the gravity of each galaxy affects and distorts the other. Think of the momentum of each part of the body as the gravity of the galaxies.

By following this interaction, your attention becomes more complex and stronger. You learn that there are spots in your body that the attention flows through well and other spots that are closed to the attention. To a large extent, you can open these closed spots by relaxing them or by having someone massage them. You can also "breathe into them" as described before.

I describe it this way. If you hold up a piece of wood at an angle and place a drop of water near the top, the drop will probably just remain in place. But if you wet your finger and draw a path of wetness down the wood, then connect that with the drop, the drop will follow the path. You have lowered the friction down that path and the drop will follow the path of least resistance.

In the body, you use the breathing technique described above to "lower the resistance" of your attention in that part of the body. What you are really trying to do is to eliminate the resistance of attention everywhere in the body. You wind up with a "field of attention" rather than specific pathways. It is this field of attention the cells and organs use to communicate with each other and coordinate their activities. It is a finer and more effective means of communication than the nervous and endocrine systems. When our bodies are dull to attention, the cells and organs have a more difficult time functioning properly.

We must also lower the resistance of attention in the bones as well. Attention can flow anywhere. It is what connects all things together. Internal energy ("chi") is a sense, like the sense of sight. Internal energy reveals to us how everything is connected to each other. The sense of sight shows us how everything is separate (I am here and you are there). Both senses balance each other. Our culture has emphasized the sense of sight (separateness) and de-emphasized (really, eliminated any reference to) the sense of internal energy. This has detrimental effects culturally and medically.

The sense of sight and the sense of internal energy are a paired sense - they work together to form an accurate picture of the world.

We are partially "blind" without the sense of internal energy and have a very distorted view of the world.

Keep your eyes Yin (relaxed) to develop this sense. Don't try to grab with your attention as if there were little arms reaching out of your eyes to grab something. That would be Yang attention. Yin attention allows the sights to flow into the eyes like water flowing over a waterfall and splashing down into the pool of the Tan-tien. The mist of the waterfall evaporates into the air. Allow some of your attention to evaporate into the air, even while most of it flows along with the momentum. This means that while a pulse of attention moves with the momentum, you keep the entire surroundings "moist" with attention as if it were a mist, filling the area.

When you start to breathe out (your body has finished expanding on the in-breath and is about to sink), new, fresh attention is drawn into the body from the surroundings. When you breathe in (your body finished condensing and is about to expand), new, fresh attention is drawn into the body from the ground. The implication in these statements is that there is attention in the ground and in the surroundings that can be drawn into the body and that "your" attention actually "goes" somewhere into the surroundings.

From the "Zookinesis" perspective this is true. Remember that empty space is a characteristic of the sense of sight – separateness. We create an intellectual framework within which the sense of sight can be arranged and be made useful to us - the "three-dimensional, physical world". But the framework of the sense of internal energy, the "spirit world" does not really have "empty" spaces. Nowhere is there an absence of attention because attention is the substance of the universe. Space is one of the things creativity "makes" with attention. This is similar to the theory of the Big Bang creation of the universe. It is not that the Big Bang shot matter and energy into space. Space itself was also created by the Big Bang.

In the "spirit world" everything is filled with attention; everything is connected. That is the experience we are trying to achieve by learning a Tai-chi form.

When you practice any form of healing (such as massage), you are aware of how attention flows through the "patient". You try to "moisten" the patient's body to allow attention to flow more freely and to connect to the body more easily.

289

You gradually become aware that part of the substance of your body is attention and that becoming an artist of attention means that you become aware of the creative energy in you. You become aware of how you can develop your body, mind and spirit in a healthy way and, on the contrary, how it can be contorted. The form teaches you that you are the creator of your own life through your artistic effects on attention. Rather than trying to change the world around you to conform to your own distorted attention, you refine your attention and through that your body, mind, spirit - your life.

Only then can you fight for justice, the environment or whatever your cause. Only when you become a master of your own wellbeing can you be effective in improving the world around you.

We learn through Push Hands, how manipulative we can be if we act from our thinking minds and how a person who is addicted to this manipulation, can himself be easily manipulated. We learn through the form how to allow our attention to flow smoothly along with momentum, and to remove the mind's grubby little hands from the flow of attention. This frees up the flow of internal energy, which follows the flow of attention.

The thinking mind always freezes attention and the Body-Mind always frees attention. Tai-chi is a balance of the two.

If you imagine attention as the substance of experience (in this case of the body), internal energy is a wave in that substance. While each water molecule in a tidal wave just moves up and down, a wave of energy is propagated through the water resulting in great power.

The water itself is not pushed along the length of the wave. It may begin as a sinking of the earth - an earthquake or underwater rockslide or as an expansion of the earth - an underwater volcano. The propagating force comes and goes quickly but the flow of energy continues. You do not need to "push" the internal energy of the body along in its path. You need to let it go. If you use a bow and arrow, you don't push the arrow forward; you draw the bow first and then, to send out power, you "release" the force; you let go. The ideas of the mind can initiate a wave of energy but it must let that wave go. Thoughts are like a shift of the earth underneath the ocean.

Each movement of the form is initiated by letting go (usually of the opposite side of the body from the direction you want to go) rather than by forcefully moving the body into place. When you push someone, you first allow your own body to be compressed by their resistance, and then you let that compressed force go (back to the pusher) before or while adding your own.

Teaching Zookinesis is the same. We first learn to let go of our tendency to force energy through our bodies. We discover the power of letting go of that addiction. We discover that our bodies already know the "correct" way for that energy to move.

We let go of the habits that manipulate our attention. The less we manipulate our attention, the more it can be used as a sense to detect the internal activities of the body.

Now when the student practices Push Hands, he can sink his attention very deeply into his partner. When he practices bodywork healing, he can heal on a very deep level. Rather than manipulate his patient's energy, he removes the claws of his patient from his patient's own energy. He makes the patient aware of the patient's body's own wisdom. Even more, he makes the patient aware of the wisdom of all of nature surrounding him and the connection of his energy to the rest of the energy around him.

When we look at a wild animal, we can respect the great wisdom of its internal energy, of its attention, and realize that its attention is the same that is inside us. It is the substance of all things. When we meet that wild animal, we look into its eyes and say, "I recognize you. You are inside of me." And the animal says the same to you. If it is an imported animal, it may still be confused about its new surroundings but it recognizes you and is familiar with you.

Each of us finds ourselves out of the habitat our bodies evolved in as if we were an imported animal, and as we look around at our fellow humans, can we detect something familiar in them? Or are they so involved in manipulating themselves and others that our attention flicks off them? The ability to absorb the attention of others is the glue that holds our society together.

If you look at old movies, the camera focuses on an actor's face for a long time as his expression changes due to some event. Your own attention can sink gradually into his as you appreciate the change in his feelings. Newer movies are based on the poorer attention span of modern times. You don't get the chance to allow your attention to mellow into the scene, like the aging of a fine wine. We don't get wine anymore, but grape juice. And this change has taken place in just the few years since movies have been around.

I hope that Tai-chi training doesn't all become of the grape juice variety. I hope there are still some teachers out there who are willing to wait for the wine. Sometimes I get calls from people asking, "How many lessons do I need to become a Tai-chi teacher - six or eight lessons". I understand that some organizations are offering two-day Tai-chi teacher certification courses.

To me, Zookinesis training is the fine wine of Tai-chi.

Chapter 7
Death and Time

The issue of death can lead us to a more powerful way to live our lives. We know what happens to our bodies at death. What happens to our consciousness (or what I call, "attention")? We fear death as if it were not already part of us. Yet the death of the awareness of our bodies, of the consciousness of each cell and organ, is death we carry with us. The death of our direct awareness to our connection to nature already places us in our graves.

We are like travelers towards the destination of death, carrying our death with us. In this way we bring death to death. When you practice Tai-chi you become more alive each day. The barrier between ourselves and the world around us gets thinner and our attention can traverse that barrier more easily. We live our lives bringing life to life.

When you hear beautiful music, the music threads your consciousness through your body into the world of sound. When you fall in love you thread consciousness through each other. We are weavers of consciousness. When others think we die, we know that we have weaved the last of ourselves into the web of life and have become that web. The issue of life is not the length of life or our wealth but the beauty of the tapestry we weave.

We are not grabbing onto life to avoid death. We are in a constant state of letting go as we live, so that our death seems familiar. It seems like the way we have been trying to let go to rejoin the world around us.

Each time you are willing to let go (of anger, fear, worry, etc.) you learn that grabbing stops you from growing. Grabbing makes you feel safe. It is like suing someone after you hurt yourself because the world wasn't made perfectly safe just for you.

A beginning Push Hands student feels more alive, more powerful, when he grabs and controls the partner, but that is death to the interaction, to the connection of the partners to each other. When you allow the partner's energy into you and work with that energy, you feel alive in another sense. You become the interaction. What you perceived to be "holding onto life" with grabbing evolves into flowing with life by becoming greater than your individual self – the basis of any relationship.

When you can trust someone, you can be open to them. To trust them you must trust your ability to "see" them – to know what is going on inside of them. Your relationship evolves by how well you know each other rather than how well you control each other.

When a child climbs a tree, he becomes that tree. He holds the branches in order to connect. When you hold someone you love, it is to become connected. The child is not trying to control the tree and, if you really love someone, you are not trying to control them. There is a temptation to control the people around you and bend them to your will. In some cases, their refusal to do so results in anger as if you had a natural right to be obeyed. A very useful exercise is to ask yourself, in any situation, "Am I trying to connect or trying to control?". Do I want to conquer the tree or become part of it?

It is difficult to release the desire to control and to conquer. Our economic system is based on one company conquering another, one employee conquering another to get a promotion and one country conquering another. It is almost impossible to imagine a world not based on conquering. How would we stand out from everyone else? If we weren't in constant battle, how could any progress be made? Don't we have to become hardened to deal with a hard world?

Tai-chi teaches us to release this paradigm. When we learn to release, we die, in a certain sense, because we are no longer a hardened object. While people may still be dishonest, we develop the courage to let the hardened shell around us die so that we may live.

It starts with living a life of honesty. You have the courage to state what you need and expect from others. You honestly assess your own limitations and skills. You do not cheat other people. Yet your training allows you to see the dishonesty in others and avoid getting cheated. You have the courage to call out lies.

Living an honest life brings you to life. Demanding integrity helps bring others to life. The issue is not "will you die?" but "what will die?" Death is no longer a time-line but a question of growth of awareness.

What is awareness capable of? Is it a captive of our concept of time and space, just electrical signals of the brain, or can developing our awareness pull back the curtain of time and space? Can we imagine what we now know as death as the pulling back of that curtain?

The ability to be open to and to see the beauty of another person or culture's story helps bring you from death to life. It helps you learn to stop grabbing (at your own story). In Push Hands you learn to not grab the partner but to flow with him. You learn to not grab the idea of winning but to allow force to be released into the partner. You learn to not grab onto your own identity that covers up the creative spirit. Traditional Push Hands brings you to life.

The "push" is not the end goal of traditional Push Hands. Letting go with every cell of your body is the goal of Push Hands. That type of letting go is a process; it is continuous. When we die, we can let go of the body because we know the whole of ourselves. We have pulled back the curtain and are ready to move through it.

When we watch an exciting movie our bodies and emotions are affected by what we see. Even when the movie is over, those hormones that were released during the chase scene take time to subside. We know the movie will only last two hours or so but it can affect our attitudes for life if it gives you insight into life itself. A silly little fairy tale is not designed to inform you about what happened to a real person at a real time. It teaches you about how to live your life.

Your life is a story. If you are the creator of the story you can make it a good one. Reading mythology or fairy tales teaches you how to write your own story and how to not let others write it for you. If your story is not working out well, you can change it at any time within the limitations of your present condition. It is the change of story that will get you beyond that condition.

While the story may change, the writer is always there. The issue really is how conscious is that writer? Did he or she spend the time to learn how to write a good story? Is she willing to continue to be creative and not let the story die from neglect?

There is a story that goes with Tai-chi training and I have tried to write that story. It is a story of whom we are, how to understand the obstacles to our health and happiness and how to heal. The story teaches how much there is to each of us, and how to unlock our power. It sets out a path that leads to health and greater awareness and challenges us about how far we can go. If there is a secret in Tai-chi, it is that there is no limit to how far we can go on that path.

Death is a fulcrum – not an end. It is stillness, emptiness. Returning to stillness, one is able to move in a different direction. Returning to stillness one can notice things that remained hidden beneath the clutter of activity. Stillness is necessary for change and movement. It is the hidden background upon which everything else stands out.

As one uses form and substance, one must learn to use stillness and death. A fulcrum is still. The fulcrum of a compass or see-saw or our own Tan-tien allows movement. Should the fulcrum move or wobble you would not be able to remain centered. Death is the center point between opposite ends of activity.

This form of death suggests renewal rather than an end. It is the source of power. Moving around a central still point, any object passes by the same point in space again and again. It shows its face and back alternately as in the case of day and night on earth. Death therefore allows continual renewal through cyclic activity. Understanding death as an end throws the fulcrum off center, preventing our lives from continuing in its cycles of development, even during our "living" time on earth.

What is it that is renewed through death and stillness? When we are still our minds and bodies rest. The continually evolving structure of thought ends. Then we can start in a new direction. If we fear the cessation of thinking, if we identify ourselves with thought, then we may fear the quieting of the thinking mind.

But if we can allow thought to end once in a while, we can be more creative and restful. Our thoughts will be more varied. Similarly, if we identify with our behavior patterns, growth may threaten us. Growth always involves change in behavior and perspective. We may fear to lose a particular structure and try to maintain that structure rigidly.

When death is balanced, there is life – a continuity of movement. You can detect that balance because your form is effortless and the battles in your life end. So we search for stillness everywhere. Within a joint we say, "rotate in place – don't move in space". This means that movement should come from the rotation of each joint with the minimum of movement of the joint as a whole, so you are not moving wildly about. This allows you to focus on "internal movement" in which the joints move sequentially to create waves of motion within the body.

We search for stillness within our thinking so that we have a "passive observer" of awareness, just watching the thoughts bounce about, but not getting disturbed by mental activity. We search for stillness in our relationships that allows us to become aware of the beauty of the connection between two people without needing to substantiate our feelings. We search for stillness in each moment of our lives that allows the curtain of self-pity and misery to be pulled back to reveal the beauty of the world. Stillness is our sword that sharpens our awareness and removes uncertainty of our power. It is courage.

We experience stillness as the central part of ourselves, not as the enemy. And when death comes at the end of our lives, we know this must be a fulcrum as well – to allow change.

It is the rigidity of our patterns that defines our boundaries. When some of us walk in a natural area, our attention expands and joins that area, yielding to its intent. The yielding dissolves the rigidity, leading to stillness, balance and peace. We can practice "death" every day by letting go of rigidity so that when we finally "die" we will be experts at it. The skill of dying is letting go of the resistance to life.

When I lived half each year in the Catskill Mountains and the other half in Brooklyn as a child, I loved both the "country" and the "city". The country was the forest, farms and animals. I spent a lot of time at a stream in the back of the property. The city was sophistication, large buildings, culture and education. They were like two states of being. If only I could have both at the same time! I now live in the suburbs on Long Island but it has gotten pretty built up over the years.

In Tai-chi and Zookinesis training I learned to combine those two states of being. The Body-Mind state is losing yourself in nature. The thinking mind is like big buildings, culture and education. The goal is to allow both states to function at the same time so they interpenetrate each other.

Life and death are like that. Death is the ultimate release, back into nature. Life is condensing a "self" out of nature. There is no reason we cannot have both release and a self at the same time. At one stage of growth, we strive to become independent from our parents. In our teens we try to integrate with our peers. As adults we benefit from what we learned about being independent and about integrating in our culture.

When we include nature as part of our culture, we can integrate life and death and allow them to interpenetrate. Death - the still fulcrum that allows our consciousness to merge with the world around us. Life – isolating and understanding each element of our world and our relationship to it. We should not be on a linear path towards death and away from life but on a path of integration of the experience of ourselves as individuals and as part of the "being of the earth".

In many ancient cultures the world of death and life are very connected. In Greek mythology Demeter was the Goddess of fertility and growth of crops. Her daughter by Zeus was Persephone. Hades, the King of the Underworld, took a liking to her and captured her to live with him in the underworld. Demeter was very angry and sad and because of this, crops failed. Zeus bade her to let the crops grow and all the Gods pleaded with her. If the humans died, there would be no one to worship them.

Finally, Zeus traveled to the Underworld and got Hades to agree to release Persephone for half of each year. That is why half of the year is warm and the crops can grow, and half cold. It sounds like a silly little tale but it shows the intimate relationship between life and death. The Underworld is not some place we go to when the body dies. It is part of life and without it our lives are not as rich and satisfying. Each of us belongs to both our culture and to nature.

The Underworld is "sung". It is sinking into the earth to become part of the world. Our Tai-chi form is the balance of sinking into the earth and being lifted into the heavens (into Mount Olympus in Greek mythology). It is the "alignment of heaven and earth". If we only lift, we will be stiff. If we only sink, we will be sloppy. The integration of these two qualities is a sign of the depth of our training. The term

298

"spirit world" that I am fond of using means the complete integration of those two qualities.

Tai-chi forms are based on the principle of "silk reeling energy" or "spiraling energy". When you breathe in and expand, you are expanding upward from your center (Tan-tien) and downward from your center. The upward and downward spirals move at the same time and in different directions so that they balance each other. If you want to expand upward and outward explosively, you must also root with equal force. After the body stretches in this way it then returns back to the center using the same mechanics.

The center is the still point that allows great activity. It is the "singularity" out of which spews a universe. Every move in the form must express this principle. Integrating "death" with life prolongs and enlivens life.

You are a singularity, in a sense. The integration of the health of your body, mind, emotions and spirit with the health of your environment is your job. You are the gatekeeper between the microscopic world inside of you and the entire living world. Cells may die and be replaced. The deadness of winter will give rise to the flowers of summer. Both inside and outside the cycles of life flow on. There is a process between the inside and outside that continues through these cycles and you are the creator of that process.

To really be human it is important to understand that process. That is what you learn in Tai-chi and Zookinesis. That process not only takes place in you, but on larger scales in the world around us. To place yourself within the process of creativity, within that singularity, within death that creates life, is to align yourself with the overall mechanics and spirit of the universe.

When you yield the deadness of your grabbing mind to the intelligence of each part of the body, you provide life for those parts. When you yield the deadness of your grabbing to the flow of nature, you allow all life to continue.

To yield in this way you need a strong sense of self so that you feel confident enough to let go. If you were to climb a cliff you would need a strong grasp before you could move your leg to a higher level. So the creation of a fashioned creature is necessary to let the energy of your attention go into your body and out to your surroundings. Too often, though, a person who mistakes the fashioned creature as himself pulls energy into it from his body and his surroundings. He doesn't use the creature as a steady base from which to yield his energy so the inside and outside can connect. The "gate" becomes rusty and won't open. In this case the softening of the fashioned creature, oiling the rusty hinges, may seem like a death, if you identify yourself as your creation.

Yet such a death returns you to life – to your original creative nature, to generating and spreading healing energy. There is no longer a difference between the individual parts of the body and the whole individual. There is no longer a difference between the whole individual and the whole earth.

The "I-Ching", written 2,500 years ago or more, describes the 64 qualities or states of the relationship between the "inside" and the "outside". Each is depicted as a trigram (three lines) representing the inside (bottom trigram) and a trigram representing the outside (top trigram). (This is my interpretation). The two trigrams are called a hexagram. Each line may be solid (Yang) or broken (Yin). You can think of the bottom line of the "inside" trigram as representing the Body-Mind, the top line as the thinking mind and the middle line as the relationship between the two. The top, "outside" trigram represents the individual (bottom line), the world (top line) and the relationship between the two (middle line). The I-Ching describes how your life will proceed with each combination of internal and external states. It has been used as a book of divination, in which you cast sticks or coins to come up with those hexagrams to forecast your future. But its greatest benefit is teaching you about your role in creating your life.

This book teaches you how to use the flow of time by switching from one mode (one hexagram) to another in order to veer your life onto a new path. It is like the GPS in your car that instructs you where to turn and lets you know how long it will take to get to your destination.

Physicists question whether time is a single moment which moves or if all time exists somewhere at "all times". It is useful to understand the concept of time according to Zookinesis.

Time is an aspect of the dynamics of attention. If a person's attention locks up in Push Hands, then time is said to lock up. If your partner changes speed suddenly, your attention may become bound to the new moment and the new situation. You may lose your awareness of everything that led up to this new situation so that your time-line of attention has been broken.

When your partner changes speed suddenly, his change of body alignment must also change more rapidly. Remember that as you move, your body must constantly re-align to be in a solid and springy position to be able to push your partner. If you change the speed of your movement, then you must also change the speed of the process of aligning.

What usually happens is that only part of the body speeds up its alignment and the rest is still re-aligning at the previous, slower pace. So some of the body is properly aligned for the previous moment – the previous situation – and part of the body is aligned for the present moment.

Your body can be said to be in two moments at the same time. You could also say that part of the body is prepared for the present situation and part for a situation that is no longer valid. In fact, the principles of Zookinesis suggest that there are parts of you that are prepared for many past moments in life and not for the present.

In Push Hands you need to be aware of a section of time. You must maintain your awareness of the history of the present moment – how the interaction of the two partners led to the present moment, and what are possibilities for the future (as you do in chess). You must also be aware of how each part of the partner's body is aligned. Is a particular part aligned for the present moment, or is it still aligned for one or two seconds before?

In this way, you can tell how well each part of the partner's body and his attention, can adapt and change to the present conditions. You see your partner as a collage of different moments in time.

Then, of course, when you look inside yourself, you try to discover if you are also disjointed in time. If your attention is more fluid, then time itself takes on a different flavor. If each moment is disconnected from the next and your attention moves in a jerky way then you are within "the round of birth and death".

If parts of our body are responding to circumstances that happened in the past, you cannot focus your whole attention on what is going on around you. You will be inordinately tied to the past and that type of time sense will have a deadening effect on your attention.

Death and Time

If your whole body is geared for the present moment, you can still remember the past. You can remember the series of movements that led up to the present. It's just that parts of your body don't think they are still in the past. Your attention is free to move and to act.

Time is considered to be the medium in which the attention moves and acts. If time is fixed, if the body is "locked up" to various circumstances of the past, then attention loses its freedom of movement. Attention will jump to each new moment, and then just as suddenly, become locked up and die in the round of birth and death. The sense of time that results is like discreet steps going up a building, rather than like climbing up a mountain where the ground is random and uneven and you really have to pay attention to where you are stepping.

The steps allow us to use less attention so that we can be thinking about other things than what we are actually doing. The deadening of attention removes us from our own lives.

In Western culture, time is the measurement of movement of one object against the repetitive movement of another object (the rotation of the earth, vibration of a molecule, etc.) We organize our lives to the movement of the hands of a clock or the increase in numbers of a digital display.

With Push Hands, we have the movement of two people. The attention of one may be more repetitive (less spontaneous) than another. Push Hands measures the spontaneity of one partner against the repetitive behavior of the other. It is a measure of the dimension of time. When the attention can move more freely – less repetitively – and is less controlled by outside forces, we say that this partner occupies more time.

The repetitive partner occupies only an instant of time if he is absolutely controlled by patterns. Such a person can only pay attention to one thing at a time, and he can either perceive what is going on or respond to what is going on. He cannot both perceive and respond at the same time.

Push Hands is designed to make the repetitive person more spontaneous. Time is a comparison of restrictive movement vs. free movement. In physics, we think of time as just the repetitive member of the pair. Time is understood as an absolute and continuous progression.

Einstein suggested that the perspective of the viewer was important in assessing time or at least that the speed of movement of an object influences the relative experience of time of the viewer.

If you can follow the movement of your Push Hands partner in real time, you can perceive more change than a person who can only follow one or two movements per second. If it takes you time to perceive and then react to the partner, then you cannot follow changes in movement while you are assessing the previous movement. If it takes you a half second to perceive and another half second to react to a movement, then you can only live second by second.

If you need only a quarter second to perceive and another quarter second to react, then you can live at half second intervals, giving you a relative life span twice as long as the first person. It is the speed of perception that increases relative life span. But again, the goal is to perceive and react at the same time.

The urgency of the issue of time is death. We only have a certain amount of "time" to be alive. The ability to be free from the tyranny of time means that you do not live your life as a linear progression from birth to death.

Seize your entire life as one moment and live that entire moment all the time.

"God does not play dice with the universe", according to Einstein. Here we humans are, with our spontaneous behaviors but the rest of the universe seems to be different from us. We are intelligent, aware and spontaneous. The rest of the universe is ruled by strict mechanics with no awareness or intelligence – no spontaneity. Many people even feel that human behavior is completely controlled by mechanical forces and that there is no spontaneity even within us. In this view, our behavior can also be linked to the vibration of an atom or the rotation of heavenly bodies. Certainly, this is the idea behind astrology. At least with astrology, the idea is to become aware of how our behavior is mechanical and to try to gain more creative control of our lives.

In such ancient systems as astrology, Tai-chi and Zookinesis, there is a bias in favor of the spontaneous behavior. It is an attempt to increase the balance of intelligence and creativity over living mechanically.

I also have this bias. And I wonder, aside from humans, is there any other sign of spontaneity in the universe. This does not necessarily need to be in the form of a biological organism – a little green man. To what degree is intelligence and creativity inherent in the universe itself?

How would we even search for spontaneity in the universe? Repetitive behavior is easier to find. Our sciences have had a bias in favor of looking for repetitive behavior. Intelligence is assumed to have evolved as a consequence of increased brain size (compared to body weight) and increased brain complexity. In other words, by increasing the size and complexity of a mechanistic system, you suddenly get creativity. In this way of thinking a reptile, for example, just doesn't have what it takes to be spontaneous and creative. Yet when you respect a reptile and when it comes to respect you, you can interact with more understanding. You can play with your interaction.

When you do not respect the animal, both of you respond with pre-programmed behavior (your screaming - its biting). Respect, therefore, has a lot to do with spontaneity, with intelligence. The more you respect the animal as an individual, the more awareness you have of its intelligence.

Could we look out into the universe, assume that intelligence could be found there, and then develop ways to recognize it, within the bounds of science? Physics is built on the foundation of mathematics and tends to compare one repetitive behavior to another. While you try not to have any expectations in the realm of science, there is an underlying expectation of repetitiveness. The repetitiveness of an experiment or observation validates it. A religious person, on the other hand, may believe that God is behind all things, and he then looks into the universe with the expectation of spontaneity. This is the great chasm between science and religion. It is a chasm that the philosophy of Zookinesis bridges.

What you would need first is to understand the underlying qualities and dynamics of attention itself – the mechanics of attention. We would need to know to what degree we could be creative with these qualities and dynamics so we can develop a "craft of attention" – of consciousness. Then we could study the interactions of attention to physical matter, for example to our own bodies.

You can perceive creativity in the stillness of the universe. Let us take one small part of the universe – you. When you are the most relaxed and still, isn't this the time when creative ideas come to you "as if" from somewhere else?

Physicists look for exciting places in the universe, places that produce complex molecules – supernovas perhaps. But where is creativity developed? In stillness – perhaps the stillness of a black hole (according to one view of black holes) or of the moment before the big bang (although the word "before" is meaningless in this case because time itself was created with the big bang). Can we look for the remnants of stillness as we look for the remnants of the background radiation of the big bang?

In our own lives, can we search for stillness? When I look at an animal, our mutual awareness can be agitated (worried) or still (comfortable). An animal may close his eyes for a moment, stilling his attention, to show he is comfortable. Still attention shows respect. Agitated tension shows fear and disconnection. It shows lack of awareness.

If everything in the universe were motionless, there would be no time. If everything in the universe were timed exactly to everything else, there would be no spontaneity or intelligence. Our spontaneous behavior creates the sense of time. Time is the measure of creativity. It is the measure of consciousness. We measure our spontaneity against the apparently mechanistic activities of other physical matter.

We know about the length of time – minutes, days, years. Consciousness is the width of time. While a person may be wide, physically, he may be very narrow in the dimension of time.

If the repetitive part of time is its length and the spontaneous part is its width, then its height is communication. It is the connectedness and interactions among attentions. Communication depends on mechanics (e.g. language) and spontaneity (what you want to say). It also depends on one person's talking being connected to the other person's listening. With mechanics, consciousness and communication, we have the three dimensions of time.

When two conscious beings communicate, you are comparing the two-dimensional space of time (creativity or consciousness) of one person to the two-dimensional space of time of another person and you are measuring the space between them – thus the third dimension.

305

Death and Time

When you stare at a snake, you are staring into time. The snake is looking for the time within you – for the space between automatic behavior and true awareness. The snake usually sees very little time within us. We can sense so much time in a snake that we are afraid of it.

A snake has all the time in the world. It can stare at you for hours without moving. Can you stare at a snake for hours without moving? It can do this, not because it is dumb, but because it is aware. You are afraid of a snake because it exists in a much larger space of time than you – even though a snake lives only fifteen or twenty years.

He maintains the "shape of time" in order to "soar" – to merge his attention with yours and yours with his so you can experience each other. The steady shape acts as a container to hold the merged attention. So your attentions, lined up towards each other, then allows something else to move into each other in the "space" thus created. This something is called, "spirit". It is what allows consciousness to merge (and conversely, to separate). Spirit is the art of merging and separating, as is Push Hands. Spirit exists in the space we call time, the three dimensions of time.

When you talk to another person, you generally are not interested in merging but in playing with the distance between you (how much you are different from each other). But when you love someone, you want your spirits to merge. You can stare at your lover silently because you love looking at him or her. There is a kind of tension – an awareness of your individuality and yet something is merging.

The snake, in essence, wants to love you. The energy of the earth wants to love you. The energy of the earth can only merge into you within a space of time. That is why artists say they feel the creativity is flowing through them from somewhere else. They have a space of time; they have creativity.

When you are healing, you are trying to create space in the patient – not physical space but a space of time, a space whose length, width and height are awareness of mechanics, spontaneity and the ability to connect.

They should be aware of what you are doing and the principles of what you are doing. They need a feeling of freedom, even if it is just the freedom of movement of a joint. They need to connect their minds and bodies and to connect with the creative intelligence of their bodies.

The strength of the connection between two consciousnesses (whether two people or one person's mind and body) depends on how much "space of time" is in each consciousness. The more conscious each one is, the more connected they can become. It is similar to the force of gravity. The more mass each object has, the greater the attraction between them. If someone is totally unconscious, it will be hard to make that connection. If they are conscious but they behave in a very mechanistic, unaware way, it will also be hard to make a connection.

The width of time is equivalent to mass of an object in regards to its attractive force. Some spiritual disciplines feel that consciousness is affected by gravity and that is what holds us to our bodies. Their version of becoming more spiritual is to escape the force of gravity and remove their consciousness from their bodies. Their version of heaven is floating on the clouds.

Zookinesis has a different view. We learn about the dynamics of attention so that we can be creative with how attentions attract each other. We learn about merging and separating so we can become the gatekeeper. While we develop a large width of attention, we also learn to move and act within that width – within the spirit world. Our version of heaven is to simply be aware and to be able to function effectively in all the dimensions in which humans exist.

For some, time is the distance between birth and death. For us it is the distance between repetitive, unconscious behavior and true awareness. The first version of time is a relentless march towards an end. The second is an expansion of time itself, a growth of the human spirit. The difference between the two is how you live your life and how you remember your life. Memory is not only a list of events but a record of your growth.

If we could only understand how our memory works, we could access deep memories, even those before birth. The study of Zookinesis and Tai-chi explains the mechanics of memory and teaches us how to access these deep memories. Natural memory, or what is called, "sacred memory" is the biological way memories are stored. It is the memory of feeling states, which includes how your body feels, skills you have acquired, and how your interaction with the world around you, changes your internal state. This type of memory is not related to time but to maintaining an optimal internal state of health, and an optimal connection to your natural environment. You do not lay down memories in a time-line. Rather, this type of memory is cyclic, sometimes moving away from optimal condition and sometimes returning to it. At a certain point in life, you learn about clock time and your life begins to revolve around that. You are taught to lay down memories using time as a reference.

Time, rather than health, becomes the reference point of a memory. You dissociate yourself from inner feeling and the feeling of health so that you can become part of the "time culture" we have invented. Your behavior no longer binds you to health but to time. Furthermore, the type of time we use as the basis of our culture is separated from the vagaries of nature. Rather than judging time by the flowering of a certain type of plant or the appearance of a certain insect, we use clock time to eliminate any variations. This allows the world around us to appear mechanistic and our lives to become mechanistic.

Zookinesis teaches us to experience every moment of our lives with our whole selves. Even when a thought comes to us, we not only experience that thought as words, but as internal feelings. Thoughts become complexes of feelings and associations with a short label of words. The words are not the thoughts. The feelings and experiences are the thoughts. In this way every aspect of life stirs the body, stirs the emotions, and stirs our connection to nature. Life is more vivid, intense and beautiful. It is much easier to access the earliest memories because those complexes of feelings are still present.

When we learn a Tai-chi form, for example, we are concentrating on the feeling of our body's alignment at each moment. The teacher adjusts our body so that we can feel proper alignment in that pose and feel how energy flows so much more freely when we are aligned. We concentrate on how each muscle must become alive and have an eagerness to move. At first, the eagerness of the muscle is to remain tight. We learn how to convince the muscle to relax. When the muscle feels the joy of relaxation and its increased competence, it becomes eager to relax and move.

We remember the process of developing eagerness in that muscle and apply the same process to other muscles. In this way, memory can be transferred from one muscle to the other. Each muscle "remembers" how it can interact with other muscles to create the proper flow of movement for the Tai-chi form or Zookinesis exercise.

The memories of each muscle interact with the memories of the others, as if they were people sitting around talking about "the old times".

Those memories of interaction then interact with your creativity so that the muscles can play with their relationships with each other. Using the memory of how they learned to cooperate with each other as a basis, the muscles are also affected by your memory of an eagle flying, or perhaps, a tiger pouncing. The muscles blend their memories of cooperation with the other muscles with the memory of the eagle flying and create a composite. This is how animal forms are developed. Each is based on proper body mechanics for a human, yet influenced by the movements of an animal.

This is an example of how we re-ignite the internal dynamics of memory that were the norm before we learned about clock time. We learn to operate with both modes of memory and not sacrifice "sacred memory" for "clock memory". Sacred memory allows you to live in eternity within each second of clock time. You have access to the memory of your whole body and spirit, and their connection to all of nature. Yet you can still show up to an appointment "on time".

A moment in life is like an animal. The moment is not "a" moment; it is "this" moment. When we see an animal, we often say to ourselves, "That is an animal". But to the animal, it is not *an* animal; it is he. To a zookeeper, each animal is an acquaintance, a friend. He has a relationship with that animal.

When we meet someone we don't say, "There is a human". We say, "There is Joe". When we have a relationship with a living being, we feel part of it, connected to it. When we can simply name it and place it into a category, we don't feel the same sense of connection.

Which aspects of your life are dismissed as "a" this or that and with which aspects do you have a relationship? Do you have a relationship with this moment in time? Do you feel a connection to the things around you right now? Do you talk to your computer (or curse at it)? If you do then you feel part of life. If not, you may feel like a disembodied spirit, not connected to this world.

Feel this moment in time as a wild animal that you have gotten to know personally. When you meet it in the forest you know you can't own it; it is wild. You can't predict when you will meet it. Yet when you do meet, the animal is happy to see you. You can tell from the relaxed look in its eyes and a mild sound, like a murmur, showing its contentment.

You want it to know that you are happy to see it too. Yet you know it is wild and will not tolerate the complex, twisted mixture of human emotions. You meet on a very pure level - a level of friendship and freedom. It matters not how you got to know each other. What matters is the connection between you.

Can you feel this way towards this moment in time? The moment greets you with all its circumstances and particulars. You are friends with this moment and are content in its connection to you. Can you sense the relaxation of the moment itself because of your presence? Can you sense this moment's acceptance of you?

Develop that relationship but always be mindful that moments are wild. They cannot be tamed and owned. You can acknowledge your acceptance of each other - you and the moment - but don't try to get entangled emotionally with a wild moment. This means keeping your inner state as pure as that of a wild animal, honest to yourself and others. Don't deceive yourself and then try to get others to go along with your self-deceptions. Be ready to meet each moment, each wild animal, with honesty and clarity.

It may be a good idea to develop a relationship with a real animal, even if it is a "captive". My preference is the reptiles. They are very clear and straightforward. Connecting with animals is, in my opinion, the most powerful shamanistic technique. There used to be a small horse, some kind of pony, which was presumably owned by someone but lived free in my neighborhood. It grazed on peoples' lawns and left fertilizer. It came begging every morning and afternoon and I had a bag of horse feed ready. The pony had its own food and water bowl in the gazebo and it would stick its head through the gazebo entranceway to eat.

The pony lined up with the students as we had Tai-chi class in the gardens and seemed to feel it was part of the school. At first, I used to return it to the fenced area that was its home, but it would get out a few minutes later. The owners didn't seem to take care of it. So we just let it wander about as it pleased.

This went on for two years and then unfortunately, it was hit by a car and killed. No one ever questioned that a pony lived in the neighborhood. The neighbors always worried that a car might hit it but the pony was its own boss and we couldn't tell it what to do. Everyone gave it food. A horse hoof expert was once brought in to clean and clip its hoofs. We brushed it from time to time. We even tried to ride it, but the pony would have no part of that!

If you live in a natural area, you get used to animals living on your property. You feel you own your property but the animals don't know about deeds and property rights. It's their home too.

The idea of ownership gives us the feeling that we can chase animals away from our property. The animals just see a mad human running after them with a broom. Our ideas of ownership, whether of a property or a set of ideas, gives us the feeling we must chase away any interlopers. Someone who disagrees with your ideas is an interloper of your "idea property". You "run" after him, chasing him with your "mind broom" as you tell him he's wrong and you're right. You gradually build up your physical, mental and emotional properties and build your world around the idea of protecting them. This disconnects you from your world and makes it hard to feel part of it.

This behavior is connected to the imbalance of the senses of sight and chi. We identify ourselves more with our separateness than with our connection to nature and other people. We want to be better than other people or to somehow stand out. The feeling of connection competes with the feeling of standing out. Zookinesis restores a balance of these two feelings by restoring the sight/chi sensory balance. We can be good at standing out and at being connected, both at the same time. The two feelings don't compete with each other anymore.

Wild animals are usually very balanced. When you enter into a relationship with it you begin to perceive that clearness - that balance - that absence of emotional trauma. A simple look from a wild animal can "put you in your place", even if it is small. You sense that you are not superior to the animal - that each species is evolved in its own way - unique but not superior. And your own twisted energy starts to untwist.

Why are we twisted? Human culture provides many opportunities to become traumatized. As an example, many people are brought up to believe that we are being watched every minute of the day and night by God. If we do the slightest thing wrong, we will go to hell. Furthermore, the devil constantly tempts us to commit sins. If we make the slightest mistake, we will be condemned to eternal damnation, whatever that is. (But it certainly sounds bad).

A person who believes this can't help but be traumatized. Fear dominates his life. And the other side of fear is violence. Why violence? This person looks at the world as a battleground for his soul. His innermost being is up for grabs.

Often, feelings of sexual and other pleasures are considered sinful - as the temptation of the devil. So this person will fight against his own feelings. He will consider his innermost being to be the devil - the enemy. He is beating himself up violently (in an internal sense). His inner creative being always fights to survive. The world outside and inside is experienced as places of violence.

Any suggestion of resolving that conflict will be interpreted as losing the battle against the devil and will be fought off vigorously. When this person sees something like Tai-chi, he or she will be aware of the implications of an end to conflict. His response, limited by social constraints, may be in the form of ridicule. Without the constraints, his response might be more direct.

Why do some religions promote such insanity? A cynical answer would be that people who are fearful are more easily controlled - a political answer.

I would suggest that the myths comprising our culture have become warped. We no longer try to understand the deeper meaning of myths; we take them literally. Myths are no longer a pathway to wisdom but become a substitute for a person's identity.

When a child asks a question, you tell him a story that will give him an insight into his question on a level he can understand. You are not concerned with the story itself, as if it actually happened, but with the lessons the story teaches. As the child grows, the stories become more sophisticated or deeper lessons are explained based on the original story.

Storytellers not only tell the stories but also keep the meanings behind the stories alive. I met a Native American whose name was "Medicine Story". His name said it all; telling stories can be good medicine.

The stories told in our society are not as good medicine as they used to be. Now the purpose of the story is to make money and the last thing you want to do is use it to teach. The less teaching and the more action and special effects - the more profits.

As the real storytellers have suffered, so have the teachings behind the stories. How does a "real" storyteller get his stories heard or read if the publishing houses and T.V. stations aren't interested?

They simply have to be sneakier. They can slip a teaching story by the editors by sugar coating it, by giving the editors the entertainment value that is their main interest. They can search for other avenues for their stories (school auditoriums, the internet, public access, home videos, etc.). I think one of the attractions of Star Treck was that teaching about the moral principles was sneakily combined with an action film. I think that "Bonanza", the old "Kung-fu" series and "Star Trek" were all basically the same show. Certainly, their common spirit was the seriousness of what they were trying to teach. Part of the job (and the joy) of teaching through medicine stories is finding your own unique venue of telling your stories.

I feel that religions are not as much a source of medicine stories as they used to be. They now act as a membership organization. They are run as businesses competing with other religions for members, money and influence. "I am a Christian, a Jew, a Muslim," but what does that mean? It means that you are defined by your membership in an organization and not by what you discover about yourself through a process of self-awareness.

The religion or political party fills the identity, satisfies it. "I am a..." I don't need to know any more about myself.

So we know ourselves as a category, not as a person. We have built our identity fence so tight that not even our inner feelings are part of ourselves anymore. And when we hear a story that can lead to self-awareness, we are only interested in the special effects. Such a person is nowhere near the spirit world. He considers his spirit to be the enemy. As he has substituted his spirit with a category, he has substituted sacred time with linear time.

The spirit world and physical world are two sides of the same world. When the spirit world dies, the physical world dies. Just look at the world today and see the truth of that. What can be more important than living in the spirit world?

There is a saying, "As above, so below." Look at the physical health of people today. Look at the health of the planet. The health and spirit of each individual is another side of the same coin as the health and spirit of the whole planet. Living in the spirit world is not just a form of "new age entertainment". It is a matter of survival.

"Know thyself" is still the beginning of wisdom. Forget the many categories you belong to. Feel yourself! Feel nature!

When you work with wild animals you don't compete with them on the basis of what group they belong to. They may be a member of the snake group or bear group but that is a simple biological fact with no ideologies involved.

The relationship of your identities is concerned with you, as an individual, and the animal as an individual. You discover how you enjoy being together. You cannot look this up in a book. You must explore your feelings.

The same is true about each moment in life. This moment, in all its intricacy, is not in a book. It is right before you and inside you. It is not against you. It is not there to cause you trouble and you need not fight it. The moment, with all its physical, emotional, mental and spiritual aspects, wants to explore how it can enjoy being with you. The moment does not belong to a group - it belongs to you and you to it. When you connect to the moment, knowledge flows to you; it flows in the form of feeling.

What was once a wild, fearful animal or a fearful moment, becomes a friend and then becomes part of yourself. The world no longer tears you apart. You no longer tear yourself apart. You connect and gain knowledge and wisdom. Feeling once again flows through you and there is no part of you that is hidden or feared.

"What a tangled web we weave when first we practice to deceive."

Not to leave out our fellow humans, we can enter into a relationship with "a" woman or "a" man or with an individual. Some marital problems can arise when one partner realizes he or she has married an individual. In this case you cannot simply look up how to behave in a book.

On the one hand, you need the courage to allow the spontaneity of each partner to express itself and not program your behavior. On the other hand, you need the courage to let your partner "inside of you" and to allow your fears and weaknesses to be exposed. Then there will be no loneliness inside you. Instead of inner fences to protect you, your partner is there by your side.

Your partner is part of you in the spirit world. The earth as a whole can be as well. Instead of retreating into the categories of our minds, we merge into the feelings of the life around us. Our experience of life is no longer a list of categories. We are a living being participating in a living world. The moment we are living in becomes alive.

When my wife and I first met, I wanted her to experience the chameleons in my mini-zoo. They are very intense and expressive yet their bodies are still and they don't use facial muscles. Simply meeting a chameleon can open up the spirit world for you.

Each eye moves independently and jumps from one thing to another. You can tell what it is paying attention to by the movement of its eyes. When the chameleon looks at two different things at the same time, this is a compound expression. "I'm paying attention to this as well as to that."

The stillness of its body in relation to the activity of the eyes emphasizes the moving pattern of attention as its mode of expression. While its facial muscles don't move, its expression has a permanent quality similar to a short, rotund talent agent smoking a cigar and trying to act important.

The chameleon's hands are very expressive as well. It may move its hand in slow motion to grip further along a branch while staring at you. Its eyes may be so focused on you that it will not even use its other eye to see where to step. Its hand gropes this way and that until it finds its branch.

If you walk over to it and touch its foot, both feet may pull in towards the body in a prayer formation while the lizard sits up like a kangaroo. Meanwhile, its eyes examine every inch of you for signs of your intention. The effect is heightened by the fact that skin covers most of the eyeball, resulting in a cone shaped eye with the pupil peering out of the tip of the cone.

We first kept the chameleons in a cage "as if" they were mere animals. We took them out once in a while for exercise. When we put them back there was a look of horror in their faces as if they were crying. Mouths open, each eye rotating around at random and arms flailing, they seemed like the robot in Lost in Space saying, "Warning! Warning!"

We then let them loose in the greenhouse. They were fed by throwing a bunch of crickets into a dry, open fish tank. I placed them in the tank from time to time to give them the idea that this was their feeding tank. It took time for them to believe we wouldn't put the top back on and "trap" them.

They are a joy to have around. You become happy just by looking at them and having them look back at you. We no longer keep chameleons as they take a lot of time to take care of.

I remember the first time that one of the chameleons which was loose in the greenhouse, walked over to me when I walked in. He sat on a wood beam above me (they always like to look down on you) and greeted me with his eyes. Then his eyes looked here and there and then back at me as if to say, "Now what do we do?"

The spirit world is like this. It beckons our attention. Our cells and organs beckon our attention. The natural world around us beckons our attention. But both the inner and outer natural world have become frightened of us. They have been injured by our clumsiness. They fear being put back into the cage and having the lid clamped back on.

When you enter into a relationship with the living creative energy of life, the nature of time itself changes. Time is no longer a dimension that theoretical physicists can include in their mathematical equations to determine the relationship between nuclear forces and gravity to develop a unified field theory including quantum mechanics and general relativity. Time becomes your path in the evolution of your soul. It is experienced as getting to know the world around you personally.

We usually experience time as a linear sequence of events, the former events "causing" the latter events. You feel as a rat in a maze having to examine each pathway to find the cheese, only to find dead-ends most of the time.

Entering the spirit world feels as if the rat has been lifted up to see the entire set up and can see where the cheese is right away. The cheese is the awareness, the intelligence of the world around you. Time is the dead-end pathways the "dumb" rat has to run through. The cheese prize is eternity - the eternity of life itself.

Eternity is the hidden message in the eyes of the chameleon, in the eyes of your child, saying, "I am you." When that happens, that moment becomes personal. Time no longer continues to plod along. It stops and lets you see something.

Whenever you stop to see that something, when you look for that message, "I am you", in a sight, a smell, a feeling, you change the nature of time. Time then no longer leads you to your death. It leads you to remember who you are and so, leads you to your life.

Linear time is the road to death. Spirit time is when you stop the car, walk off the road and roam around the countryside. It is more than just "smelling the roses". It is realizing that there is another type of road that is not paved, in which trees and plants have not been cut down to make the way clear.

It is a road some part of you knows. The lizards tell you when to turn. The plants urge you to continue straight when you don't need to turn. The rock lets you know whether to go up the hill or around it. There are highway signs all around but it takes a different part of you to "see" them. You will learn to trust and respect these signs just as you now respect traffic lights. You know that if you don't respect those traffic lights you may get into an accident and die.

In the same way, most of us are now in an accident and are dying. The spirit path is the way out of that accident. In a sense it is a way we can turn back time and try again. I think most of us have imagined going back in time. How would we live our lives knowing what we know now?

When you walk the spirit path, you don't have to go *back* in time; you go sideways in time. It is as if you were on a train track and a train was heading for you. Would you run along the tracks as fast as you could to try to outrun the train? Or would you simply step to the side a few feet and let the train go by?

Many of us have been trying to outrun the train all our lives. Yet, eternity is just a few feet to the side.

I like to use the analog of the science of theoretical physics and astrophysics, which tries to understand the creation of the universe and its underlying principles, or laws, using my limited understanding of that subject. The universe is believed to have begun at the "Big Bang" and expanded to its present form and will perhaps one day end with a "Big Crunch" or it may simply continue to expand and fade out, or expand and contract in a cyclic way. It is one of our modern ways of trying to understand what is going on out there.

Before the "moment" of the Big Bang, (which is called a "singularity") the laws of physics are said to have been not valid due

317

to the fact that you would have a basically infinite mass in an infinitely small space and physics has a hard time dealing with infinites. At least, we don't understand it at this time. So at that time, anything was possible. As soon as the universe began to take shape, the moment after the Big Bang, not only did matter expand but time and space were created as well. So much of theoretical physics is devoted to finding the relationships between matter, time, space and the forces of gravity, electromagnetism and subatomic forces - in other words, what is going on out there?

But let's look at the question of time from the point of view of "primitive" people. Look at the singularity as centeredness, as the "center of the world", a place where sacred time and profane time meet. It is a place where the everyday mind, scurrying about, reaching for extremes and away from the center, is actually centered and balanced. It is the entrance into our spirit world.

The thinking mind is linear time, jumping from one idea to the next, in linear sequence, to give us the impression of time as a march toward an end (the conclusion of the ideas which brings us the "truth"). The Body-Mind is sacred time, always moving to the center, maintaining balance, keeping the "gate to the spirit world" open.

In the spirit world, many of the assumptions and expectations that hold us to the world we have created, no longer have to hold true. We no longer sit on top of the pile of mental constructs and wonder how we will ever get down again. The spirit world is said to be "magical" which really means that it is natural, a state in which the creative energy of the human spirit meets nature on a one-to-one basis.

The study of the creation of the universe with the Big Bang, its expansion and perhaps, eventual return to another singularity is the study of the birth, growth and mental development of a person. It is his realization that the world of mental constructs he has learned, to give him power in this world, needs to be balanced by a return to the awareness of the spirit world. The end is not a Big Crunch but a balancing of mind and Body-Mind, of the sacred and the profane.

Gravity is what pulls things together. In that sense, it is like the movement of attention towards the center - towards the spirit world, aligning us with the spiral staircase of life. (Remember that even rocks and planets have attention.) The "center of the world" is the singularity - where the sacred and profane worlds are balanced. It is where the "altar" is placed in many cultures (a piece of ground designated to represent this concept like our modern-day churches and temples).

To put it very simply, the thinking mind moves away from direct awareness to create a universe of thoughts. In this artificial universe, we can be free in a sense because we can make believe anything is true and act accordingly. You can be a child and make believe that your room is a jungle and that you are on a safari. But then your mother comes in and tells you to clean up the mess in your room. That kind of breaks your creative imagination and instead of tall trees and monkeys, you see dirty underwear and an old pizza box strewn about. Physicists would say that our journey away from the singularity into our universe of thoughts has allowed entropy (disorder) to increase. Your mom would just say that you are lazy and if you don't clean up our room right now....!!

So, feeling that dessert and TV privileges are more important than tall trees and monkeys, you move into a state of decreasing entropy, away from our artificial mind universe and towards a neater room. You have returned to your mom's (God's?) reality - what that child might call, "The Big Crunch".

Within the Big Crunch, anything is possible because you can create something completely new - instead of a jungle, it may be a space ship and you are trying to save the Queen of Saturn. Once you have cleaned up your room, you are ready to mess it up again (after being inspired by watching some television and eating a bowl of ice cream).

When you become centered, become aware of the spirit world and its relationship with your everyday world, become aware of the Body-Mind and the spiral staircase, and their relationship with the thinking mind, you finally understand how the concepts you have learned have truly shaped the world you experience. You understand the great value of life, of consciousness in all living things and the gentleness with which we must encounter nature, both around us and inside us. You understand that the creative intelligent energy of life is not an anthropomorphic God fighting against you nor a barren wasteland of molecules destined for ultimate annihilation. That new understanding is where our culture is now heading.

We can find the story of our groping for this understanding in stories of old and in modern physics. Instead of Gods warring against each other or princes and dragons, we now have quarks, neutrons and black holes. If we wonder how real those mythologies of old were to the "primitive people", we have only to look at how our own cosmologies seem real to us and how our careful scientific observations seem to bear out our most incredible hypotheses.

I am not saying that physicists are deluding themselves or that their work does not give us valuable information but only that each culture tries to understand their relationship to nature and the nature of their own spirit, in their own ways and terms. Our modern version is no greater or lesser an achievement than that of the Taoists of thousands of years ago. The human mind was just as vibrant then as it is today. Technology arises from modern culture, validates it and conforms our lives and minds to it. To what degree does it determine who we are?

I believe the important thing is whether the mythologies improve human life and allow us to live in harmony with all our living neighbors. Perhaps we cannot run after absolute truth with the hopes of ever catching it. With science we know where we stand – what is going on out there. Mythology tells us what more there is to explore. Science gives us facts. Mythology gives us perspective.

I feel that in some ways the efforts of theoretical physicists to understand the nature of the universe is like trying to outrun the train of knowledge on legs of mathematics. And as they know, the faster you run, the heavier you get.

The tendency to devise conceptual worlds in order to predict future observations puts us in an uncomfortable position of only looking for those observations which make sense within that conceptual world and of devising instruments based on that conceptual world. When an observation confirms a prediction, we wonder if it shows that we are closer to the truth or closer to isolating ourselves within that conceptual world.

I mention this analogy to theoretical physics, not as a physicist or as anyone even remotely understanding that science, but to point out something more personal and immediate. Our personal feeling of time is that we have to get things done "on time". We have to get to work on time. We have to finish our project on time. We have to get the kids to school on time, get dinner cooked on time and have enough time to clean the clothes.

Time is usually associated with work and specifically, work which we try to get out of the way so we can do something else (enjoy our lives?).

Now our lives are lived mechanically due to time. Has time, a plane of reference in the mathematics of physics, become the God of our lives? Think of God and think of time - Both are absolute. We are created and die in the dimension of time. To early humans, time was cyclic and even though they died (at an earlier age) the feeling of time was different (as far as cultural anthropologists can determine).

I believe that the linear feeling of time began with the monotheistic God. God created the universe at a particular time and it will end at a particular time (in some religions). This gives us a feeling of heading towards an end and our life as part of that journey towards an end.

Yet relativity theory requires that time is not absolute. This is because light travels at the same speed regardless of the observer. A traveler going at 1,000 miles per second towards a light source would not see the light going relatively faster towards him than a traveler going 1,000 miles per second away from that light source. They would both experience the light as going the same speed. This requires that time itself not be absolute.

The changing concepts of time, as trivial as it might seem to most people, can throw the science of physics into upheaval. More importantly, it as a sign of the change of our culture.

In earlier times, the Gods were humanlike, arguing and carrying on with each other in all sorts of ways. Half the time, they didn't know what was going on. The monotheistic God not only knows what is going on now but for all time. HE is absolute and all-powerful. We had better obey all HIS rules (which the Priests or Rabbis or a book conveniently list for us). When time itself is not considered to be absolute, HE must be worried about HIS power.

When time is not absolute then the future is more in our own hands (God help us!) and the nature of time becomes part of our own creativity rather than God's. Our sense of time is determined to a large extent by how rapidly things change, by how rapidly we go through the day, by how much of our day is mechanical and how much is creative - in other words by the nature of our culture.

If culture progresses not on any outside absolute basis but on the collective creativity of all people, then you have democracy! When individual creativity becomes the basis of culture then you have a more personal relationship with the world around you and more interest in, and awareness of the creative individuality of other people, other cultures and other life forms. You have a cultural movement towards a spirit culture.

God then becomes life itself, the slimy as well as the sublime. The prophets are not necessarily holy men with wise sayings, but chameleons rotating their eyes and ponies eating your lawn. God lives in the back yard and leaves fertilizer for your lawn. This is called "pantheism" and was what monotheists tried to overthrow. It is culture based on the creative energy of life rather than the rules listed in a book.

I believe the next great step in that direction, the hallmark of the beginning of this next millennium, will be the uniting of modern scientific knowledge with ancient spiritual knowledge. That's hardly a prediction - just look around you. When "energy healing" is practiced by nurses and is now considered a legitimate part of medical practice - that certainly deserves a double take.

I hope this book is a contribution to the understanding of this ancient knowledge and a guide to its incorporation into our culture. The exercises given in our instructional DVD's are a way each of us can incorporate that training into our own personal lives.

Science makes the most advances when two or more sciences join together to enrich their individual views. Cultures make the same progress when they share as well - and no one can argue that our culture, in the state it is in now, can use some progress.

Do me one favor. Read this book again a year from now, and see if you understand it at that time as if it were a completely new book.

There is a moment between an outside event and a habit getting triggered. There is another moment between a habit getting triggered and that habit creating a physical response. A Tai-chi student needs to "widen" those moments so they stand out very clearly and so he has the "room" to interact with those processes. You can "widen" the moments by noticing them and not interfering with them. Watch them as a scientist watches the behavior of an animal in nature.

Then you can intercede with your creativity – choosing a different way of responding. Notice how the habit resists your creative choice. It is like first waking up from a dream but wanting to finish the dream,

322

even though you know it is just a dream. There is a momentum to the habit and the dream that pulls your attention.

If you were to intercede with your creativity too strongly and just freeze so that you don't carry out the habit you would not be doing Tai-chi. No freezing is allowed. The Tai-chi way is transformation of the habit, not overpowering it. If you can "see" the process in great detail you will understand its components and become an expert in the anatomy of a habit. And, just like a doctor who has to be an expert on the anatomy and physiology of a human body, you will learn how to heal that process. Overpowering a habit is like taking a strong drug that has many side-effects.

The spaces between trigger, habit and behavior are the Gnostics' "bridal chamber". Those spaces are where creativity lives, where God lives. They are the spaces in time that allow you to move from mechanistic behavior to creative behavior.

You also look for those spaces within your Push Hands partner, but in this case to trigger his habits and shrink the space for creativity in him. Each of you is competing to make each other's behavior more mechanistic and less creative. This can be done by simply tiring out the partner's attention, causing him to freeze and overpower rather than to transform. The goal of course is to make each partner more aware of this process.

When you do Push Hands, the teacher has to move very slowly at first because it takes time for the student to perceive and respond to the teacher's movements. As the student's attention follows more quickly, the teacher can move more quickly.

The finer resolution, increased agility and increased stamina of your attention is key to integrating all the elements of yourself with the world around you – and this is spirituality.

The key is to be aware of attention as a substance, its qualities and its activities. Attention is at the center of your being. Everything else is what you pay attention *to*.

In Zookinesis, we say that an important issue is where you are paying attention *from*. If I say "pay attention to your feet, you would normally go from your head to your feet because your eyes are on your head. But paying attention is not the same thing as looking at something. Attention does not need to be controlled by turning the head and aiming your eyes.

Death and Time

There is a mechanism inside you that can move attention and we have forgotten about that. And so external forces control our attention to a large extent. The mechanism that can move attention is sometimes called, "heart", - not the physical organ of course. It is a metaphorical name, as in "the path with heart".

The physical heart beats its steady rhythm but its pace can change along with the activities or emotions of the person. The timing of heartbeats relates to the minute-to-minute life of the person.

In a larger sense, our lives can be linked to the variables of nature or to the non-varying clock time. Removing creativity from inside of us is similar to removing the varying pace of nature from our lives. We are no longer expressions of nature. We are expressions of a clock.

The elements of our being should relate to one another in a creative, varying way. When that creative variability is removed, when the "heart" is removed from us, then all we have left is to obey an external organization or philosophy that serves to regulate us in a way devoid of creativity.

That variability, the "heart" of life, tempts you to remove yourself from the machine and be creative. The idea of "your heart" and God being the same is an anathema to someone who has externalized God. They have used time (clock time) to wash God out of themselves – to sterilize themselves.

Clock time has become their God. Clock time is absolute. It is perfectly mathematical. It is absolutely correct and unforgiving. If you arrive at 2:01 instead of 2:00, you are late.

The heart is part of nature. Nature has its own rhythms necessary for its health. When your time is regulated by heart, the internal chemical activities of your body can vary so that your health is maximized at every moment. The health of your family, community and of nature is also maximized. That becomes the basis of the movement of your attention. When the clock regulates time, nature's rhythms are cut off. It would be as if the carburetor in your car never varied and so you had no control of the speed of the car.

Clock time is useful to regulate our work behavior for a company. It organizes workers to perform a larger task in harmony with each other. But clock time has become more than that in our culture. It symbolizes how we have severed the connection of the nature within our bodies to the natural world around us. Now, the very purpose of our culture is not to keep both healthy but to keep us disconnected. That's why it's important to create your own subculture, even if you're the only one in it, that is based on connection.

When a Yoga teacher holds a Yoga posture in a class, does he hold it for 30 seconds or 60 seconds? Or, does he assess the conditions of each of the students at each moment to judge how long to hold it? In the latter case, time is determined in a live way, in a way connected to the real situation in all its complexity. In the former case, it is determined by the numbers on a clock.

Our culture requires less and less attention. According to the three statements of Zookinesis, attention is the very essence of what we are. (Attention is not the same as what you are paying attention to. You are attention. When you know yourself – the play of attention and creativity - you know God.) As attention seeps out of us, we die. We die as vibrant, living beings and we become machines to spur the economy.

We identify with what we own, with how we look, with our job title, our bank account, our house and car, etc. Our attention gets stuck on things.

Worse yet, attention is so unaware of itself that it is at the mercy of distractions. It is like a pinball, bouncing around the pinball machine. The dynamics of your attention in this case, are merely a reflection of outside forces and are not connected to creativity. In your life, do you feel more like the pinball or do you really feel like the person controlling the pinball?

When you live a life with "heart", it is creativity acting in the world. If you lose your dreams you lose your creativity.

This is really a discussion of the subject of the "thrust-block" or the "floor". The body needs something to stand on if you want to push something. The floor is the thrust-block; it is what your body pushes against. It provides a solid platform. Many martial artists use the body's tension as their thrust-block rather than the floor.

In a similar way, many people freeze most of their attention to use as a thrust-block. and just allow one part of it to move. This is the process of linear thinking, one thought following another. So most of the attention becomes the thrust-block and does not participate in your life at that moment.

In Zookinesis, we use the patterns of attention and energy flow we have learned from the animals or the exercises, as our solid platform, our floor. We internalize these patterns to such a degree that they seem very solid to us. There are no abrupt stops. It's like in baseball when the short stop catches a ball and, in one motion, throws it to the first baseman. There is no stop in-between. In fighting, the body and head are always in motion, creating a moving target for the opponent, but also allowing you to execute your technique from a moving start. If you get hit, your body just continues its movement, neutralizing the force.

A Tai-chi form should be the result of the circular movement of muscles and joints within the body, bubbling up into external movement. We start with internal patterns in the relationship of one part of the body to another. The movement of the body as a whole is the release of these patterns through the torso, arms and legs. The movement someone sees should be the release of an internal process. *You* should also be able to "see" this internal process. Your attention as a whole person is willingly yielded to the intelligence of each muscle and joint that continually catch and throw the "baseball" (energy) to each other in a seamless flow.

As the whole-person intelligence yields authority to the muscles and joints, it still retains influence. The balance of influence of the intelligence of the whole and the parts is another meaning of the term, "The Golden Elixir". That balance varies from moment to moment. Nurturing that relationship is part of the joy of practicing forms.

Some musicians get to the degree of skill where their fingers start creatively taking over. The musician wonders, "Hey, where are you taking me now"? Should the balance of authority of the "whole musician" and his fingers go too far either way, the music would suffer. It is that balance of authority – the "Golden Elixir" – that obviates the need for frozen thrust-blocks.

We may shift the patterns that serve as our attention's floor (of course, keeping them rooted into the ground). By using creative patterns as our floor, our attention remains alive and it stays connected to creativity. Attention thus becomes a living connection between creativity and the physical world around us. It is said in Taoism that we are "aligned between heaven and earth".

When a Push Hands student pushes his partner, the student also absorbs the resistance of his partner, balancing or neutralizing his force. When you move forward in a Tai-chi form, you breathe in, so that the air in front of you is not displaced but flows into your lungs. In this way the air is not disturbed. When you shift back, you breathe out, letting the air stay in its place. This is an expression of balance. When you move forward into the world (with creativity for example) you also allow the world to flow into you (appreciation of beauty for example, which allows the world to affect you).

When you rebalance the relationship between attention and the body, between attention and creativity, between the influences of the world around you and the influence of your biological spirit, you are learning to allow the God within you to grow. This is a perspective of God not as the holy terror yelling at you, but of God as the artist of balance, as the gatekeeper controlling the flow in and out of the gate.

In Push Hands class I explain that your attention must merge into the force of your partner as he tries to push you. At the same time, part of your attention must flow, from the point of his push, downwards into the floor to ground his push. These two movements of attention proceed at exactly the same pace. This neutralizes the push.

In the same way, the gatekeeper allows attention to move in to your "inner world" and out to the greater physical world at the same time to keep the system balanced. From that balanced state the gatekeeper and the Push Hands student may then exert the slightest effort of their own, to cause a desired effect. For example, you can slightly alter the angle of your hips to change the entire relationship between you and the Push Hands partner. This change then destabilizes all the joints of your partner. If you were to concentrate on that change of hips so much that you lose your awareness of maintaining your overall balance, your own alignment would become destabilized. So the awareness of the change must be balanced with maintaining overall alignment.

In order to move your attention in both directions at once, you are really "extending" your attention, while the center of the attention remains at the gate. In the expanded state, an effect on one end will affect the other end because they are connected. In the case above, you must expand your attention into all your joints to maintain alignment at the same time as you extend your attention into your partner's joints to detect where you gained an advantage. Yet you can't get too caught up in awareness of that advantage or your attention can get "caught" in what you "see" and freeze as you figure out what to do about it. The goal is to "see" yet not freeze – to continue to function so the attention remains alive.

The part of you that makes changes such as changing the angle of the hips, the part of you that sees the results of that change in the partner that gives you an advantage, and the part of you that responds to that opportunity, all work together at the same time. They are all aspects of attention. If any of these aspects of attention were to freeze, it would freeze the other aspects as well.

When attention is a well running team, it becomes the "self". The thrust-blocks, which are the frozen habits and the frozen identity (fashioned creature), are not the "self". The saying that there is no "I" in the word "team" refers to the individual as well as a group. Even "God" or the creative energy of nature, becomes part of the team.

Some people may feel it is presumptuous to place God, attention and the physical world on a more or less, even plane, but that is the nature of balance. It is the nature of a relationship with God and with the world not based on fear and subservience but on respect and joy. Fear is the brother of violence and anger. Respect and joy are the siblings of love and beauty.

A fear-based religion has traumatic effects on the personality, making it difficult to enjoy life and feel close and loving to other people. Why is it that people need drugs to feel good when there is so much love and beauty in the world? If fear keeps you from that love and beauty, you feel inadequate, like something is missing inside of you (joy). You understand that love and beauty exist but you can't appreciate it. Therefore, you feel angry.

Some people relate every aspect of their lives to their religion. The word "God" and "Lord" is inserted into every sentence. "Praise be God" for this and that. The concept of God is their thrust block but it can become a blockage to joy. When I meet people who express their devotion to God in this way, so that it becomes an overwhelming addiction, I notice that they seem to be crying. If you didn't understand what they were saying and judged them only for their behavior and tone of voice, they would seem to be in great distress even though they are supposed to be expressing their joy.

Their distress is that they are running faster and faster towards a concept, which in the end offers no joy. The concept of God is not creativity itself. That concept is a thrust-block; it is a freezing of the living experience at the core of their being. Their feelings of joy and of fear have become isolated, one from the other. Heaven is total joy and hell total horror. It is possible to create such isolated experiences only in the thinking mind and these people live in their thinking minds. They seek relief in one concept as opposed to another rather than in balance and in the connection of all parts of their lives.

Your personal mythology about whom you are and your purpose in the world, can change how you see the world. It can change how your life progresses. Change your dream and you will change your world. Share your dream and you will change *the* world.

People get angry at life's ups and downs. Yet I have never seen a child, when playing see-saw, angry at being down for the moment. When your life is based on developing the dynamics of attention, the ups and downs don't throw the center off balance.

There are many ways of being off balance. Focusing on God too much is off balance. Focusing on the ups and downs of your worldly life is off balance. This is why Zookinesis places creativity and the physical world in a balanced position with attention at the center. They are really all one whole, with no one part cut off from the other.

You take your first breath of life in the spirit world when all of the elements of your being are aligned. Rather than identifying with any one religion or nationality, you identify with life itself. You identify with creativity and beauty, not with the fights among people.

A parent doesn't take sides with fighting children but tries to stop the fighting by giving the children a broader perspective. "There are many toys on the floor. You both don't need to play with this particular one and if you do, you can find a way to play with it together." The parent just wants peace in the house.

Some people think of our lives as a battle for our will (the element of fire in the West) by our spiritual (wise) side and our physical (desire) side. Two parts of our lives are fighting for our will. Thus, the body feelings are often depicted as the devil and our spiritual side must fight against those feelings.

But when you become aware of the spirit world as a broader perspective that brings peace to the house, the battles end. The spirit world is the awareness of ourselves as completely connected to all life and that creativity and intelligence flow through us.

If a population suddenly became aware in this way it would be a politician's nightmare because he would no longer be able to pit one group of people against another. The hard part in developing such awareness is to not create yet another religion. When you create a religion, you create a division.

Imagine what you would do with the main street in your town, to make it so enjoyable that you would want to visit it every day. The main street is the center of the town.

If it were so beautiful that everyone would love to spend time there it would help unify the people of the town. They would see each other while in an uplifted mood. What is the center of your life? For each person it will be different – house, family, work, a particular interest or field of study or an artistic talent.

To many of us the center of our lives has become our work and our material possessions. If our work is not beautiful to us, then the center of our lives is not beautiful. Our material possessions may indeed be beautiful but is that a fruitful center for our lives?

Our bodies can also be a center, as we try to keep it healthy and in good shape. Our creativity can be a center, as we get involved in artistic pursuits. Our connection to life itself can be a center and we may spend time in natural places, tend a garden or houseplants, breed reptiles as I did or practice chi-gung, which develops the flow of life energy throughout the body. Learning may be a center as you read books, attend lectures, etc.

When a particular religion is a center, it should be both beautiful and creative to you or it will turn sour. If wealth is your center, you need to be creative with how you use it to help people in a beautiful way or it will undermine your humanity.

Is the center of your life creative and beautiful? Can you make the center of your life like a beautiful main street that draws the townspeople to it so they can meet in an uplifted spirit?

That is like the balancing of the elements. The parts of your life are aligned around a beautiful, creative center. When you visit the main street or town square, you are fulfilled by its familiarity but you also are excited to experience something new. There may be a band playing, or a restaurant offering samples from its menu. You may see new people. You enjoy the unexpected and come to the town square prepared to be surprised.

In an internal training, the whole point is to leave yourself open to new experiences and to accept them as they are. To some people this is exciting. To some it is uncomfortable.

Taoism gives you a conceptual framework for the new experiences you encounter in Zookinesis or Tai-chi training. This framework allows you to feel more secure about new experiences because, at least you can place them in a context.

The context, or framework of Taoism is based on practical everyday usefulness. This system avoids abstract intellectualism. The student should strive to remain open, to be ready to receive the unexpected with open arms. Taoism provides the "inner town square" to experience surprises you as you develop your awareness.

We instinctually know to pull attention through the eyes of a baby to begin the flow of attention and connect it to this world. It is like threading a needle, as explained before. Tai-chi practice pulls our attention through the body, teaching it to become connected to the natural world and its energy. It does this by teaching us how to align our body to most easily let force move through it.

If we want to push in Push Hands, we establish a line of force by bringing our attention to points along that line - for example, the foot then the center of the hamstrings, center of quads, then the center of gravity of the partner's body. If we do this correctly the force will naturally flow through your Tan-tien.

Your attention and physical force must flow narrowly through this path and not spread out until it reaches the partner's center. If it spreads out early, it will be like a fraying thread and it will be difficult to put the thread through the eye of the needle.

In one of the Indiana Jones movies, he sought the Holy Grail. He found the underground caverns in which a knight hid the grail.

Jones came to the edge of an underground cliff, hundreds of feet high. About a hundred feet in front of him was another cliff.

His instruction on how to traverse the gap was to take a "leap of faith". So he stepped out into the gap and landed on a rock bridge just inches below where he stood. When the camera angle changed, you could see that this rock bridge blended perfectly with the opposite cliff so you couldn't really detect it.

To move your attention and force through empty space to the Push Hands partner is such a leap of faith and there is indeed a path. There is an empty space between your hip and elbow, for example, and the force must move directly from hip to elbow. Beginners bring the force up to their shoulder and then through the whole arm and into the partner. This is an inefficient route.

There is also a bridge to the next level of attention when you die and the intelligence of nature is there trying to thread your attention into that next level.

The goal of a student is to traverse that bridge while still alive and come back.

To practice this, we allow our attention to be "absorbed" by the things around us. Allow a plant, a rock or animal to "absorb" your attention. This takes place in the practice of "soaring".

You are fully aware of the levels of consciousness within you, like the thinking and Body-Mind and you are also aware of how that is part of the consciousness of a habitat or the whole earth.

The great goal is to be able to traverse all levels freely while still alive. It should not be death that brings our attention to higher levels, but our own efforts, operating from within our bodies.

During our daily routine our attention goes to this and that. We clean the dishes then pay our bills, watch some television, etc. When you die, this whole life seems like one thing the attention is doing and now we move on to do something else. It is a shame that we become so focused (attached) to this one thing we are doing that we forget that anything else exists. We can live our lives but still be aware of the other levels and allow those levels to empower us.

When you allow your attention to be absorbed by something outside of yourself, you will feel a little initial tug on your attention. It is a subtle feeling. It is like the jolt of thought that is subtle at first because you are not used to perceiving it.

The tug of your attention is like the bite of a fish on your line. You let the fish bite and take some of the line before reeling it in. In the case of attention, you let the rock or plant take your attention and absorb it into itself. In this way you will get to know the rock or plant, as you "know" the behavior of the fish by its tugging, even though you can't yet see it on that level.

We do the same thing to become aware of the dynamics of consciousness in our own bodies. When you practice a form, parts of your body may have their own "ideas" about how they want to move. You as the "parent" consciousness can encourage each part of your body to be creative and work with the other parts, like a parent encouraging cooperative play among his children, rather than just telling the consciousness of your body to shut up and "do what I tell you to do".

The spontaneity and creativity within your body is like that fish tugging on the line of the parent consciousness. You become aware of your own body as a conscious being just as you marvel at the creativity of your own children. You begin to understand that the degree of consciousness inside of you is directly related to the ability of your child to develop theirs.

Art is like this as well. You may learn the techniques of the art but at a certain point the art teaches you. It pulls the creativity out of you, allowing you to see it. It makes you grow, as does raising children. You take a leap of faith that, with all the nonsense and craziness going on at the moment, that child (or art project) will turn out just fine.

The child grows from the creative energy inside of you and from your willingness to let them connect to it. You may not understand how by just being aware of and true to yourself, this will lead to the child's emotional and physical health, but you must have as much faith as Indiana Jones.

It is like a person, new to these ideas, reading this book. At first that person says to himself, "What is all this nonsense?" Then one or two things make sense to him like a fish tugging on his line, and he says, "Maybe there is something of value here". He takes a leap of faith, that I, as the writer, know what I am talking about and that it is worthwhile to read this book, even though he may not understand it all at this time. Once he takes that leap of faith and opens himself up to new ideas, he can travel far, to new lands.

When you push, you set up several points through which your force will flow, perhaps from the bottom of the foot, the elbow and the palm. You thread your attention through each as you breath in and push. At the same time, the resistance of the other person moves into those points, informing them of the partner's balance, state of readiness, etc.

Death and Time

When you interact with the energies around you there is this same interaction so that each point, each eye of the needle, each "space", is a center of interaction of the flow of intelligence. This feeling of being absorbed into the world, balanced with absorbing the world you encounter, informs you about your relationship to that world. In our modern culture, that experience has been eliminated, especially as concrete replaces earth and glass and steel replace trees.

A couple of years ago I visited my alma mater, Cornell. When I attended from 1966 to 1970, the buildings were all gray stone and covered with vines. Since then, many new glass and steel buildings have been built in between the other buildings. The effect was jarring. The new buildings seemed like unwelcome intruders. But they are cheaper to build than the old stone buildings.

I could feel how my college experience was not only about filling my mind with facts and ideas. It was also about the great natural beauty of the campus and how that made us feel. When you practice Tai-chi and Zookinesis you enter an old campus with stone buildings covered with vines. You remember the feeling of being part of the world around you energetically.

You no longer consider intelligence to be one particular sequence of words as compared to another particular sequence. Intelligence is not words. It is the live interaction of nature's energy flowing through you with your own energy flowing out to her.

I recently told a student to redistribute his attention in Push Hands. I said that attention is like a light that needs to always be even. He imagined a searchlight located at the point where my hand pushed against his body, shining down on different parts of his body. From the vantage point of the light shining from my push he "looked" down to see which of his parts needed more attention.

I told him the light *is* the attention and shouldn't be stuck in any one place. Don't turn light itself into an object like a physical flashlight.

When Jesus said, "I am the light", this was true, but it is true for everyone. Each of us is the light. Each of us is attention. But people have turned Jesus into a flashlight.

I told him that each part of the body has eyes and those eyes should be open and bright, with attention threading through them. Some of the parts of his body were asleep. Keep all those individual eyes open.

In many everyday situations we freeze our attention before acting. Awareness is considered female energy (it receives). Acting is considered male. Zookinesis or any spiritual discipline teaches the continuous interaction of male and female energies. The "chi ball" or "puzzle ball" expresses this well. This is a ball, often around four to six inches in diameter, made of stone, jade, or, in the old days, ivory. It is carved in such a way that there are several concentric spheres within the ball, so each ball is actually several hollow balls, one within the other. Amazingly, they are carved from one piece of material. The outer ball and perhaps the next one or two, are intricately carved with figures of the dragon and the lotus flower (representing male and female energies). This carving represents many of the basic principles of Taoism, such as the continuous, circular interaction of male and female energies.

When these energies are unnaturally separated, a state of mind is created similar to stop and go traffic. (Perceive then react, perceive then react, etc.). Each stop is a death and this leads to the deterioration of the individual. If we understand attention as space then we can see that it is what allows action to take place. The empty spaces in the chi ball between each layer, is what allows the spheres to move. You can stick your fingers through the holes in the outer balls to move the inner balls.

When the roles of male and female in a culture are rigid, the male and female energies cannot interact within an individual. This blockage of energy transformation results in exaggerated behavior.

Anyone involved in a precise sport cannot allow his attention to freeze. He must enter a state in which attention and action are perfectly balanced.

This is true of the thinking mind as well. Too often thinking consists of repetitive action. There is often little attention involved in the thinking process. The quality of attention is revealed in the dynamics of your own thinking, just as it is revealed in the dynamics of body actions in the form. Repetitive stating of opinions has little attention in it. Two people joking together have a lot of attention; it is creative. When attention and action are balanced, there is creativity.

The Buddhists call action coming from the balance of creativity (male) and attention (female), "Right Action". The action can be thinking or living one's life.

Death and Time

When you step in the form, there is a tendency to first align yourself over the weighted leg, freeze the weighted hip and leg and then step. Rather, you should continue aligning yourself in your weighted leg throughout the step. The attention and the aligning should never freeze. This allows the stepping leg to move out effortlessly.

We may shut off attention while stepping because we feel that now, we need to do "man's work". There is a great effort coming up and we think that the exertion of effort requires the shutting off of attention. You feel you can't do both at the same time.

But Tai-chi is based on the principle of the attention always being alive during action. It requires that you constantly readjust to stay aligned so that your efforts are always maximally effective.

In this way we "end the round of birth and death" and become "immortal". The attention no longer plods in single, heavy steps; it glides and flows. Information in terms of feeling flows from every part of the body to every other part so that all the joints and muscles can act as a coordinated team.

This does not mean your body will never die. Your attention not dying in the present is what constitutes immortality. Your body never dying just means that you will become very old but from the attention's point of view, you may be dead most of your life.

When we use our attention in stop and go fashion, it is like an artillery gunner who sees his objective and then fires. He then sees the effect of his firing – how close it got to the enemy. He can then readjust and fire again more accurately. He hopes the enemy cooperates by staying in the same place.

When you look into someone's eyes you can see the extent of their death or life. You can see death and life in a struggle. With the slow movements of the Tai-chi form, action becomes slow and continuous. Here attention can flow with the action and you learn how to remain alive.

Death is not eliminated. It is transformed into patterns of movement that constitute our "floor", the "thrust-block" as has been described before. Rather than use our own freezing to "act from", we use the patterns of flowing motion; we use the downward pull of gravity and upward expansion resulting from pressing our feet onto the floor. We use the spherical expansion of breath and its sinking into the Tan-tien. We use the rotation of the joints.

We transform death (freezing) into the proper mechanics of the motion of the body and of internal energy. As these patterns are constantly changing and shifting, death is transformed into movement, and movement is time. Death has been turned into time itself – into eternity.

When attention and action are connected in this way, you are free to "play with the form", to express it in different styles. As you introduce a new quality to the form, the joint and muscle actions are appropriately adjusted by the web of attention.

Creativity affects the attention by introducing a quality, and that changed quality of attention, in turn, affects the action. Creativity on one side, body on the other, attention at the center. Attention is like the central of three pennies touching each other on a table. If you hit the central penny with one of the outside pennies, the penny on the other side will move. Yet the central penny stays still, especially if you hold it down with your finger. Even if you hold it down, the vibration still gets transferred.

Attention, being connected to every joint and muscle, transfers the quality introduced by creativity, individually into each joint and muscle, which body part in turn, expresses that quality in its own way. It is like the energy of the earth, connected to each individual that allows each individual to express the earth's energy in her own way.

This is similar to a teaching. We all hear the teaching but understand and respond to it each in our own way. We each respond to art differently. Let the body respond to your own creativity as a group of people respond to a great teaching or to art.

In this way creativity and the body can each be alive and independent. Attention, as the female aspect, provides the connection between the two; it provides the aligned center.

When that center is always alive and aligned, then creativity and the body can be more playful without throwing the whole thing off balance. The "thing" is your life.

In Push Hands, your partner tries to "freeze your attention" (to make you dead). He does this by changing his pace of movement and the amount of tension in his arms. He tries to "jar you" into death of the attention.

We can neutralize these attempts by creating a buffer. This is a way to neutralize his disruptive actions. The buffer is similar to what tropical fish enthusiasts used to do in the old days with piston pumps. These pumps produced short bursts of air so the air bubbles in the tank came out in bursts. To create a continuous flow of bubbles, we connected the air tube from the pump to a glass jar with tubing and from the jar to the fish tank. The air in the jar served as a buffer, to turn the short bursts of air into a continuous flow.

In Push Hands our attention, connected to each part of the body, is the buffer. The jar, which maintains a constant pressure, is proper body alignment. The alignment channels the partner's force into our interior – like the inside of the jar. There the changes of pace and pressures are buffered, while the jar itself, the alignment, is maintained.

While the buffer neutralizes the attempts to destabilize you, the container remains connected to the partner and does not withdraw from the partner.

This is a strong theme of Gnostic training. Do you withdraw from this crazy world and be passive or fully engage in it and forget who you really are? The Gnostic solution is to engage in the world and experience the fullness of humanity but not forget who you are. It is to be *in* the world but not *of* the world. Easy to say, isn't it? It's the same theme of *The Last Unicorn* (book and animation) by Peter Beagle.

When you are fully connected to and fully neutralizing the partner, you are then free to be creative to destabilize your partner. When each partner plays Push Hands this way, you sharpen your skills. Furthermore, you become aware of this dynamic inside your partner. When you look at other people, you become aware of how the alignment and movements of their body reveal the structure and aliveness of their attention.

In the same way that your partner's force enters you without disturbing you, you can also enter the world around you without disturbing it. And you can leave yourself open to allow the forces of nature to enter you without disturbances. This is "interpenetration".

Attention then has a creative relationship with your physical body. In the same way that the joints are loose and relaxed so that there is fluidity in them, the attention provides fluidity between your body as a whole and the rest of the physical world.

With loose joints your body is not rigid because each part can move individually to a large degree. The shoulder can move, for example, without bringing the whole body with it. You can neutralize the push of your Push Hands partner just by rotating the shoulder. Otherwise, your whole body would be thrown off balance.

Similarly, when you can perceive the interplay of attention and creativity in your perception of physical matter, then your perception of this hard, physical world becomes more fluid. The new fluidity of the world doesn't disturb you. This perception is not an illusion of melting clocks like a Salvador Dali painting. You immediately recognize the validity of this way of perceiving because something inside you recognizes it. It is soft, more relaxed and less harsh. It is more natural. You already understand how to perceive this way.

The harshness is not in the physical matter itself. When your body is relaxed, even a hard floor seems soft. When my wife taught her foam roller classes, the students' experience of the floor changed. Before, you are lying on a hard floor. After the exercises you feel as if you are lying on a soft mattress. Was it the floor that was hard or your back? Your own tension made the floor feel hard. Physical tension changes your perception of the world around you.

When you approach life using "interpenetration" rather than conflict, your world changes. You are now really *in* the world; your body and the world are not so separate.

The key to achieving this awareness is holographic attention. Attention must become a three-dimensional field rather than a single point. Perhaps it should be said that attention should be innumerable points as the stars in the sky. As each star has worlds within it, each point of attention (the shoulder joint, for example) has many subtleties within it.

This is what the Gnostics mean when they say that the nature of humans is distinctiveness. You don't expand your attention in such a way that you become flaky. As you expand attention you also strengthen it and increase its resolution.

In the chi (or puzzle) ball, each sphere is hollow and has several large holes drilled through it. It is made by first drilling holes through the solid ball and then using little saw blades attached to sticks that cut each sphere free. When the holes line up, you can see all the way to the inner ball.

When you push in Push Hands, there must be a similar lining up of all the Yin "spaces" within your body. Your Yang force moves only through the empty (relaxed) parts of the body. If you tense up as you push, your internal energy can't come through. Lining up these spaces (lotus flowers) allows your energy (dragon) to flow through your body. It is called, "Dragon jumping through the lotus flower" in Zookinesis.

You must trust that you can send your force through empty space. The path of power is paved with trust.

When Indiana Jones stepped onto the bridge of stone to retrieve the Holy Grail, the metaphorical lotus flower (emptiness) was in the gorge below him. It was also in the cup (the Holy Grail). Jones had to find this cup because it was filled with a fluid that could save his father's life. The knight guarding the cup tested Jones' pure heart by making him choose the proper cup from among many. He chose a simple wooden cup from among many fancy ones. Jones then had to drink some of the liquid in the cup. If he had chosen the wrong cup he would have instantly died.

Cups are a symbol of the power of emptiness. The cup's usefulness is in its emptiness. Jones had to trust jumping out into the gorge and trust drinking from the cup, just as you have to trust that the words in this book are meaningful and useful.

The Holy Grail turned out to be the simplest cup. Its elixir gave life. The role of emptiness (simplicity) in your life is to heal you.

This book is not designed to add more facts to your mind. It is really a step back to challenge your assumptions. Understand the words in this book on their simplest level. You may ask yourself, "what does he really mean by this?" I mean everything I write in its most direct simplicity. The simplest explanation is often the hardest to believe.

The spirit world does exist. It is the world we perceive when we have regained all our perceptions. Attention is a force of its own. It exists as much as physical matter exists. We are, in our simplest form, attention. The movement and dynamics of attention is what we call creativity, or God. Spiritual development is the development of the senses that allow us to live fully in all worlds – while we are still physically alive. And anyone can achieve this through proper training of Zookinesis, Tai-chi or other related disciplines.

When we first begin to learn about time and start organizing our memory according to time, we can do this in one of two ways. 1. We can abandon organizing memories in terms of feeling or 2. We can interweave our feeling memory and time memory. Zookinesis helps us to weave that cloth. With time memory, we see our lives as a progression of events. With feeling memory, we see our progress as an enhancement of the ability to feel and experience.

If we lose our ability to feel, the progress of events becomes a metaphorical journey back to feeling, represented by money, power, etc. This creates the idea of a time after death when feelings will return. This is really the death of the separation of the inside of ourselves from the outside, that deadened our feelings. Being "trapped in a body" may then be interpreted as a separation from some more "spiritual state" and the death of that body as a return to that spiritual state.

But you are not trapped in your body, if that body is connected to the rest of the world. To weave the cloth of linear time and feeling time you need decentralized attention – the ability to be aware of the relationship between the two. When the cloth is well woven, your ability to experience, to perceive, grows through linear time. The world around you seems to change because the world inside of you changes.

This change of perception creates the impression of a more fluid world – one in which our internal states affect the perception of our external world. When we demand that the world be perceived as unchanging, we lose this balance between the inner and outer. The relationship becomes fixed and rigid, not conducive to growth.

Just as physicists assume that the laws of physics are the same everywhere and unchangeable, we may assume that we must be unchangeable and so must our perceptions. When you lose the balance of internal and external, we lose a form of movement – movement through the spirit world. If a compass falls down on one side, it cannot continue to rotate. Similarly, there is a pivotal point of perception, a point balancing the internal and external, a kind of gatekeeper.

The two types of perception (changeable and unchangeable) can reinforce each other, providing a full understanding of the world we live in. We can understand the role of continuity of principles yet allow for flexibility and change. It can allow for being open to receive the messages of nature that transform you and to be independent and create your own life. You can explore the laws of physics while also exploring how everything you experience is subjective. You don't need to flush out subjectivity from your life. You can swallow a contradiction whole, as it is said in Zen. Weaving the two experiences of time gives us a broader view and allows us to live our lives more fully.

Chapter 8
Fear and Power

The ability of fear to control behavior is an impediment to developing the full power of your attention. As you develop the sensitivity of your attention you will notice many things that you were too dull to notice before, such as the flow of energy in the world around you. This new awareness may trigger fear because it is an unexpected perception. You may turn that perception into something familiar in order to make it more comfortable to you. If you experience energy around another person, you may turn it into seeing a color around the person and call it an aura, for example. You may not be ready to experience the energy directly as such.

Most of what we experience through our senses is our own interpretation. When we experience sight, for example, we are experiencing two tiny spots of light, one in each retina. The impression of experiencing a large scene in front of us, filled with very solid objects is our interpretation of those spots of light, based on prior experience. This keeps us rooted into experiencing what we expect to experience (what I call the "Echo of Expectation").

With a practice such as Zookinesis or Tai-chi you must allow yourself new experiences. As you experience new things, such as the flow of energy (chi) you may be uncomfortable because you are in "new territory".

When a student tells me that he is afraid to experience these new things I tell him this:

343

Fear and Power

First of all, you are not afraid. By saying you are afraid you are saying that what you are, is fear. You are identifying yourself as fear. "I am afraid" rather than "I am Joe". The truth is that you perceive or experience fear, but you are not that fear. You are experiencing fear and the new experience that you believed caused that fear. You tell yourself a story. "I must not feel fear. If experiencing chi causes me to experience fear then I must not experience chi."

So you emphasize the importance of not experiencing things. In Zookinesis and Tai-chi we emphasize experiencing things in as much detail and clarity as possible. So you can experience the chi and experience the fear as well. Don't push the fear away. Pay attention to it. How does it feel in your chest, in your back, in your arms, etc.? Get to know the feeling of fear. At the same time, get to know the feeling of chi. It is all right to experience two things at once.

Emphasize getting to know your experiences and realize that you are not just those experiences. You are that which experiences. Fear is just another experience. It may make sense to avoid dangerous situations but that is not the same thing as avoiding a situation because you experience fear. The feeling of fear may suggest to you that there is a danger, but then look at that danger and decide for yourself whether the danger is real.

If you are afraid of trying something new because you may fail, for example, you know very well that is silly. Yet the feeling of fear keeps you trapped. In this case, get to know the feeling of fear as a by-product of a whole process. The more clearly you see the fear the more you know it is not you. It is a combination of physical and emotional feelings that are triggered by events or thoughts. Unless it is a direct reaction to an immediate attack, it is programmed behavior that causes you to freeze.

View your own fear as a scientist views animal behavior. From then on fear will serve to warn you of possible danger but it will not trap your behavior. It will help you rather than hinder you.

You may feel anger and fear within you because of someone's aggression. Then practice the following exercise: Feel the anger or fear. Know how it feels in each part of the body but don't judge it. Don't feel that you have to get rid of that feeling. Just know it. Let fear and anger be like the raccoons that try to steal your food at night. You shine your flashlight on them and they slink away. Their power is in their sneakiness. Light steals their power. Really knowing fear and anger, how they physically feel in each part of the body, steals the power of these emotions. They only control you if you don't know them.

The only Tai-chi trick is to "see" and to "know". If you know the fear and anger within you, then you understand it inside of others and you will say to yourself, "I know you." When you know yourself, you know others. Once you can hang out with the raccoons, you can really do Push Hands.

When I worked as a zoologist, I introduced a lot of people to the joy of playing with snakes. People are afraid of snakes because they don't know them. It is wise to be careful with an animal (or person) you don't know. Some peoples' reactions were so strong that their breathing became restricted and they began sweating as I took out a snake. But after a few minutes I had that snake around their necks and they were laughing. They laughed at their own fear. Fear turned into joy in one instant. That is how closely related those emotions are. You might even say that fear is the blockage of joy and joy is the flow of chi.

Snakes have two types of hisses. One comes from fear and the other comes from joy. They obviously feel joy when being handled. But if you didn't understand the two types of hisses, you would be afraid of both. The joyful hiss is like an "Ahhh". The other is like a "Hey!" When someone confronts you and you react according to Tai-chi principles, you are transforming their "Hey!" into an "Ahhh", especially if you begin your response by acknowledging their point of view. "I can see what you're saying, but the way I see it is..."

This shows that you respect the person even though you disagree. The same is true with a snake. When a snake first sees you, it takes a moment to assess how you are reacting to it. It can tell if you are glad to see it (or is there a pistol in your pocket?). They can assess your state of being. They can sense chi. When you handle a snake, you can feel the consciousness of every muscle in its body. Sometimes you have to feel something to understand. You know that every part of its body is consciously alive.

My wife tells me that I should do Push Hands with every new student just so that they can feel something of its dynamics. My hesitation in writing books is that it may just seem to be a bunch of words if you aren't feeling anything in the "real" world. Ideally the words should go with your practice of physical experience so you don't misinterpret the words.

You need to be relaxed in order to rally the forces of your skills – the "spirit animals" (individual consciousness) of each part of the body. When you fear, each little spirit animal rears up and cannot function. The spirit animals all run into their burrows within the dragon's lair at even the shadow of the falcon of fear.

When you relax, they start to poke their heads out of the burrow. They look around to see if the falcon of fear is gone and then your spirit animals go back to their living.

If you can feel the "rearing up" of your spirit animals, then you can balance that with courage. Courage is the awareness of and faith in your power. You do that by relaxing, which energizes the spirit animals to get back to their living. Relaxing sends them out. It sends out your powers. Relaxation is power.

There is another way to get the spirit animals out of their burrows. You can push them out. You can make them go out even while they are scared. This results in a constant internal battle.

A culture that encourages its people to develop their skills and empower their lives is ruled by the consent of the governed. They feel good. They also have courage because they are used to taking their lives in their own hands. A culture ruled by being pushed out, that is, ruled by fear, does not develop great skills and self-respect among its people.

There is a culture within each person's body. Zookinesis makes you aware of the factors you control on a whole person level that affect the internal culture. This is how you can transform yourself.

The balance of fear and courage and the way they interact in an individual, largely affects a person's personality. Someone who acts brave or aggressive may actually have a lot of fear. When fearful, you are not comfortable with yourself. You don't trust in your own power or your desirability. You focus on the issues of power or popularity. You try to convince yourself that you are these things.

A person who is comfortable with himself can focus on the joy of life. So we are really talking about the power to enjoy life.

In the martial arts, when you spar from fearful aggression, you are trying to use anger to overcome your fear. This immediately robs you of power. The internal styles, like Phantom Kung-fu, understand what contributes to power. It is better to learn to relax, to let go of fear, than to overpower the fear. In hard styles, fear and tension are always your main opponents.

The internal stylists let go of these two opponents and only fight the sparring partner. The spirit animals are always out and always on and around the sparring partner. This is called, "sticking". This means sticking to him with your attention, not just your hands.

The attention can penetrate his body and stick to the inside of his back. When you push a person (or punch) you first place your attention on the inside of his back so your force penetrates. This also eliminates the tendency to withdraw the arm first, before striking (winding up). You are so connected to your focused attention spot that the force of your strike explodes into his body from the inside of his back.

Fear is related to the tyranny of time. Your spirit animals carry out their activities in time. We remove the issue of time in effecting action. For example, when we strike, each joint sequentially but almost simultaneously, expands. The entire action of the strike takes place very quickly. Each part of the body works in close coordination with each other part (at the same time). They are in communication with each other.

So we don't concentrate so much on a sequence of actions through time but on coordinating all the actions at the same time. The ability of each part of the body to act independently but in a coordinated way, moves the focus from time to awareness. Awareness ends the tyranny of time.

The purpose is to show you how developing awareness eliminates fear as light eliminates dark. Dark is just the absence of light. We fear what we are not very aware of.

I don't fear snakes. I *am* cautious with them but I don't fear them. My awareness of their behavior makes me relaxed and comfortable. It is a relaxed and comfortable caution – not a fearful caution.

A snake can read the "culture" of your body. They have preferences, just as we may like certain cultures and not others as we travel the world. While we may not know the language of another culture and not understand every conversation, we can sense its qualities. Each person in a culture is different but there are general qualities to the whole culture, the way people relate to each other.

Zookinesis is a study of the culture of the spirit animals. You encourage your spirit animals to grow in strength and awareness and to develop a joyful relationship with each other.

We become aware that spirit animals are in everything; that all is alive since they are part of the earth. So another part of this practice is to develop relationships with the spirit animals all around you. This relationship will be based on the internal relationship among your own spirit animals. If it is one of joy then you will probably also have a joyful relationship with "external" spirit animals.

When you meet someone, the spirit animals within both of you want to meet as well. This is just as if two people were each walking a dog. If the two meet to talk, the dogs will also want to interact.

Keeping pets is very valuable. First of all, it represents to us that we have spirit animals. In a culture that is not aware of internal dynamics, the pets really take the place of our spirit animals.

Another value of the pets is that your spirit animals can interact with the spirit of the pet. The pet can teach things to your spirit animals. When aware spirit animals of one person meet deadened spirit animals of another person, the lively ones can wake up the deadened ones. That is really the job of the healer. In a culture that deadens spirit animals, the best healing is to strengthen them.

How is it possible for a person to forget the spirit world? How is it possible to forget awareness itself?

Babies must start developing their awareness by being aware of their own bodies – all its joints, muscles, nerves, etc. When you stop using the body as an adult in our sedentary society, you lose that awareness. Part of awareness comes from being connected to and acting from the cycles of nature. When you disconnect from that, you lose awareness. We isolate ourselves from the natural ground, and the weather, and our food comes from packages.

I am affected by the change of the seasons. For a few days in the spring and fall, I get tired as my body adjusts to the changes in weather. This is the price I am willing to pay to be that connected to my environment. Yet each time I am affected, my first reaction is to worry that I am sick and then I remember what time of year it is. It is like when you bring up a new program in your computer and a pop-up asks you if you are willing to have that program make changes to your computer. It asks if you know this program and trust it. I know nature and trust it, and by developing my awareness, I can know other people and thereby trust them because I trust my awareness.

Part of our awareness comes from allowing another person's attention energy into us, in a Yin, open way. In this way we can sense what is going on inside of them. This awareness ends when we develop an aggressive attitude towards life, scratching and clawing our way through it. When we whine and complain, we develop an angry attitude towards the world and our energy goes out against it as if we were battling.

The student of Zookinesis is in a precarious situation. He must become more and more open in order to feel more. Part of what he begins to feel is the pattern of whining and blaming inside of him – blaming others for his problems. But he must accept responsibility for his life. This means, most importantly, that he must search for any lies he has been telling himself to hide truths about himself he cannot face.

As he is faced with the stark discipline of facing himself as he really is, and accepting himself, he might bolt. It is too painful to admit the lies, because so much of his life is based on them. If all the lies come tumbling down (as in the Tower card of the Tarot), his world will fall apart.

The solution to this inner battle is to remember "the passive observer" – that perspective in which you view yourself as a character in a play. You see the silliness of it all, accept yourself as a silly human being and laugh (the dragon smacking your fear with its tail) and maybe cry. From the vantage point of attention itself, the follies of the human character can be more easily forgiven and self-forgiveness is a powerful tool in any spiritual discipline.

You will see yourself, not as a series of behavior patterns played out in time, but an awareness that is continuing to grow and develop. Your identity is not tied to the rigidity of the patterns but the fluidity of creativity. In the former perspective you (your patterns) were found to be at fault and so you are bad. The viewpoint of Zookinesis is that you have found an escape from your own behavior patterns so that you can more clearly understand who you really are – that your spirit is part of a larger community of consciousness. You can then understand the fundamental values that are part of our humanity. The passive observer is a "relaxed vantage point", devoid of judgment. It sees what it sees and sees it in perspective. It does not get riled up.

From this vantage point you see the feeling of fear as just another force that can be channeled to hurt your body (make it feel bad) or heal it (allowing this force to flow through it). It is our reaction to this force that really is the fear. Fear isn't the force itself. From a higher vantage point, you can distinguish the forces flowing through your body, from your patterned reactions to them. You can use each force more efficiently. Fear is really power flowing through your fixed behavior patterns. If your focus is on defending your patterns, fear is felt as negative. If you "let fear take you" as you do with music, then it can be a vehicle for internal change. It can be "Shiva".

This does not result in losing your conscience. The passive observer's absence of judgment is not a green light to do whatever you want. It is instead, the ability to clearly see the origins and results of your behavior patterns and their relation to fear, the interaction of creativity and attention and the effects of all this on your body. It is like a rat, lifted from its maze, being able to see the whole pattern of the maze and knowing how to get its cheese.

When we recognize fear as the powerful ally that it is, we turn a negative emotion into a positive force. When we do that with a snake, we can see the beauty of the snake. You are learning to appreciate the beauty of healing power, just as when you feel the beauty of music.

Now when you look into the eyes of a snake, you can look at it as an equal. And when you look into the eyes of your own fear, you can appreciate it as a beautiful healing power.

To appreciate any beauty, you must let go. You must empty yourself. Then the beauty can fill you. If you listen to beautiful music, you let go of your cares and concerns. You "give" those cares and concerns to the music and the music takes it away, so the creativity of the composer and the talent of the musicians can spend time with you.

You let go of your world and enter theirs. They take you on a tour of their world of creativity.

The snake's awareness is its world of creativity. Nature composes her music and plays it through the eyes of the snake and the eyes of all the animals. The music of nature is attention, and music represents the creativity of nature.

When you are faced with love, it can seem like the stare of a snake at first. You are not sure of its intentions. It may bite at any moment. And while you always understand that you may be dealing with a "wild animal" and must be careful, you can appreciate it and love in return.

We are all wild animals, we humans. You may meet wild animals in nature and you must be careful yet you can appreciate their beauty. The ability to appreciate beauty is directly related to your power. It takes power to appreciate beauty.

If you have a band in which one member plays poorly, the interaction among the musicians will be limited in creativity. Increase the one member's skill and the beauty of the interaction goes up. When you interact with a wild animal you are in a band of attention (or at least a duo).

This awareness, this connection to life, forms the basis of your fulfillment on a day-to-day, minute-to-minute basis. There is less anxiety that you "don't have enough" (material things), or that you haven't gotten enough done. The frantic pace of our culture to produce and purchase as many products as possible arises out of fear and contributes to it.

Zookinesis teaches you that, who you think you are, controls a lot of your life. If you think you are your opinions, your life may unfold very differently than if you think you are your body. Both of these are part of you. But which is the "real" you? Who is in charge?

Zookinesis emphasizes creativity and awareness throughout the body as the main focus of your identity. To this end we are suspicious of locked patterns of behavior because they can block creativity and awareness.

We use our awareness to determine if a particular pattern or tension serves any useful purpose. If it does not, we feel free to drop it because that pattern is not us. It is a product of our creativity that has become hardened and "stuck".

Dropping tension is like getting rid of old things stored in the attic or basement. You are afraid to get rid of it because it might be useful someday.

I had an old, rickety director's chair made of two sticks of wood, joined at a pivotal point by a thin wooden dowel. A piece of nylon, stretched across the top, served as the seat. It could be taken to outdoor concerts. I bought it in my college days in the 1960's. I was afraid to throw it out because I was sure that as soon as I did, I would need it.

I thought that one day, after I threw it away, a visitor might come to my house. I would say, "Would you like to sit on my couch?" and he would say, "No. What I would really like is to sit on an old rickety director's chair that is so flimsy that I will probably fall right through it and break my ass. Do you have one of those?"

I would say, "I just had one of those and I threw it away yesterday," and then, wouldn't I feel foolish?

Our tensions are like that. They represent our fears. We feel that we may need our fears so we'd better keep our tensions always ready. If the imagined fear did actually show up, the tension would do us little good anyway. We would fall right through the tension and break our ass.

Zookinesis suggests that the only way to prepare for the feared event is to develop our awareness. And that means letting go of our tensions. If we are fully aware, then we can trust that, if anything were to happen, we could react to it effectively.

The more you invest in awareness the less you need to invest in defenses. You will be able to catch the problem before it gets too severe.

This is certainly true in the field of health. Many people fear getting old. They fear the frailty, the loss of body function, loss of energy and dulling of the mind. You can invest in nursing home insurance and hope for the best. You could also invest in maintaining your health and youthfulness. So practice your Zookinesis and Tai-chi.

Meet fear with head lifted. This means that you recognize that fear is just energy and that all energy is a gift of life. There is beauty in all forms of energy. Meeting your fear with head lifted means that you recognize the beauty of the energy of fear. You recognize that fear is not you. There is a Zen saying, "There is fear, but no one who fears".

Fear is a reaction to power. It is a formation of energy that can stand by itself and act. The problem arises when you engage in a struggle with fear. You grab it as you would grab a snake's neck to prevent it from biting you, even though it only wants to bite you *because* you are grabbing its neck. It is the grabbing that gives the energy of fear its negative quality.

Fear can act for you only if you release it. If you grab fear, you will pull each other down as a drowning person pulls on the lifeguard to save himself thereby drowning the lifeguard as well. Let the lifeguard do his or her job. Let fear do its job. I call it power. Power must be released to be effective. When power is released it is no longer being pulled down and it can act "with its head lifted".

To release this power, you must relax the muscles of your body. When you are relaxed the power will leap forward to act for you. The act of releasing or relaxing is called "emptiness". When you hold onto power you are full of "fear" and experience it as fear. Many politicians may be familiar with this experience. When you release it, this energy becomes beautiful; it becomes your competence. Muscular relaxation is the key.

Fear is a problem in your relationship with power. Releasing your fear does not mean that you get angry or violent. This energy acts by neutralizing aggression through an equal exchange of power. As you spar, notice what you are grabbing onto within yourself. Yield that to the partner. Yes, releasing energy may be in the form of a punch or kick, but if there is no internal grabbing, then it is not born out of anger. It is not grabbing for power over the partner.

You learn what role the act of grabbing plays in your life. How is owning a lot of things a type of grabbing? How are you grabbing onto your habits? How are you grabbing onto expectations of other peoples' behaviors? In each case, releasing your grabbing leads to a better and more powerful life.

When the internal culture of the thinking mind grabs onto the body it imprints that culture onto the body. If you are filled with negative thoughts, that pattern will impose itself on the body's functions. If your mind is filled with the beauty of the world around you, with its mystery and grandeur, your body will respond more positively. But it is also important that your mind, even a positive mind, doesn't grab the body. That would be like a missionary, who feels his message is positive, demanding that the "primitive" people of another culture abandon their culture and adopt his.

The act of grabbing is a violent act that damages the body. When we practice animal forms and hold an image of an animal in our minds, we don't impose that image on the body. We offer it to the Body-Mind as a gift as you would offer a child a toy. It is up to the child how he plays with the toy. Our Body-Minds play with images in accordance with their own inner culture. It is common for an ancient culture, exposed to our modern culture, to take some elements of the modern culture to weave into theirs.

Sometimes a student will be afraid of new experiences such as letting fear flow through him. This is why it is important to welcome the feeling of fear as if it were a new toy for you to play with. Allow the feeling of fear to coexist and play with all your feelings. You are the ability to experience feelings, senses and thoughts. Allow them all to exist in peace and not battle; otherwise, you will become that battle. In that case, the central focus of the feeling of who you are will shift from pure awareness and creativity to a battle in the mind that has been violently imposed on you by the greater culture. Dissolve the battle within yourself first in order to be able to dissolve the battles of our culture.

Once you can release fear and transform it into the power to be gentle, you can do anything - even heal the world.

If you hunt for power, you welcome its arrival. If you are afraid of the power people have over you, then you are afraid of power. You don't welcome it. A hunter seeks to understand power, to copy it. You learn the nature of power – what it is that makes a person or a painting or a situation powerful. You admire that power. That doesn't mean you copy someone's behavior patterns. Instead, you distill the understanding of power from each situation.

Power should be balanced with mercy. That balance yields a powerful life. Power without mercy yields a troublemaker. Mercy without power is ineffective. If the feeling of fear arises when you confront power it is an opportunity to become a hunter. First perceive the feeling of fear clearly and learn how to let it flow through you (rather than pushing it away). When you interact with the power (a strong person or situation) see how allowing the feeling of fear to continue to flow through you and to be released, turns the feeling of fear into kindness or mercy. Condensed fear becomes anger, and fear condenses when you grab it or push it away.

In this way you come to realize how a lack of understanding of these dynamics of interaction drains your power. You don't need to be intimidated of or jealous of power. You need to understand its nature and learn from it. When you spar and are beaten you can get angry or you can laugh. Anger is not a good way to learn. If you do get angry, you can laugh at your anger.

If you can meet power without thinking of it as power over you, you can learn. If you are sparring a big person, you can be more agile and move within his spaces. If you spar a more skilled person you can do your best and realize that it is really your own frustration that is interfering with your power. If you do not welcome the partner's power (their punches for example), you will interact with that power in a negative way. Welcoming a punch allows you to be more creative with it. This means that you connect with it and move yourself out of the way rather than knocking the punch out of the way. Allowing the feeling of fear to continue to flow through you smoothly and unimpeded allows you to clearly perceive what is going on so you can react appropriately. You are not dividing your attention between his punch and your worry.

Once you have the power to let fear flow through you smoothly, you have power for anything. But how can you gain that power? To gain power, you have to give something up. Give up the "I" who is afraid. There is no "I" who is afraid. There are only body sensations. You can try to block the body sensations, which takes a lot of work and attention or you can stop blocking them. When you spar it is not about "you" winning. It is about releasing your spirit into the world. Your sparring partner is birthing your spirit. Fear is the womb that is holding onto you. When that spirit is released you can't help but make noise – perhaps a laugh or a shout. As a hunter, you are really hunting for the exit for your spirit to join the world.

And then you realize that power is just joy. You realize that joy isn't the absence of fear. It is the appreciation of beauty and your creative participation in every interaction. The feelings you have about the interaction are not based on battle but on connection. Even if someone is acting in a hostile or unbalanced way, you trust your own balance and your own physical abilities, gained from Tai-chi practice. You can forgive that person their lack of perfection. You are clear about the limits of your participation in their actions and discussions and have learned to say, "no" in a way that is convincing.

Your own power allows you to forgive. It allows you to choose how your body and emotions will respond by choosing your relationship to the encounter.

Fear and Power

In Push Hands, you try not to control the movements; you let the partner do all the work. But you control the relationship between you and the partner so that it works in your favor. It is not easy to resist the temptation to control the movements and base your relationship on emotional patterns. But when you are skilled you flow around the partner like water. This frees your creativity because you are no longer bound up in battle. Each muscle of the body "plays" like a little child, who enjoys just running around.

We want to return our bodies and emotions to that playful state by disengaging from those stories of the culture that pit us against each other. You are trapped when your emotions, tensions and health are controlled by playing a role that others have chosen for you. You are attached to that story and that story plays you like a violin – a very bad sounding one. The term, "non-attachment" means that you are not controlled by that story, but can chose or create your own story.

Chapter 9
Review of Internal Mechanics

FORM

The first thing you are taught is to relax. Relaxation though, is not as easy as it sounds. After many years of being tense, most people have not only forgotten how to relax, they have forgotten that they are tense. The key is to understand that to relax any part of the body, there needs to be "space" under that part of the body to sink into. If your chest and ribs are tense and you try to relax your shoulders, the shoulders have no place to sink into. First relax the muscles of the feet so they sink into the earth like wet clay. Then relax the knees, hips, ribs, etc. Allow each part of the body to sink like sand sinks into a hole you dig in the beach. The sand fills the hole from the bottom up.

When you shift weight from one foot into another, don't push yourself into the front with your back foot. Allow the weight to sink into the front foot as though sand was sinking into the front foot from the back leg. This releases the back leg, making it "empty".

The degree of relaxation and tension of the abdominal muscles is vital for proper movement. As an example, when you begin to step, the abdominal muscles (on the side of the stepping leg) relax at an even pace. This relaxation helps to extend the leg. You do not extend the leg by using the muscles of that leg. Stepping is a result of the rotation and relaxation of the opposite hip and the relaxation of the abdominal muscles on the same side as the leg. The hips are never locked. Allow energy to flow through the hips and stepping leg, to allow the step to take place. It feels like the back of the weighted hip sinks into the

357

hamstrings of that leg and the energy flows out from there along the bottom of the stepping leg.

Use your sinking and turning to move out the stepping leg. You can slightly straighten the stepping lower leg to make the heel land first. Keeping the stepping leg off the ground as you step, is done by relaxing the rear of the pelvis so that it tilts under and slightly forward, slightly raising the stepping leg. The adductors (muscles on the inside of the thigh) of the weighted leg must stay firm as your stepping leg leaves the ground. If you let go of those adductors you lose stability.

When you take a step forward in everyday life, you need to release your rear foot. Progress comes from letting go. Letting go of the bowstring releases the arrow. Letting go of the pebble into a still lake releases the waves. Letting go of your habits releases your power. Release the flow of energy at the end of the in-breath and out-breath. Don't let the energy pull you with it when you release. Don't do anything extra. The mechanics of Tai-chi are very simple.

When you release in the form (on the in-breath and out-breath) release the attention as well. Let attention flow through you. It is in how the attention flows through you that you know yourself, not in how the attention is held.

In the form the hips generate the movements. They work in three planes. The frontal plane allows you to bend from side to side. The medial plane allows you to bend forward and back. The transverse plane allows you to turn your body left and right. As the hips move in its planes the created pattern of momentum moves out into the torso and head, the arms and legs.

At the same time, each joint sinks as you breathe out and rises as you breathe in (so the body sinks and lifts about an inch). This creates an additional pattern of momentum. While these patterns are largely created by the hips they must also pass through the hips as you sink and rise, without interference. So the hips are empty of resistance to allow the passage of momentum patterns from the legs up through the torso and from the torso down through the legs. The hips both generate and yield to momentum.

In Push Hands the way you deal with the incoming force of the partner is like the way you deal with momentum in the form. Do you meet oncoming force with resistance or with grounding? Does your attention leap towards the force or does it open a pathway to the ground? Does it open a pathway into each joint and muscle so that it joins the force to the entire body and ground?

Sometimes we change from one plane of movement to another. It has to be a smooth transition beginning at your center, specifically the tailbone and sacrum, which will direct the rotation of the pelvis. From there the change in planes emanates throughout the body. This requires that the rest of the body wait its turn to change planes as each joint sequentially changes its rotation. The pelvis (along with the tailbone and sacrum) thus acts like a rotating ball and the student understands and keeps track of the circles the pelvis makes.

At the moment she changes planes, her attention must be seated within the pelvis to make the most efficient and smooth change. If the attention comes from outside the pelvis (for example, the head) and moves toward the pelvis, ordering it to change planes, the movement will be awkward. This teaches the student to seat her attention within the pelvis. From the pelvis the attention then seats within each successive joint allowing it to follow the change. This teaches the student to seat their attention within each joint.

Eventually each joint, each muscle, each part of the body will have its own seat of attention so that the movements of the body become like a symphony. Each instrument is played by a skilled musician who is completely connected to her instrument, yet also completely connected to all the other musicians.

One of the most effective exercises you can do to improve your health is to move your hips. I have taught thousands of people over many years and almost all of them came to me with locked hips. All the muscles in that area, including the low back and the gluteus muscles were frozen.

The hips connect the activity of the upper body to the legs. Whenever you step, the weight of the upper body should smoothly sink into the legs. When the forward leg presses up so you can take a step, that upward force should flow through the hips to the upper body. In this way the forces the body experiences are always gentle.

With locked hips the upper body meets a solid "floor" at the hips instead of at the real floor below you. The forces generated by the legs also hit the bottom of the hips and reverberate back down the legs. It is no wonder that so many people have hip replacements.

Any activity that moves the hips gently and in all directions, can greatly improve your health. Elvis Presley was a health innovator in that sense. He was called, "Elvis the pelvis". The chi-gung system of "Zookinesis" emphasizes movement of the hips and of course the hips move slowly and gently in the Tai-chi forms.

In modern Tai-chi there is no such training. The pelvis doesn't rotate at all. I mourn the imminent death of traditional Tai-chi.

The moment between changes in the pelvis is a still point. The tailbone seeks its root. The movements of the rest of the body root into the pelvis so they can "taste" the quality of the change. When the whole body expresses that change, it then releases its momentum out of the body and the momentum carries with it the quality of all these changes.

At the point between release and subsequent sinking of the body into a new movement, there is another still point. The plane of movement can change again at this point. Again, it is the pelvis that relaxes first and the rest of the body follows.

When you are at the still point, either at the top or bottom, you are suspended and your body has a chance to re-adjust to prepare for the next movement. So stillness allows movement. The still points are like the big bang – the singularity before the universe was created. That singularity allowed the creation of the entire universe. It was a suspension of the laws of physics that allowed a new universe to take place.

Take the time to sustain that still point for a second or two or more so that the body can more easily prepare for what is to come, to adjust each joint and muscle for the new direction. Create still points in your life each day to allow your spirit to incorporate all that has happened that day and allow for new directions and opportunities. As you gain skill you won't need to spend as much time for the body to prepare for the next movement. Stillness will be a part of your form at all times, in one way or another.

When the tailbone seeks its root there is a downward release of the momentum, carrying with it all the dynamics of the body leading to the release. The student is trained to not interfere with the "story" of the mechanics of the body contained within each release, to follow the releases to make sure that those mechanics continue within it. Of course, the attention and the momentum are united and act as one force so that the attention follows the dynamics of the momentum even as it leaves the body.

You are releasing your control of the attention, letting it be controlled by the momentum, which in turn, was created by the attention in the first place. This is a central "play" that takes place at every moment in practicing the form. It is like paddling out towards a wave on the beach carrying a body surfboard, and then placing the surfboard down on the water and lying on it so the surfboard can be moved by the wave. It is like the overtones of the last note of a symphony that take a couple of minutes to drift off. The audience hesitates to applaud until they are sure that the last bit of overtone has disappeared through the ceiling of the concert hall taking their attention with it.

At that point the audience is suspended and is taken away by the drifting tones. The audience and the music are one and their dissolution into the universe of music is complete. Their applause serves to consolidate them from drifting musical tones back into humans as well as to thank the musicians.

We go through this transition in every movement of a Tai-chi form. When we look even more "internally" at each joint we find an even more intricate dynamic. As each joint "waits its turn" and then expands, the previous joint settles back to a neutral position, so that the energy moves like a wave through the body. The ability of the previous joint to relax after expanding is crucial for the following joint to expand. If the previous joint expanded and then just stayed that way, the body would be stiff and removed from its root by the time the energy moved to the top. It would be difficult to release.

The dynamics of the "ebb tide" continue as the "flow" goes forward. Each tide moves through each other. The dynamics of that interaction are part of the creative artistry of the student. Again, the "ebb attention" and the "flow attention" move through each other, yielding to the momentum. In this way the student develops a more three-dimensional attention so the relationship between attention and the body is a world in itself.

Within that world, the dynamics of healing are clearly seen, as a tree that is in the way is clearly seen by a skier. It is easier to avoid self-destructive behaviors. The subconscious becomes conscious. Any habitual condensation of attention or tension of the body interferes with the flow of momentum like the tree interferes with the momentum of the skier. The source of that interference becomes obvious.

The interaction of attention and momentum is the interaction of creating and yielding to the creation. This teaches us how we have created ourselves and can re-create ourselves. After all, what we consider ourselves to be is a set of behavior and thought patterns that have been set into motion. But we have drifted off through the ceiling of the concert hall and left the musicians stranded, without applause. We are like one movement of a Tai-chi form in which each joint remains expanded and does not then relax into neutral. The stiff body that results is like our stiff sense of self – our rigid behavior patterns. Rather than our lives being one movement that results in rigidity, Tai-chi teaches us to be an entire form or symphony with all its nuances.

A good exercise to develop yielding is to have someone poke you in various parts of your body while practicing form. You continue the form at its pace but yield to each poke and incorporate it into the movement. As you are poked, you blend yielding with returning to the proper position. You will discover which parts of your body are not willing to "play" with outside influences. Those pokes can teach you how you are "closed" to the flow of energy and to your own attention.

The inability of attention to penetrate some parts of the body or some aspects of the emotional state is, by definition, subconscious. Our practice dissolves this artificial barrier that allows parts of us to hide. Hiding takes a lot of energy and when we practice form or spar, we need as much energy as we can get. We want the form to be a revelation of our spirit, not a representation of our hiding. Hiding also inhibits you from engaging in activities that might expose what is behind the subconscious barrier. Every hiding part of you that is exposed to your own attention, frees you. This allows all of you to participate in your life and to feel life more fully. It also allows all the cells of the body to function to heal you rather than to hide you because even the cells are affected by and called upon to assist the hiding.

If you practice a spontaneous form in which your body moves as it wishes, each part of the body expresses its "desire" to move at each moment. You may find that some parts of the body will love the opportunity to move spontaneously and others may not know how to or fear to. It depends on the degree of penetration of your attention into these areas. If your attention has free movement in part of the body,

362

that part can be spontaneous. The physical body and attention "desire" to dance with each other. By practicing in this way, you will detect those parts of the body that are hiding from your own attention. The end result of this practice will be that every part of the body will dance freely.

The understanding of proper body mechanics varies greatly among Tai-chi teachers. Some sink down when they move forward and lift as they shift back. I teach the opposite. Some lean forward throughout the form. I teach a vertical stance. There are variations in breathing, if the joints are locked or flowing, if you sink and raise each joint just a little or only sink and raise the knees. I teach students to be aware of the role of each part of the body in each movement. As you shift back, for example, the insides of the shoulder blades widen to the sides. As you begin to shift forward, the bottom of the blades sinks down. As you rise up in front, the bottom of the shoulder blades presses forward toward the sternum.

We emphasize the flexibility and activity of the tailbone and low back in general. Before you can expand, for example, the tailbone must press into the root. As the spine expands upwards, the tailbone continues to root downwards. The tailbone never leaves the root although it follows the circles of the hips, as if it were digging beneath the ground.

The trapezius muscles lengthen from the neck toward the shoulders as you rise, so that the shoulder area relaxes (as the bottom of the shoulder blades press into the sternum). The head participates in the fluidity of the body so that it circles within a diameter of an inch. If the neck were to be stiff, this would radiate stiffness down throughout the body.

We are taught not to call different approaches "wrong" but to just say they are different (no matter how much we really think our approach is better). In this way, we keep peace in the Tai-chi community.

Part of the differences are in the goals of the teacher from simply memorizing a series of movements to a complete healing of mind and body and learning self-defense. The teacher's background influences how he teaches. He may have learned another martial art or healing system before, or he may never have learned Tai-chi-Chuan as self-defense and can only imagine the self-defense applications of each movement. His mind may be relaxed or troubled. If troubled, his internal issues may influence his external movements.

It is important for the student to take what he feels is valuable from a teacher but be discerning and not necessarily take everything. Explore other teachers and views. Ask your teacher "why". Don't accept the answer, "Because that's the way my teacher did it".

How do you know what to take and what to leave behind? Listen to your body. If it says, "This make sense" – take it. The thinking mind can be easily fooled. A Tai-chi teacher's job is to teach you to listen to your body.

PUSH HANDS

Being connected to the world around you and to your creations in a living, creative way leads to health. Grabbing the world around you and your creations leads to deterioration and death. It limits you because there is only so much you can grab. The harder you grab, the more locked up you are.

Push Hands students will feel that way when a joint, such as the shoulder joint, is pushed to its "end" and the student feels he can't move it any further back. He forgets that the shoulder joint can move in a circle and there is no "end" to a circle. If the student concentrates on circularity and continuity, he will never be backed into a corner. If he concentrates on grabbing and opposing the partner's force, he locks up. Even if the shoulder can't continue its rotation for some reason, he can then rotate the hip or other part of the body. Concentrating on the continuity of the flow makes you more powerful than tensing up your big, wonderful muscles.

You can also become locked into a pattern of behaviors in everyday life. Consciousness is continuous. The personality, which is the pattern of behaviors, continues only as long as it is maintained by the consciousness. The personality can become like a living thing if it is based on flow. It becomes fragile when rigid.

The artist of a painting always keeps in mind the flow of the viewer's eyes. A painting that can stimulate the flow of attention keeps the viewer enthralled. One that can't just gets a quick glance and then the viewer moves on. Art that takes you on a "magic carpet ride" heals the attention by stimulating its flow. It can dissolve resistance, or it can playfully create resistance and *then* dissolve it. It is the dissolving of resistance, tension and blockage to chi that we seek, even for those who seek it in drugs. We seek to restore the living connection among all the parts of our body. Chi is that connection. It is also the sense of the flowing dynamics of that connection.

You can pit yourself against the partner for the purposes of conquering or you can connect. In the first case your attention leaps to the partner to oppose him. Yet in the second case your attention also moves into the partner because your attention is *released* into the partner. This is different from "leaping towards" the partner or the pushing hand to stop him. You are not conquering the partner; you are *becoming* him. Just as the form teaches you to allow your full consciousness to create intention to move your body, releasing your attention into the partner allows your full consciousness to move *his* body. If your attention is within each of his joints and muscles and his is not, you are more informed than he as to the state of his body and its readiness to respond to your intentions. The release of your attention into his body is then followed by the release of your physical energy into his body – into every joint and muscle of his body.

If you watch competition Push Hands the back generally tenses and the front closes. That closes off any possibility of releasing your attention into his body. With traditional Push Hands your back relaxes and your front opens. It is not until your attention has been fully released into the partner that you then push as you breathe in. Your push starts from inside the partner and from your breath pressing into the root, not from way back there in your shoulders and back.

To allow your attention to be released into the partner you need to allow him to control the movements of the pushing. If you resist or try to take control of those movements, you stop the release of your own energy into the partner, and then it's just pushing and shoving. At the same time your hips and legs constantly align themselves with the position you have been pushed into, so that you are always in an alignment that will allow you to push. This process is really most of the push and the actual push itself is just like physically knocking over the king in chess at the end of a long game.

Releasing your attention into the partner allows you to feel within his body. The states of tension and improper alignment within his body register within your feeling sense, illuminating his interior. They allow you to make subtle changes within each muscle and joint of your body to energetically expand into those specific points within his body that are the most vulnerable. Each of your joints and muscles are like a chameleon's eyes that can move independently and pay attention to different things.

The hips are free to continually align themselves while the torso is free to allow itself to be moved by the partner. Each part of the body becomes mobile including the low back, which plays a large role in alignment, so releasing attention into the partner can only happen when you release tension and resistance within yourself.

Your energy has to "live" in the body of your Push Hands partner. But that partner usually has no intention of letting you into him. So we have to absorb his resistance into our connective tissue, which is a network of rubbery tissue that surrounds all muscles, bones, organs, and body cavities and forms ligaments and tendons. You are trained to allow the partner to stretch your connective tissue like an archer stretches his bowstring. In this case, the arrow is aimed at the partner. His resistance stretches your "bowstring" and then you release it. Your hand may be the "arrow" that delivers the force but the force comes from releasing the stretch.

Your body remains stable so the energy comes out cleanly. It is also important that all of the connective tissue of your whole body bends equally to receive and release the force, just as the bowstring bends equally throughout its length.

In this way each joint will be dealing with only a tiny fraction of the original whole force. That will be much easier to deal with. When your joints and the connective tissue, ligaments and tendons are all dealing with his force, what seemed like a powerful push now seems like a bunch of tiny pushes that are easy to neutralize.

At the moment of your push, you are letting go. We say that "letting go is power" or "did I push you?" As to how to direct the partner's force to just these tissues of the body, a competent teacher is necessary to help you learn this principle.

Power comes from allowing the "external" forces to re-align your internal mechanics so that it has a desired effect. When done correctly, the absorption of energy and the release happen simultaneously so that for each inch of stretching your connective tissue, there is an inch of push. Since it happens quickly the effect is that the pusher is pushing himself. The creative skill is to absorb his push into the connective

366

tissue in a way that will result in maximum release, aligned directly towards him and connected to the root (your connection to the ground).

As his energy enters you, yours simultaneously enters him. You can think of your energy within him as the bow, your body as the bowstring, the arm connected to him as the arrow and his body as the target. Each joint of your body responds to his push by aiming to the centerline of his body. The energy released from your body flows through this entire energetic system and explodes from the inside of his body. It is not a push of the hand against the outside of his arm or body but an injection of energy into him, which then explodes within him. It is the ability to be affected by his power and have each part of your body respond individually and cooperatively to your energetic advantage that gives you power. This is known as "transformation of energy" or "Taoist alchemy".

You can also completely neutralize his force if that force is released upward and downward from each of your joints. You can begin to practice this by letting his force expand your spine both upward and downward at the same pace. Feel his force fill the spine and then release the energy up and down, as you would do in the form with your own momentum. Your goal is to receive into all the joints and "align heaven and earth" from each joint at the same time.

This brings your attention into each joint and then, as you release, allows the attention to flow smoothly from each joint through the whole body upward and downward as well as spherically outward. As your partner's force is released in this way, (if your goal is to just neutralize his push), his alignment is affected. He has to re-align as you drain his force out of his body because he depends on your resistance for his alignment. To practice correctly, neither of you should depend on the other's resistance, because that can be suddenly removed. You learn to interpenetrate the partner while maintaining your own alignment. This changes Push Hands from "push and shove" to "interconnect" and learning to use dynamics related to that connection. It allows Push Hands to represent situations in life and metaphorically show you how to become more effective in life.

You must learn to allow energy to flow through your body, into the earth and from the earth, through your body, into the partner. This process will focus your attention within you, revealing your inner dynamics. It will also give you the confidence to let others closer emotionally. This is so for two reasons.

1. You will have spent lots of time seeing inside yourself and getting to know yourself, therefore you will be less afraid to "lose yourself," your identity, in a relationship.

2. You will learn how to neutralize the negative energy of others *after* it has entered you. This will give you the confidence that you can always clear yourself of unwanted energy, behavior patterns, tensions, etc.

You will allow the beauty of the world to affect you more and will feel more alive. You will reverse the hardening process that most of us learn as children to shield ourselves from pain.

The principles of Push Hands, the methods of dealing with your partner's flow of energy represent principles of personal growth. When the partner tenses up, we flow around him or absorb his tension and push through him as water can both flow around rocks or seep into rocks.

The mind can feel good about "winning" over someone else. The body and attention feel good about being healthy and moving freely. Even when you are working out on equipment there is a different relationship with the resistance. Resistance can stretch your body if you allow it into your body. You feel that you are stretching "into" the resistance and it is stretching into you ("interpenetration"). You are connected to it rather than fighting against it.

Each muscle and joint receives the resistance from its own vantage point and so is lined up with the force. As the angle of your arms or legs or the angle of the equipment changes, the force gets distributed into just those parts of the body that are lined up to receive it. Each muscle only works within its own most efficient range of motion. That is what you are paying attention to, rather than to maximizing the tension of the whole body and grunting loudly. The more the control comes from the "head", the less efficient you are.

You try to separate yourself from your partner (by pushing) and yet in order to be successful, you learn a complex system of connecting to him. It is a contradiction. As it is said in Zen practice, "You need to swallow the contradiction whole". If you think about pushing it will be hard for you to connect. So you push without intending to push –

"Did I push you?" It may seem like the whole purpose of the game is to push but as you can see it is more to learn to connect.

Make sure that the connection with your partner through your arms and hands remains steady. Keep that pressure constant even though the pressure should only be "four ounces". You may have a partner who is extremely tense. In that case the pressure should be four ounces lighter or heavier than his, depending on whether you want to lead him into you or away from you.

If one of the partners thinks to push, there are subtle changes in his body to prepare for the push that the other partner can detect. If each partner can detect even the intention of the other to push, the exercise takes place without much movement as each partner counteracts the intention of the other before it manifests in physical movement. Yet a partner may purposefully create such an intention as a diversion to trap the other partner. Push Hands takes place on many deceptive levels and this teaches you to detect intention.

It teaches you to detect the origins of your own intentions. Are they creative or do they come from habit? Are they composed of spirit animals leaping out of the dragon's lair or are they composed of fear? The former keeps attention alive and the latter leads to death.

When you are about to push, don't telegraph your intentions. This means that you don't raise up your force to your upper body as if to say, "I am about to push you." There is a psychological impulse to prepare for the push. You must remain in an aligned position throughout the Push Hands so that you can push at any moment from where you are. Needing to prepare for the push means that you were not aligned before.

Watch for this telegraphing activity in your partner. As soon as he prepares to push, push him at the moment of preparation. His force will be top heavy or locked at that moment and he will be easy to push.

The first tendency is to become tighter, harder, more condensed than your partner because that makes you feel stronger. To many who practice Push Hands, feeling strong is the benefit. Two people tightening their muscles, grabbing each other's arms tightly, perhaps gritting their teeth, moving around aerobically, leaning in to each other, makes them feel strong. They don't want to feel, "Did I push you?" They want to feel, "I pushed you!" They are feeding their personality, not their connections.

Don't tighten up if you feel your partner is about to successfully push you. It is better to get pushed than to tighten. The whole point of this exercise is to learn to remain relaxed, to neutralize the opponent's force through relaxation and to issue your own force with a relaxed mind and body. You are only cheating yourself if you tense up to avoid getting pushed because you will never learn real Push Hands.

Don't think of the force of your partner as "his force" pushing against you. Accept all force as part of your own energetic system and realign your body to distribute that force equally throughout your body. If you remain even in this way at every moment, his force will have no effect. You are like the ringmaster of a circus. You are coordinating all the acts so the show runs smoothly. Similarly, coordinate all the forces you feel (gravity, momentum, the partner's force etc.) so that nothing gets jammed up. Don't think of the partner's force as an attack but just as force that needs to be aligned and balanced within your energy system.

When you do any chi-gung exercise it is important to balance the chi, not only within your body but with the chi of your environment as well. It is dangerous to hold chi just within your body and isolate it from the environment. Push Hands teaches you the importance of balancing your internal forces with outside forces.

I have learned a lot about Push Hands from my many years of snake handling, which in essence involves doing Push Hands with the snake. Imagine a large boa or python curling around your body and intertwining your arms. You cannot force the serpent to do your bidding because it is stronger than you.

By tuning into its flow of energy, you can harmonize with the snake and enter into an energy union. Your motions would be identical to Push Hands.

The snake, of course, doesn't have hands but uses its entire body. Its attention is distributed throughout its length and allows the snake to instantly respond to the slightest touch or change of balance of the handler.

In Push Hands, you don't really push with your hands or arms. These appendages act as springs, cushioning your interactions with your partner. They can store energy as a spring can store the energy of something pushing against it.

370

One's body becomes very spring-like and force is cushioned, stored, grounded, redirected and released. The physical energy is more obvious, more concrete and easier to see, but the lessons learned in dealing with physical energy also apply to emotional, mental and spiritual energy. Practicing Push Hands creates a springier emotional and mental attitude. You become less fragile in all ways.

This teaches us that we don't have to fight our way through life. Our softness can neutralize the hardness of others.

A student should try to think of how each Push Hands lesson relates to his or her life. If he has difficulty learning some aspect of Push Hands, does that student have a similar problem in interpersonal relationships?

I also feel it is the teacher's responsibility to name these principles with common English words that relate to one's personal life. "Push," for example can also mean anything in one's life that "pushes your buttons".

A partner may capture your attention by faking a small push on one side, only to come in on the other. The advertising industry does this "bait and switch" to us all time. Use simple words which are practical rather than mystical words designed to impress.

Many cultures use mythological stories to encode lessons of growth. The reader becomes aware of the deeper levels of meaning and understands that the mythological characters represent universal qualities within all people. Push Hands encodes these lessons in physical movement and makes the lessons much more graspable - more immediate.

Do you always try to repel the partner or do you allow his energy to seep into you to feel that energy deeply? Is your main concern to push him more than he pushes you or to develop a harmony, a blend of your two energies?

Do you think of technique or trust your creativity to serve you each moment without preplanning? Where is your attention - on thinking the next move, or on feeling the flow of energies?

The more you think of winning and pushing, the more rigid your attention will become and the more you will get pushed. Push Hands thus becomes a form of death and re-birth.

Let go of the desire to win over the opponent, to struggle through conflict. And then a new self-identity will emerge - creativity, harmony and spontaneity, a channel for the flow of nature.

Whenever you feel a "point of pressure", use that as an opportunity to shift and adjust something in your life so as to make that pressure irrelevant. Before we are about to attempt anything, the attention assesses the body, mind, will - all the "elements" - to see if you are prepared to accomplish the mission. If your attention feels that you are not ready, it will cause you to hesitate or stop trying. By building your inner strength you feel more prepared and are more willing to try new things. You no longer consider a new challenge with fear. Your attention assesses your elements and finds them strong and ready. This creates an entirely new attitude that leads to success. That "inner strength" is really the ability to readjust as conditions change, to be able to let go of behaviors that have become irrelevant.

Even though we may be dealing with a mental or emotional challenge, the attention also assesses the body's physical condition to determine if you are ready to deal with the challenge. Is each part of our body flexible and strong and is it filled with our awareness? Our intellectual way of interacting with each other in modern society is a more modern form of behavior. Our biology still works on a physical "flight or fight response" mode. So in order to feel confident to tackle a modern type of interaction, we still instinctually assess our physical readiness.

If we are ready to respond to every change instantly, then we don't need to control our situation by preventing change. A Push Hands "volley" that consists of each partner trying to control the movements is very different from one in which the partners are playing together. The expression "playing Push Hands" means that you are not trying to prevent the partner from functioning but that you are freely interacting. It is like journeying together into uncharted lands.

When you practice by letting go and connecting with your partner, and letting the body and attention go where it goes, there are no mistakes because you are not judging where things should go. Your thinking mind just watches and wonders – and learns. The main thing it learns is that it is not the smartest part of you. It is a plagiarist of the genius within you. We are trying to access that genius directly. That is done by dissolving the blockages to chi, and the blockages between the flow of chi within the body to the flow of chi in the natural surroundings.

Chi cannot be worked with by grabbing with the grabbing mind. It is "worked with" by letting go of it. It is "worked" by the entirety of the flow of chi of nature. As a band member plays with his band mates, your chi plays with nature's chi, and that is your real Push Hands partner. The drummer may think he is in control because he sets the beat. The guitarist may think he is in control because he is playing the melody. The bassist creates the setting to give meaning to the music. The keyboardist may play with the guitarist's melody so that they are dancing with each other. Yet no one really controls the music. The music controls the musicians.

The music happens because of the connection of the musicians to each other and to their instruments. Their creativity strums the connections. But if they did not feel completely connected to each other and to their instruments, they would be concentrating on how to hold their hands or which note to sing. Their minds would be playing and you can imagine how that would sound. Nowadays there are electronic devices to make up for that poor sound because we don't want to inconvenience the musicians to spend the time learning to gain more skill.

The more connection you have to your own body and to the world around you, the more you can let go and allow creativity to be the center of your life. Let it play through your life so your life is great music.

The skills that are passed down from generation to generation are the structure that allows creativity to flow through you. It is like the alignment of the body. If you are leaning over, your Tai-chi can never give you the health benefits for which it is famous. Proper alignment allows chi to flow. When you receive your Push Hands partner's force into your connective tissue, the force will go into the structurally weakest part of the body. So the structure of the body should have the characteristic of Yang (steady and aligned). Yet the inside of your body can receive the force and transform it. The inside has the quality of mobility and flow (Yin).

The reason Tai-chi-Chuan is considered to be an internal martial art is that action arises first from the dynamics of attention which causes the transformation of energy and that takes place inside the body. That transformation then has an effect on the structure, causing it to move (but not to distort). You should be able to see something taking place inside the Tai-chi person's body before it turns into movement, if you are trained to see it. Indeed, the goal of a teacher is to train the student to be able to "see". The student should see the flow of chi, especially if she is involved in healing.

The Tai-chi student "knows" the flow of chi like the musician knows the flow of music or a surfer, the flow of the wave. They don't order the music or water or chi around – they want to be taken by it. Yet they also want some minimum of Yang, so they have something to say. In each case, the golden elixir, the proportion of Yin to Yang, changes constantly and becomes the relationship of the artist to her art. In your everyday life, isn't the ability to let go or be firm, the balance you are trying to achieve?

Sometimes in Push Hands, when a partner gets pushed over, he grabs onto the partner's arms to "avoid" getting pushed. This is someone who doesn't know how to let go. He is reaching into his bag of tricks to make up for his lack of skill.

When doing Push Hands, you are constantly assessing every muscle and joint of your partner. Are they in a state of readiness to respond or are they tight? Are the individual parts consciously independent, so that you are dealing with many partners or are they controlled by the "king" (thinking mind), so you are only pushing one consciousness? The more you allow your parts to respond individually (and in coordination with the others), the more "soldiers" you have. Can the king let his generals make their own choices? Are you willing to take that chance? It depends on how much you trust your body and the skills your teacher taught you.

That trust is one of the greatest benefits of Push Hands. You will forget how many times you pushed people over. But you will never forget the time you saved yourself from getting hurt by using Push Hands principles. The first time that happened to me I was running in a parking lot and a little round pebble rolled under my feet. I went into the air, flipped, landed back on my feet and kept running. My mind was a little perplexed and then it felt like my body consciousness said to my mind, "Who's your daddy now?"

The mind enters into a relationship with the body consciousness (Body-Mind), like the guitarist playing with the keyboardist. That relationship has to become "Ahh" not "Hey!" like the two types of snake hisses. Tai-chi practice makes that transformation. You go through life making transformations based on the one you made within yourself and that becomes the basis of your friendships and your interaction with situations.

When you experience the many little consciousnesses of the body parts and how they work together, it is like how there are many species and individuals in an ecosystem and many ecosystems in the world. It is hard to claim ownership of your consciousness. And what is it that makes that claim – the personality (which I call the fashioned creature)? You created that personality in the first place. Does the creation claim ownership of the creator?

Yes, that is how most people live their lives. The fashioned creature becomes the self and the creator is possessed by that which it created. Once you realize that you are the creator and not the creation, you are free. The fashioned creature was fashioned, not only by you, but mainly by the way our society molded you. If you become the fashioned creature and not the creator, the culture has you by the cojones.

When I was eight years old, I apprenticed with an artist of oil painting. One of the main things I remember from this experience was that he emphasized to keep looking at the subject I was painting rather than the painting itself. I complained that if I didn't look at the painting, I wouldn't be able to see what I was doing.

He explained that he didn't want my painting to come from my mind but from the real world itself. The art of the painter was to allow one's body to transfer the real world to the canvas in such a way as to coax out one's creativity and allow it to participate.

In other words, he didn't want my painting to become a fashioned creature but rather to showcase the way my creativity was in charge. There is nothing wrong with sneaking a peak at the canvas once in a while but my main focus was to be on the relationship of my creativity to the real world – not just be a manufacturer of paintings.

To create is your nature. To let go of your creation is your skill. If you grasp the creation, you lose yourself.

It is sometimes difficult to trust that the body's intelligence ("Body-Mind") is completely adequate to control Push Hands or sparring. Your thinking mind and tension want to take over. Part of the concept of "nothing" is to "let go" and allow the body intelligence take over the Push Hands or sparring. It is like riding a bicycle. You can't think your way through it. You may fall off the bike a few times but eventually you will gain the skill.

Awareness of internal energy also allows you to do healing. I was taught Tai-chi massage. The healer is aware of the pattern of attention of the "client" and of the attention of each individual muscle. The client concentrates on particular areas and the healer then relaxes those muscles. The ability of the healer to perceive the movement of the client's attention essentially allows the client to "massage himself", using the healer to do the job. The healer can also influence each muscle to relax by directly connecting his energy to the energy of that muscle and then using energetic techniques (rather than brute physical techniques).

This trains the client to become very aware of the relationship between the pattern of his attention and the structure and behavior of his body. He can take this knowledge to the Push Hands and sparring to refine his awareness and the ability of his body to respond. And of course, the ability of the healer to perceive the client's pattern of attention and the condition of his body makes him better at being aware of these same things in the Push Hands partner. So healing and sparring practices help each other.

There is an expression that teaching these practices is like "selling water by the river". The teacher teaches you to be aware of your own body. That awareness is right there inside of you but you don't see it. The teacher is really providing you with what you already have.

In a sense, that is what most salespeople do. You don't sell the car; you sell giving the customer a better image of himself. You don't sell the shampoo; you sell the admiration of others when they see the customer's clean hair. But once you realize that people are really impressed with someone who is just comfortable with himself, you don't need the external representations of that. Just be yourself and you don't need to buy the products (maybe shampoo).

The Tai-chi teacher doesn't really just teach you to memorize movements. He teaches you to be able to feel your body, and through that, to feel your connection to the world. The teacher teaches you not just to push someone over in Push Hands, but to bring back the awareness of internal energy and of the dynamics of attention in your body and in other people as well. The teacher opens up new worlds of experience that should have never been locked up in the first place.

The Zen expression, "Selling water by the river," means that you already have all you need to be fully healthy and active. All a teacher can do is point out to you, skills you already have and health that is already inside of you. Our modern culture teaches us to lock up our skills and our health. It takes a lot of effort to make us unhealthy.

It is almost as if I am teaching people how to see by telling them to open their eyes. But in this case, I am asking the students to open up their inner eyes – their ability to feel and use each part of their body. How much sickness and misery could we avoid if we all opened up our inner eyes?

The freedom of the movement of attention within the flesh of the body results in the joy of movement, as in a young child. It is the yearnings of the attention and body to interact that result in movement rather than the yearnings of the thinking mind. The thinking mind is formed by the mythology of the culture that tells it how to feel good about itself. The interaction of attention and the flesh already know how to feel good. It cannot be coerced to be self-destructive or other-destructive.

Since we do not mirror the power of the opponent, our own responses can be more creative. In fact, we allow creativity to completely take over. Each organ and cell of the body is a living being with an independent will, wisdom and awareness in its own way. Given enough information about external conditions ("someone is about to push me"), all the parts of the body can organize a response. Since all the activities on a cellular level are magnitudes faster than on our own level of awareness, the reaction time is very quick. When the wisdom of the entire body is allowed to fully participate in our lives, we are at the point of maximum creativity.

After an action has taken place we can look back and remember how the body responded efficiently and marvel at its competence. When we are more advanced, we can watch this process as it is happening without interfering with it. We develop a trust in the body's competence and are willing to let go of the tension and emotional upheaval that comes from the thinking mind trying to do the body's work. This allows us to understand the proper role of thinking and of action, a principle we can apply to our everyday lives.

Action requires intense attention but not from the head. Attention is the fuel that both the body and mind need to function. Tai-chi training should result in neither robbing attention from the other. The mind and body develop a creative relationship with each other rather than an antagonistic one.

The antagonism between the mind and body destroys both. The mind may not trust the body because the body has failed the person or is in constant pain. In most cases I have found that those failures and pains of the body actually arose from the poor relationship between the two. By healing that relationship you can heal the whole person in many cases. That healing simply consists of allowing attention to fill the whole body and its surroundings. We let go of narrowing and condensing attention all the time.

I used to breed mice as food for my reptile collection. When baby mice had to be transferred to a new cage, I had to reach into a swarming mass of them, grab a tail and pull the mouse (upside down) to its new cage. There were dozens of mice in each cage so I had to continuously and rapidly grab to get the job done. My attention had to keep track of the movements of the mice so my fingers would wind up where the tail would be a second later. (For those of my generation, I felt like Lucy at the chocolate candy conveyer belt.)

All this translates well into Push Hands and sparring. Humans are used to single pointed attention. We can learn to switch our attention rapidly to keep track of several things but the speed of that switching has its limits. Instead, we learn to decentralize our attention so that we can be aware of everything at the same time and respond to everything.

If I were to ask you what is in your room you would just look around and see it all. It might take some time for you to verbally list each thing but you would be aware of it all at once. In the same way we need to be aware of the opponent's balance, the readiness of each of his muscles, the pattern of his attention, the quality of his attention, etc. all at the same time. We need not only continuous attention but also modes of perception that have degenerated in modern humans.

To begin this type of training we need to always remember this idea of not locking the body or mind. We need to catch ourselves as we do indeed lock in some way, during our daily lives. We may, for example, lock onto a thought loop, repeating words endlessly in our minds. This removes our attention from what is going on right in front of us. We

378

may lock our backs and shoulders as we begin to type into our computers. We may lock our muscles around a pencil as we write or lock up our jaw muscles as we think of something unpleasant. If it is cold, we may lock our shoulders as if that would keep us warm. We might hold the steering wheel of a car much more tightly than necessary.

We may also lock onto anger. Perhaps something happened that truly deserves an angry response. Yet we carry that anger with us for the rest of the day because we locked onto it.

There is a story of two Buddhist men walking on a path in the woods. They came to a deep stream and saw a woman hesitant to cross. One of the men lifted the woman up and carried her to the other side of the stream. Then the two men went on their way. After a long time, one of the men said, "I just have to say something to you. We Buddhist men are not allowed to touch woman yet you picked that woman up and carried her across the stream." The other man said, "I let her go on the other side of the stream but you are still carrying her."

We cannot be emotionless and sometimes anger can be appropriate. But when you lock onto that anger, it can turn violent. It is much easier to simply express why you are feeling angry to let the offending person know how you feel. That might not solve the problem but it leaves you free.

You can also be locked onto your self-image. If you feel that you must perpetuate this image, you may be locked onto behavior patterns that are not necessarily to your advantage. With some people, helplessness is a large part of their self-image. "Oh, I just can't go to class today. I'm too tired or too bored or too busy. It's not my fault. I'm just too helpless". Let's not even get into the people who are too helpless to stop their addictions. While there are physical and emotional components to addictions, often the helpless self-image is a large part of the problem.

How does your self-image keep you locked into certain behaviors?

Many people feel that if they became unlocked, they would fall apart. If they gave up their excess tension, they would fall down. If they gave up their emotional and mental locks they wouldn't function anymore. They are not functioning now if they are locked up. Flexibility can be their cure.

Businesses that are flexible can survive. Bands and musicians that once earned a living from the royalties of their records and then CDs, now make very little that way. They have to go back to touring. That's why it's called "Jurassic Rock". When I first produced videos on Tai-chi, I used a VHS editing system. Then I switched to Super VHS. Next it was Betacam SP and finally digital. And don't get me started on transferring from the old VHS tapes to DVDs! It was expensive to make the switches but I had to keep up with the increasing quality people expected. I didn't appreciate having to keep changing, but that's life!

The key in Push Hands is to not mind changing. Don't try to keep from changing by grabbing your partner, tensing up and resisting. The whole point is to learn to make changes on the fly based on proper body mechanics; it is to get used to living your life with flexibility, so important in modern times with so many changes taking place so rapidly.

Just release whichever of your tensions that are the easiest to release in Push Hands. If a release starts to be difficult, switch to another one that is easy. Recognize those parts of your body that are closing even as you may release another part. The goal is no condensing. When you switch from one release to another, bring your attention into the new part already in a state of releasing. Don't first go into the new part and then figure out how to release. Allow the state of releasing of your attention to "melt" the part you are entering. You don't have to release only where your partner is pushing – just whichever part of the body is easiest to release at that moment. You release to move. You do not move to release. If you respond to your partner by releasing resistance, he will have nothing to push. You can even lead him to his instability by the sequence of muscles you relax.

Unravel the relationship between your hand that is on your partner, and the rest of your body. The pressure on the hand remains the same and the direction of your energy is towards his center. The rest of the body should be able to move independently by relaxing. Unwind the mind into the body and unwind the body into the mind. This allows the thinking process of the mind to turn into the consciousness of the body which then generates your movements. Allow the body to go where it wants. Don't use your mind to manipulate your body.

Let the legs release downward while the rest of the body releases front & back, side-to-side and upward. Don't release with the intention of pushing. The push is just the final release. Seat your identity in the releasing, not the condensing. You *are* the release.

You might get the impression from this book that the exercise of Push Hands is part of a larger training and is not just designed to help you push people better. It may surprise you that many people "learn" Push Hands just by going to Push Hands groups and pushing people around. They do not learn form, chi-gung, healing or the philosophy of Tai-chi. Each part of Tai-chi, including the fighting, forms an integrated tapestry that acts like that empty barge lifting the sunken boat, as mentioned earlier., You are learning to see the world in a new way and that allows you to respond more creatively to every encounter. It allows you to understand yourself more fully so that you can really enjoy your life.

The entirety of the training aligns all your "elements" to heal you on all levels. Faced with a life-time of training, some students may opt for short-cuts. Others relish the idea that their learning will never end.

When my mother was 65 years old, she enrolled in courses in Brooklyn College, which required a long train ride from all the way out here on Long Island where our family lives. People asked her, "Why enroll in college now, at 65 years old?" She answered, "When you stop learning, you start dying".

So when I reached 65 years old, I wondered what I would do to keep learning. My wife, Jean provided the answer. We both started training in classical Pilates exercise in New York City – a three-hour trip each way and five or six hours of training once we got there, twice a week, plus many three- and four-day workshops besides that. This went on for three years.

The point is that, if you understand the depth of Push Hands and the rest of Tai-chi training, you won't take short-cuts. You won't grab the partner's arms to avoid getting pushed. You will wait until you have learned a basic form and some chi-gung before you begin training in Push Hands. And you will practice Push Hands a few years before you do full sparring.

FIGHTING

381

Review of Internal Mechanics

Tai-chi-Chuan training consists both of physical techniques and training the dynamics of attention. It requires a refined awareness of proper body mechanics and the relationship of mind and body. This martial art is an excellent way of learning about the Taoist principle of Yin/Yang and of the power of relaxation.

The strength and skill of attention can make up for less physical strength than the opponent. In fact, the opponent's physical strength accounts for very little against Tai-chi-Chuan. It is common for a fighter's attention to give out before his physical energy gives out.

Most importantly, the skills learned in Tai-chi-Chuan are useful in every aspect of life. They make you more aware of your body and of other people. They bring back the sense of the dynamics of attention and of internal energy. And Tai-chi-Chuan teaches you to be peaceful and centered in the midst of turmoil.

It opens up a whole new world of opportunities to increase your skill in combat. By greatly increasing your ability to perceive and react, by learning to not waste energy and time and by learning proper body mechanics, the principles of Tai-chi-Chuan enhance any other martial art.

I studied Tai-chi-Chuan fifty years ago with Grandmaster William C. C. Chen, a system based on the movements of animals. Luckily, I owned an animal importing company and had a ready supply of subjects to study. I learned the pattern of attention of each species and tried to adopt that pattern in myself, to apply to sparring and chi-gung. The imported animals were often not in a good mood as they emerged from their shipping containers and I was attacked frequently. Many of the animals were stronger and faster than I so I had to use my skill in controlling their attention. There were many close calls and I had many scars.

I also traveled to the jungles of Central America several times to study the animals in the wild. I would buy a dugout canoe and spend a few months paddling along rivers, meeting the wildlife and people.

The result of this study is the system of chi-gung I now call "Zookinesis" ("animal exercises") and the fighting system, "Phantom Kung-fu", the result of Tai-chi-Chuan influenced by Zookinesis. Each teacher is influenced by his or her many teachers and experiences.

This type of self-defense is very fluid and requires special training to develop the range of motion of the joints and their coordination so the body can twist and turn easily.

Tai-chi-Chuan teaches you how to avoid attack on the street and to make it difficult for a sparring partner to defeat you in class. Even if you are not strong or are not used to fighting, there are ways you can thwart the attacker's efforts.

A mugger is looking for an easy attack on someone who won't or can't fight back. He mugs for a living and doesn't want to get hurt "on the job", just like anyone else. The mugger must assess the physical abilities of his victim as well as the victim's state of awareness.

There are three qualities you can develop to lessen the chances of becoming a victim. The first is the alignment of the body. If your body is not aligned properly you are probably not involved in any physical activity that requires coordination. The mugger can sense this. Any training, such as Tai-chi, Zookinesis, Yoga or Pilates can teach you the proper alignment of the body. Even the use of such physical therapy aids as the foam roller will improve your posture. This will also improve your overall health.

The second quality is the fluidity of the body. If your body is stiff and tight, you probably can't move very well and won't be able to defend yourself. A person who walks fluidly and is well connected to the ground may offer the mugger trouble. If your body seems bouncy and alive you may have the energy to run after him. Trampoline, Zookinesis and the animal forms of the martial arts are especially good at adding that bounciness to the body.

The third quality a mugger looks out for is awareness. If you are aware of what is going on around you, you can prepare for an attack. Strong awareness also shows that you have had some training, as the awareness of most people is very dead. All of the above training helps with awareness, especially Push Hands, sparring in general and the Zookinesis exercises.

You can take advantage of the generally poor state of attention in your sparring practice. Make your partner's attention move rapidly. While a properly trained martial artist has a "field of attention" so that he can deal with many things going on at a time, most have a single-pointed attention. That person's attention has to jump from one place to another and it gets tired.

So you should strike to different parts of the body. You can punch the legs as well as the head and body. You can integrate kicking with the punching rather than using kicking for a while and then switching to punching. Add a little bit of grappling as well, just for a second or two, here and there and then go right back to punching and kicking. If your partner cannot predict what you will do next, his attention will be uncertain and will wear out quickly.

Keep the body fluid. Allow your hips, lower ribs and elbows to rotate in small circles and allow the head to reflect this movement. This will allow you to respond quickly and will make it difficult for your partner to aim. It will require his attention to follow your movements and most people cannot do that for long.

These are but a few simple ways that proper Tai-chi training can teach you to be uninviting to attackers and to make it difficult for an attacker to defeat you.

Tai-chi-Chuan uses a fundamentally different fighting strategy than any other martial art. When this strategy is applied to everyday life and to conducting business, it provides a more powerful and effective approach. This is a summary of that strategy.

In everyday life the defeats we constantly experience are like the strikes of an aggressor. If we focus on the defeat, we are like the fighter who blocks the incoming strike, focusing on the aggressor's power. If we are thrown by the defeat, we are like the fighter who moves away from the strike. If we contemplate the change in our life situation caused by the defeat and re-adjust our focus to take advantage of this change, then we are like the fighter who moves away from the strike but towards the body of the opponent at the same time and delivers his own strike.

As a fighter you know that the aggressor will not just stand there and take your punches and kicks. Most of your efforts may never reach their target and some of his efforts will reach you. If you thought of each of his strikes as your defeat, you could never psychologically muster the nerve to practice sparring. Your own emotions would destroy you more than would the opponent. This is why the sparring partners punch each other in the face around thirty times before we begin sparring in our school. You don't evade the punches, but just stand there and receive them. This is a warm-up. Then, if you are punched again during the sparring, it is just another punch.

384

Much of the impact of a defeat is not the effect of the situation itself. It is more that it hurts your self-image. It is your self-image that is being beaten, more than your body or your life situation. Once you realize that your self-image is not you, then you are on your way to victory.

True humility is not acting as if you were a lowly human being. It is the understanding that your self-image is not you. Needing to maintain that image no longer controls your behavior. If, while sparring in class, someone strikes you, you can appreciate their skill and be happy for them, even though you got hit. In life you can appreciate the challenges you need to overcome and the skills you gain as you turn each defeat into an opportunity.

An internal style punch comes in loosely so that if blocked, it can softly bounce off the strike or slip around it and spiral on in to a different area without having to "reload". This softness or looseness is very conducive to paying attention. Once you harden up, the attention tends to freeze. You become "blind" for that instant.

The punch in Tai-chi-Chuan is an expansion, an explosion of the entire body, which is expressed through the arm and fist. It is not an act of the arm and fist itself. Each joint of the body, beginning with the foot, expands sequentially, creating a rifling effect. The back of the body drops into the ground at the same pace as the front of the body expands. This keeps the body in balance and connected to the root.

The opponent's returning force (the force of his body's resistance) is drawn into the sinking down of your back. His resistance force is then recycled up the front of your body as it expands. In this way his resistance adds to your force rather than subtracting from your force.

We always try to strike the other person at the very moment they are striking us. At that moment they are blind and we are not, so we have the advantage. At the moment a hard stylist's punch is completed, he freezes for a fraction of a second to harden up even further. Thus, we have even more time (a larger fraction of a second) to land our own punch.

Much of Tai-chi-Chuan's strategy is in freezing or tying up the opponent's attention. For example, if you are grabbed, the question is often raised, "How do you get out of the grab?" Getting out of the grab is the last thing I want to do. While the opponent is grabbing me, his hands and attention are tied up in the grab and he is usually not paying attention to the rest of his body.

Rather than fighting against his power (the grab) I would bring another part of my body (hip, leg, other hand) into a different area of his body and work in that area. Our bodies are loose enough to let the opponent have his grab while other parts of our body can move independently.

When we are grappling, we also need to assess the partner's readiness. We need to use our attention to assess his body. His grappling behaviors will come from his own sense of physical readiness. We need to be more aware of his readiness than he is of his own. This is the skill that Push Hands provides to us. We can also block the ability of his attention to assess the readiness of his body. This can easily be done by constantly shifting the meeting point of your lines of force on his body (coming from your arms or hands, hips, etc.). His attention may be able to assess if he is ready to deal with any particular pattern of pressure but if that pattern shifts slightly and regularly, his attention will be worn out quickly. You don't want to shift it enough to throw your own body off - the smaller the shifts the better. As you practice this you will begin to vividly feel how his attention panics and his body tenses when you shift the pressure and how his attention tries to re-assess the situation. The grappling game is then played on the basis of attacking his attention rather than his body.

When common sense is applied to grappling, we can easily deal with the strongest opponent. Rather than fight back against the pressures, we examine the nature of those pressures and neutralize them. In one technique we can imagine the pressure as a line drawn through the body. The line starts at the opponent's hand or arm, where he is applying the pressure and then continues in the direction of the pressure. Each of his hands or arms is exerting a pressure that creates a line of force. You feel where those two lines will meet within your body and then relax that point. You only need to relax about one inch of muscle.

When the point at which the pressures meet relaxes, the opponent's force is neutralized. The skill is to relax just that exact point and to not relax more than about an inch of muscular area. Once the opponent is neutralized, you can do what you want with him.

The meeting point of the pressures shows you how you resist the force of the opponent with your own tension. You can then more easily let go of the resistance. The opponent depends on your resistance to control you.

Yet the remaining muscles of your body maintain their firmness to keep the body's structure intact. You do not simply collapse your body but strategically relax only the meeting point of the lines.

In our everyday lives we are faced with many pressures – financial, emotional, etc. The meeting point of those pressures show how we fight against the pressure. If we imagine ourselves as victims in a world battling against us, we will wear ourselves out. We can just as easily ask ourselves, "What is this pressure telling me? Why am I battling against the pressure?" I have found that the reason most people feel pressured in life is that they are unwilling to change as they go through life. Perhaps they feel they are entitled to a certain high standard of life and resent having to control their spending. "The other guy can buy these things so why shouldn't I be entitled to do the same?"

Perhaps you demand certain patterns of behavior from other people. After all, you are entitled to be treated in the manner to which you would like to become accustomed. You want the world to conform to your expectations and it usually doesn't.

We punch and kick at the same time. We do not just get the kicks out of the way and then punch. The punch sets up the kicks and the kicks set up the punches. Our legs must be as flexible and manipulative in their movements as our arms. Most of the kicks are to the opponent's legs but we may also use our leg to create a false floor by just pressing it into his leg and then punching him. Kicking his legs undermines his root and makes him feel insecure, afraid to advance.

An arm may dangle loosely in front and then strike downward on top of the opponent's head or circle around to the side of the head. When the fist comes in loosely and compresses with the impact, it is protected against the hard skull. The compression of the fist prevents the hand bones from breaking. You also have to bend the elbow at the moment of impact to protect the elbow and shoulder. If it is blocked, the arm can maneuver around the block. When kicked, we move in to the side of the kick to punch or hold under his leg to throw him. If he kicks to our head, we drop and kick his supporting leg. We may combine some grappling with punching and kicking at the same time. In all cases we never lock ourselves up. The grappling technique may last as little as one second just to throw off his balance.

With decentralized attention, in which each part of the body has awareness, several techniques can be performed at the same time. It is as if you were several people fighting against one person. If you have to fight against several people, then it is even – because you *are* several people, all rolled into one.

Our bodies represent the entire history of our species that originally evolved from many species of single celled animals joining together into multi-cellular animals like us. It is the history of all the symbiotic compromises among the cells that allow them to live in harmony with each other.

When we reproduce, this whole cellular community is concentrated into a packet of information – the reproductive cell. The combination of a male and female cell then reproduces the entire cellular ecological community with all its interactions.

The moment of impact of a strike or a push is a time of great awareness for us. It is the time when the dynamics of the body are compressed into a packet of energy to be reproduced within the sparring partner. The resultant force explodes into the opponent's body – a little pulse that rapidly expands, just like the growth of a baby. In this way the punch represents that ability of nature to compress a history of events into a tiny packet and allow it to expand in a similar pattern into the future.

If such histories of activities can be compressed into a tiny package, then the martial artist can compress the dynamics of his body into very small movements and still retain the same power. He doesn't have to make a big show with his fighting but can remain calm and relaxed. This gives away less information to his opponent. It allows him to move more intricately because each change in his movement is smaller and takes less time.

This makes him faster – able to make more adjustments per second than his opponent. If he can adjust much more often than his opponent, then the latter is basically motionless compared to him.

The fist comes in without being completely tight so that it can feel the opponent's balance, resistance, etc. and feed that information back to the body. The body then realigns itself to better place its force in relation to the opponent. Each joint of the body adjusts to create the most direct line of force from the root into the opponent's body. So there is a history (short as it may be) of the alignment and compression of all parts of the body.

This is similar to the compression of the entire cellular community into a reproductive cell. Just as the male and female cells join in reproduction, the force of the strike has a male and female component. The male component is the generated force. The female component is the yielding of each joint of your body to the resistance of the opponent, to align itself with him so that your force moves cleanly through your body and is released into him..

As the body aligns itself into the punch it must feel how the opponent is preparing to resist or neutralize the punch. The body then compresses in such a way that the resultant expansion can overcome the resistances. This is done by a constant realignment of the body as the punch is carried out. The moment of the impact is alive with interactions.

The advantage a student of this system has over others is this type of training of attention. He may not be big or strong, but his attention is strong and accurate.

On the other side of the moment of impact, that force which was compacted must now expand into the other person to create its effect. The Tai-chi-Chuan punch is not felt on the surface. It penetrates and explodes inside

In hard styles of martial arts, this is not the case. A punch is sent out. If it lands – good, if not – too bad. Try again. But one does not pay attention to the intricacies of the feeling of the moment of impact. The hard stylist's attention cannot perceive that quickly, let alone respond in that fraction of a second.

That is what the Taoists did when the Tai-chi form was invented. They took the entire wealth of their knowledge and compressed it into a short series of movements. It is the job of a teacher to allow the wisdom compressed within the form, to expand into the student and create a new teacher. It is like "unzipping" a computer file.

Students have difficulty practicing the form in class when I stop to correct them. It is hard to get back into the flow of the form. We practice "reproducing" the entire complex of muscular and joint movements and the flow of momentum from a dead start in the middle of a form. It is hard enough to pay attention to this complexity without being interrupted. But at a certain point in your training you should be able to initiate the proper mechanics of all the individual parts of the body "at once" as if you weren't interrupted.

The "packet of information" when doing this exercise is your body memory of how the form feels at that point and how it flows to the next position. You are copying the mechanics of the reproductive cycle in your attention. Now, when you practice the form straight through, you will be aware of the entire complexity of each moment of the form without interfering with the flow.

While sparring, one "eye" is on the inside and one on the outside. Our efficiency depends on feeding information from our senses to all parts of the body and then making sure that our ideas, attitudes and programmed behavior patterns get out of the way. There may be some areas of the body that are closed to our awareness. While we may not be able to penetrate this area with our attention at this time, it is important just to notice that it is closed as you practice (and not have a negative attitude about that). Use the metaphor of gently inviting it into awareness – into the "inside and outside" connection. You may need to spar very slowly at first to keep track of all this and you will need a willing sparring partner to slow down.

VANTAGE POINT

We train to respond to force by allowing attention (and the body) to sink by feeling the force of gravity. If each muscle and joint sinks one inch, then the overall movement of the body is only one inch down. It might seem that you would add all the individual sinking and get several inches of sinking. But each joint sinks in such a way that it is better aligned. Each muscle really lengthens. The real effect is that the attention is now oriented upward to the partner's force, meeting that force from underneath. This undermines the incoming force because all of your actions are in relationship to separating the opponent's actions from the ground, like digging up a weed. It is like putting your eyes on your hips or feet so they are looking upwards towards the action. These "eyes" create the pathway of Yang energy rising up and expanding into the partner's force, lifting the weed out of the ground.

Changing the origin of the "seat" of attention changes the energy dynamics of the interaction on a very subtle level. For most people this is impossible as the "seat" of their attention is in the head and will forever remain there. If you change your perspective you change the nature of any situation to suit your goals. When we first practice this principle in a physical exercise, it is easier to then apply it to daily life because you have developed the skill to move the "seat" of your attention more freely to get better "leverage".

The fluidity of the head in the form prevents the head from being used as a "floor" from which the thinking mind can be opinionated about everything. The head says, "Well, from where I stand it looks like this." Then don't stand there. Jesus said, "…The son of man has no place to lay his head." This is generally interpreted as meaning that he didn't live in any one house but traveled from place to place. I interpret it to mean that he didn't rest his head on any particular dogma from a religion but used his common sense and sense of humanity. He could see things from different vantage points. The more rigid the head is, the more stuck the person is. Free the head, in the quite literal sense of movement, and that will change the emotional rigidity. Yet freeing the head is a difficult part of Tai-chi training. It always wants to butt in.

The attention also sinks into the root along with the weight. Since the attention is "seated" into every muscle and joint of the body, the attention roots from every part of the body individually, providing a pathway for the physical sinking of the muscles. If the attention doesn't sink, the muscles won't sink either.

When attention sinks, it is like a mist sinking into the ground. You can then see the land before you. When attention sinks into the ground you can then see the reality of your being – you discover that which guides you. This doesn't mean that you lose consciousness. It means that you no longer isolate and contain consciousness but let it return to its nature, which is grounded but fluid movement.

The containing of consciousness is a battle. When the battle is over, consciousness returns to its home in your flesh and in the world around you. No one has won the battle; it's just good that it's over.

The greatest obstacle to achieving control and awareness of the mechanics of the body and attention is what I call the difficulty of achieving "nothing" ("wu"). Nothing is the word Tai-chi-Chuan uses to describe the feeling when everything is aligned and energy flows completely effortlessly through and out the body.

When everything is aligned you feel no pain, imbalance, tightness or resistance. You don't feel strong, angry, tough or weak. At first you feel nothing because you are unfamiliar with the experience of relaxed alignment. But then within that nothing, you begin to discern a very refined awareness of the body, attention and of the flow of energy. You realize that every part of the body has intelligence and awareness; that each part of your body is able to connect with the other person and to respond to his intentions before they turn into actions.

The sinking of attention into the body is really an emptying of programmed patterns of thinking. In other words, it is an emptying of the cup of tea as in Zen meditation. When you empty your cup of programmed thinking, you are then able to really "see" the internal energy, which connects all things together. To someone filled with excess patterns of thinking, emptying the cup may seem like there is nothing left. How can one function if your thinking machine is not constantly churning?

When that cup is emptied of tea, it is really being filled with air; it is never really empty. When your mind is emptied of constant thinking it is filled with awareness of the body's intelligence. The body is aware of how to maintain its proper structure and flexibility. It is aware of how to coordinate the interaction of the fascia, ligaments, tendons, muscles and skeleton at every moment for maximum power.

Lead your partner into your center (pelvis and lower abdominal area) when practicing Push Hands. From there you can make slight adjustments in the angle of your hips to lead him off balance. If his force is connected to your center then you are controlling the action from the center of your body. Imagine you are picking up a heavy metal pipe. If you pick it up from one end, it seems heavy. Pick it up from the center and it seems light because it is balanced.

When you connect the partner's force to your center and work from there, you need much less effort and movement. This requires that your attention works from that same center. Your attention then expands into his body followed by your energy as you breathe in for the push.

With beginning students of Tai-chi form, the head and eyes lead and pull the body with them. In extreme cases, the head is far forward of the body throughout the form. A basic principle of Tai-chi is that the center of the body leads. The "Tan-tien" is a spot just below the navel at the center of the body. That is the center of the center. When you move, the center moves first and then the rest of the body follows as if someone were pulling your belt. The head and hands move last. The center then becomes the new "head". It is the center of attention and initiation of movement. This gradually re-distributes the attention away from the head and into the body. When the attention is more evenly distributed, the body more easily becomes aligned properly. The center of gravity sinks and the back relaxes (although the legs get more of a workout).

You can't easily let go of the concentration of attention in the head. Just paying attention to the center, for example, doesn't work because you are paying attention to the center *from* the head and that just re-enforces the head. By moving the center first in your form, Push Hands or other exercises, the center becomes more aware. Its attention strengthens. At a certain point it doesn't need to be directed from the head. When you have an action to perform, the center knows what to do and takes charge. Each part of the body is trained to be aware and this eases the clog of attention in the head. The consciousness of each part of the body feels confident that it can do the job itself.

THE FLOOR

Push Hands and sparring can be very emotional. If the thinking mind is engaged it can stir up emotions and become more engaged in the emotions than in the real action. This will cause abrupt, tense movements. If you pay attention to the fluidity of your movements, your emotions will join with that fluidity rather than with your thinking mind. This will unlock your emotional state from the mind. Emotions will then arise from the consciousness of the body. Switching your "floor" of action from the thinking mind to the body, changes the nature of your emotions from fear and resistance to excitement and joy of action.

Our "floor" is the principles of Tai-chi which involve fluidity (and of course the floor beneath your feet). Release your emotions through you and out into the world. When momentum flows fluidly through the body, you can easily notice the resistances that interfere with that momentum. The method of connecting emotions back to the "real" world is to first connect them to the flow of momentum, which is part of the physical world. Then you notice how the thinking mind wants to grab those emotions and control them. If the thinking mind were purely benign and spiritual that might not be a problem. But "making" the mind spiritual is a foolhardy endeavor in my opinion. It is too tricky of an opponent.

Momentum is more trustworthy. It either flows or it doesn't. When your emotions are part of that momentum and your practice is to dissolve the resistances to the fluidity, you are "taming" the mind without directly confronting it.

The term, "floor" also refers to that part of the body that serves as the origin of a strike. This should always be the real floor, the one you are standing on, but it rarely ever is. In Tai-chi-Chuan the force begins at the bottom of the foot then upwards along the inside of the leg, the hips, the Tan-tien, then the elbow (in a punch) and then to the fist. Your force should never rise above elbow level.

If you tighten your back and shoulders and punch with your arm, the floor is the back of your shoulder. If you twist your waist abruptly and turn the upper part of the body in a snap, then the floor is your waist.

The floor is obviously not the back of the shoulder or the waist. It is that relatively flat surface beneath your feet. Any mechanics not based on that reality is a false mechanics.

There is also such a thing as semi-false mechanics. You start your force from the feet and then perhaps up the inside of the legs but then skip the hips and the Tan-tien and go right to the back of the shoulder. In this case you are skipping some of the essential steps and adding irrelevant ones.

In Push Hands, each partner tries to create "false floors" in the partner. This is very simple to do because it is so difficult for a student to keep to the true floor. All you have to do is apply a very small amount of pressure (a few ounces) to any part of the partner's body. He will press back to oppose your force and that will cut him off from the ground. His mechanics will then begin from the point of your pressure. That point will become the new floor.

The proper response to pressure is relaxing the part being pressed, not opposing the pressure. We practice relaxing each muscle individually so that our response can be specific. We don't want to move the entire body away from the pressure, just that part which is being pressed on. In this way our movements can be small, exact and quick. While relaxing that part of the body, your attention moves into the partner, towards the origin of the pressure. This helps to align each of your joints towards the force so that you are ready to send out your own force. The force you received from the partner by relaxing can be added to your own force as you push.

The force used in creating the false floor must be light enough to escape his notice but strong enough to elicit a subconscious response of resistance. This can obviously be used in grappling as well.

Position yourself as a wedge between your partner and the floor with no frozen part of the body in between. There is a tendency to freeze your attention in order to push. This is a difficult issue to learn about on your own and requires a competent teacher. This is "the round of birth and death" (of the attention). It is similar to the issue of "telegraphing". You feel you must solidify your attention in order to act. Push Hands teaches you to maintain the fluidity of your body and of your attention at all times.

Your fluid patterns of movement are also a floor in the sense that any action must come from the flow of motion. If you disrupt a pattern of motion in order to prepare for a strike, you become disconnected from the interaction and the floor beneath you. That punch, from your root to your fist, cannot disrupt the patterns of fluid movement of the body. Those patterns, resulting from the interplay of the partners, are in a creative relationship with the release of force, so that each joint participates in that release. You are taught the mechanics of how the minute changes in each joint all over the body, work to magnify the force that is released into the partner – all within a very short space of time. You come to experience the creativity of the joints and muscles and learn to trust it.

Excess tension disrupts the conscious connection of all parts of the body that creates fluidity. The back is often the victim of this tension. This is the origin of many back problems and back pain. Since our attention is directed forward there is a tendency to feel that your back should be your solid base and the front of the body should be the area of activity. Even when we step, there is a tendency to lock the hips and back as this gives you the feeling of more stability. It is as if the more tense your body is, the more balanced it will be. This of course, is not true physiologically. In order to stay balanced, every part of the body must be fluid and functional to constantly adjust to the changes of balance as you step. The intricate awareness of how to use all the joints of the body at the same time is what keeps you in balance.

The back should never be used as a solid base. If your back is tense, then your front cannot move very well either. The back is connected to the front. We say that the back (and every other part of the body) should be like the hands. This means that we are used to fine manipulation with our hands. Every part of the body should have the same intricate sensitivity as the hands.

It is only the floor itself that should be solid. In the self-defense applications, power comes from expanding the legs downward into the ground. Since the ground doesn't move, this action causes a reaction of the rest of the body to expand upward and outward. Other forces are added to this such as shifting forward and turning so that you have several forces lining up to deliver the punch or kick.

In everyday life, the health benefits of staying loose are obvious. But we have this same locking behavior mentally as well. Zookinesis training teaches us that most people freeze a large part of their attention and their internal energy to serve as a sort of attention and energy base. This is a difficult thing to discover about yourself but when you do, it becomes obvious.

In the "jolt of thought" exercise, for example, the words translating the initial "jolt" is like a base. The jolt itself may be too fluid and alive for most people to "work with".

The label, the translation, is a safe, solid base that does not require much attention on your part. It also neatly fits into all of your mental programming. Just as we consider the patterns of movement to be a sort of base, one that should not be locked, we use the living intricacy of the jolt of thought as our living base, rather than using words. This provides a different experience of interacting with other people as you cannot plan what you want to say. It must come from the true awareness of what you feel.

LEVERAGE

I have always strategized how to use my life for the greatest leverage for positive goals. When I was a zoologist, I discovered a beautiful lizard called the leopard gecko. It has such physical beauty and such a great, friendly attitude that I felt it would be a great ambassador of nature. At the time there were only a handful in the country, so I contacted someone in Pakistan and imported a thousand of them over ten years.

Over those years I developed methods of captive breeding and promoted the breeding of this lizard. Then I went on to other things. A few years later the cricket breeding company that supplied crickets for my animals started breeding leopard geckos and soon many more people got involved. Now they are the most widely bred lizards in the country, supplying the pet industry. It is important for the pet industry to use captive bred animals, first of all so they are healthier but more importantly, so we don't keep taking animals out of the wild. Now there are leopard gecko clubs with thousands of members and those people really love their leopard geckos! My goal was to get people to love nature.

Each of us can find ways to exert a little leverage in our culture to move it in a positive direction. We can learn the principles of leverage in Push Hands. Grandmaster William Chen loves to work with leverage and has even crafted his form over the years to emphasize that principle.

The fulcrum can be placed anywhere in the body so that any part of the body can provide the leverage, like a clam using its upper shell to push you as it opens, so long as its lower shell remains grounded. We can create leverage with any part of our lives at any time; especially by the way we treat other people. Even the aliveness of our bodies can affect other people, calling to their Body-Minds – "the Body-Mind in this body became powerful and so could yours!" Consciousness can receive that visual message as it flows in through the eyes and moistens the dry earth of a "dead" body. You may not know whose Body-Mind got the message and began its triumphant return, but you can be assured that the message gets transmitted.

In Push Hands, we fill the spaces between our partner and us by moving parts of our body towards those spaces. This grounds our body in the center of the interaction. From there we use leverage. The concept of the fulcrum holds true, not only within our body, but in the space between the partners as well. The fulcrum can be placed anywhere because the issue is how the dynamics of your body are interacting with the partner. If the center of that interaction is within your body, in the space between you or even within the partner's body, that creates different types of leverage. This is the art of the game. This teaches us how interconnected we all are.

When the perspective ("seat" of attention) of one person or culture changes, this changes the whole attitude of the person (or culture). Changing the perspective is like changing the rules of the game in your favor. It is more powerful than if you argue back and forth within the same perspective.

You can engage in a Push Hands interaction in which you are both using one particular fulcrum and then you suddenly switch the fulcrum to another spot. The partner is then in the wrong position for the movements he is involved in at the moment. He had better take that switch into consideration or he would be thrown. The switching of fulcrums strengthens the attention and helps functionally connect the attention and body.

It is like someone arguing with you and the expression of your face suggests you will argue back. He argues more and more forcefully and then you say, "I think the same way". That would certainly have an effect on him. Then you might say, "But I also think..." In this case he has become destabilized by your agreement so that your counter "argument" has more power. The purpose is not to manipulate another person but to steer the conversation to relaxed reasonableness.

In Push Hands, you might suddenly yield to the partner's force so he falls into the "hole" and then switch your leverage to push him in a different direction. Your yielding destabilizes the partner. But before you yield you have already prepared to set up your alternative direction of leverage.

That may sound mean, but it helps the partner realize his weaknesses. You have to be aware of what is going on every second and not be too attracted to your own plans. If during one second the partner yields, you switch your leverage. It is played second by second and that strengthens the attention and increases the flexibility and responsiveness of the body. It makes you aware of what is happening in the real world more than living in the patterns of your mind.

ENERGY
Each muscle lines up with incoming force so it is in an efficient position. This cannot be done mentally; it has to be trained into the

muscles. Each muscle has its own line of force and they "dance" to maintain those lines during the interaction. Their ability to individually respond increases efficiency and also stimulates their innate intelligence. Particular muscles will "kick in" to manipulate the incoming force very cleverly, without your thinking mind's involvement. It is a "dance" the thinking mind can sit by and watch as an audience.

This is similar to an audio speaker that contains several speakers within it. I have an old "Criterion 6" speaker with 6 speakers within the cabinet. Each is efficient to reproduce sound within a specific range of frequencies. When I had to replace the midrange speakers within it, they had to be that specific model of speaker that would receive and reproduce the specific range of frequencies it was designed for.

At the moment of impact of the punch or kick, we do not lock the body but realign the joints as described above, using the feedback received from the initial moment of impact. The fist comes in loosely and compresses with the impact. That compression controls the re-alignment of the puncher's entire body. The moment of impact is only a fraction of a second yet our resolution of perception is fine enough to make that small amount of time seem large enough to make these changes.

The larger that fraction of a second seems to us, the more changes we will be able to make per second. If we have eight turns per second and the opponent only one turn per second, we will easily win. The goal of the sparring then becomes the development of perception and the refinement of attention. It would therefore be beneficial for anyone from any style to learn this system and then to adapt the internal skills to his particular techniques.

If you perceive your body as a system of joints suspended in rubbery connective tissue, force can be re-directed easily. In grappling, the change of a single joint can entirely change the relationship of force between the combatants. There is always a free joint somewhere that can be moved. This is preferable to merely applying more and more force in a relationship that is not in your favor. As you can see, these same principles also apply to one's personal life as well.

It is important to recognize and utilize the unique characteristics of the connective tissue (or "fascia"), including the ligaments and tendons. Together these tissues form a rubbery network, similar to the rubber "spider's web" found in many playgrounds.

If you try climbing up a ladder and compare that to climbing up this "spider's web" you can begin to understand the difference between sparring against an external vs. an internal martial artist. The internal arts make great use of the rubbery parts of the body. The strikes are shot out like an arrow out of a bow. The opponent's strikes are received like a trampoline "receiving" a falling person.

One of the problems one can develop with the emphasis on tension in the external martial arts is the tightening of the fascia. This tissue, surrounding all the organs, muscles and bones, can be very confining and destructive if it is too tight.

Even people who can do a full split may have tight fascia in most parts of their bodies. The ligaments in their legs may in fact, be too loose, causing a hyper mobility of the joints (and loss of stability and springiness). The fascia can be loosened with certain types of stretching (using a foam roller and exercise ball for example) and by massage.

When the fascia, ligaments and tendons are not over-tight, when they are rubbery and flexible, then each joint can move freely and independently. You can also feel the alignment of the body through the structure of the fascia and not just though the alignment of the skeletal structure. This gives you a whole new range of biomechanics to work with within your body and to take advantage of in the opponent's body.

The earth is solid. Heaven is gaseous. Align the body in such a way that all of your weight sinks into the earth. The legs are heavy with weight and the top of the body is very light. The hips are in-between so they feel rubbery. The hips connect the lightness on top to the heaviness on bottom. While "loose lips" may sink ships (a World War 2 saying), loose hips relax the whole back that then relaxes the shoulder area and the neck.

When students are finally able to move their hips they say, "I feel for the first time that I actually have hips". I suggest that as they do a form, that they drop the lower front ribs to the hips as they sink and breathe out. As they breathe in and rise, they should relax the rear part

400

of their lower ribs towards the back part of the hips. The lower ribs then act as a see-saw. This starts to bring the mobility of the hips into the upper body. It also helps to eliminate a lot of back pain. If you try this, it is important to keep the rest of the upper body stable as you "rock" the lower ribs towards the hips. Each rib can move independently and separating the activity of the lower ribs from the rest of the ribs is important in bringing mobility to the ribs.

There is a tendency, when force is applied to you, to tense up on top, bringing your weight upwards. Think of yourself as a pyramid. You have a wide base on bottom. Your head is like the point of the pyramid. When someone pushes you on top, your chest for example, they feel that there is nothing there; that most of you is underneath their push.

A new student wondered about the "magic" of the use of chi (internal energy). He wanted to be able to knock someone down at a distance by holding up his hand. There are several ways to approach this issue. The main point is, why do you want to be able to knock someone down? What are the inadequacies in yourself that cause you to want to be able to knock other people down? The second point is that these teachings require very detailed, long-term study. The mechanics of chi are very exacting and specific. The relationship between chi and the physical body takes years of study and practice to understand, feel and master. When the term "magic" is used, it generally means, "How can I do this without any effort on my part?" It is a sign of laziness. You just want to be able to use a magic word, for example, and not put in the years of study. So a real student would need to examine his tendency toward laziness. Magic is only magic when you don't understand the mechanisms behind the result.

I met a couple of teachers who claimed that they could knock someone over at a distance. They even demonstrated it on their own students. But onlookers insisted that they do the same with them. The teachers did not want to demonstrate their skills on anyone but their own students. After much insistence these teachers did try to demonstrate this "chi at a distance" on others but failed.

The point is that this chi at a distance is a training exercise. The student must be very sensitive to the teacher's chi. When the student feels this chi, he allows his body to move according to the characteristics of the chi he feels. The chi doesn't knock him over but the student cooperates via his reaction to the chi.

There is great magic in chi training. It is not the magic of seeing great things and not knowing how they happened. It is the magic of being able to see simple things and know how they happened.

When an experienced teacher practices his form, the onlooker will see the slightest movements with barely any effort used. A beginner at learning a Tai-chi form will use exaggerated movements and seem to use a lot of effort and tension. Most onlookers will think the beginner's Tai-chi is spectacular because it is big and "loud". The experienced teacher barely looks as though he is doing anything and is not very exciting.

Magic in this case would consist of being able to see the incredible control of internal movement (within the body) resulting in such slight external movement (movement of the body in space) of the experienced teacher. Magic is the ability to see the great in the insignificant. It is the ability to let go of all the habits of tension, mental patterns and chi blockage to arrive at the simple, natural state of being. Magic, in the real sense, should not be a compensation for feelings of inadequacy that appeal to your laziness.

Another point that was brought up dealt with acupuncture points. I was taught that every point on and within the body is an acupuncture point. Every cell and even every part of every cell is a center for the *transformation* of energy, not just for the *generation* of energy. The acupuncture points that you see on the charts are just useful points for healing purposes. If you work a specific point it will have a specific result. But this doesn't mean that only those spots marked on the charts are acupuncture points. I believe that in any good Oriental healing school this point is brought out. But the students often fail to appreciate or even to hear it. Many such students think that chi only runs through the meridians and not everywhere throughout the whole body. My teachers emphasized that chi must flow through every organ and cell of the body.

BREATHING

"The form begins with the breath." You will hear the old teachers say this. As I move to my right, the right lung fills first and then the left, shaping the movement of the body as a balloon assumes its shape when filled with air. The breath fills the bottom of the lungs first, then the middle, then the top. It fills the back as well as the front of the lungs. There is a lot of disagreement about proper breathing among Tai-chi teachers, from those who say breathing doesn't matter to those who consider breath to be the center of their teachings. I am of the latter group.

As with the reaction to conflict, breath is intimately tied to emotion. If there are problems with one, there are surely problems with the other, and there are also surely health problems. The "clamshell breathing" I teach helps heal these problems.

Clamshell breathing starts with the diaphragm pulling down, inflating the lower part of the lungs first. Next the lower ribs expand which inflates the center of the lungs. Finally, the upper ribs expand which inflates the upper part of the lungs. This assumes that the diaphragm works well and the ribs (and intercostals muscles) are flexible enough to move sequentially. The back and front of the lungs fill together so that the in-breath also expands the lower, then middle, then upper back.

When practicing form, the first expansion, in which the diaphragm presses down, "presses the breath" into the legs, grounding you and creating a balancing force up through the body. Grandmaster Chen compared this to stepping on a rubber ball. The pressure of the compressed ball then radiates upward through the body. When you spar, pressing the forward leg down to the root provides power for the punch or kick. It's like when you press your legs down to jump.

Expanding the center of the lungs (and the lower ribs) connects you to the partner in front of you in Push Hands, destabilizing him. The upper breath releases your force into the partner, sending him off balance. So the push is really just about breathing in. The breath is called, the "soft bones" because it provides solidity to your mechanics.

The breathing principles are part of leverage. Your diaphragmatic breath (the lower breath) is like the clam anchoring the lower section of shell on the ground. Then the foot can come out (middle breath) and the upper shell lifts up (upper breath). The hinge of the shell is the fulcrum. The "seat" of your attention acts as the fulcrum. As force moves up to your Push Hands interaction, more force moves down to add to the grounding. As force moves up and to the left a counterbalancing force moves down and to the right, creating that barbershop pole spiraling energy. Where you place the fulcrum is important in creating the right leverage.

Breathing in when you exert is very difficult for most people. That is because they don't breathe fully and in a way that is connected to the earth. So to teach Tai-chi-Chuan it is essential to teach proper breathing. It is also essential for physical and emotional health. Just as breath leads the movements of the body in form, it leads you to greater health.

People normally associate issuing force with breathing out and condensing, as if you were posing for a bodybuilding contest. If you condense while striking, you compress the force within your own body and it doesn't move into the partner's body. Breathing out is also associated with a relaxing mode, ready to lie down. The Tai-chi-Chuan strike is like an explosion – a rapid expansion of air. It is like the sudden expansion of a car air bag, pushing you back so your head doesn't hit the steering wheel. You breathe out right after the strike.

The goal is to generate force in an explosive way and then to release all the force into the opponent, leaving nothing behind. Striking is a result of the explosive expansion and is therefore associated with breathing in. We do not tighten the force within our bodies but release the force as an archer releases the arrow. The arrow does not generate the force; it just transmits the force of the bow. Our arms do not generate the force of the strike; they just transmit the force of the whole body.

When you take in a full breath of air with each inhalation you are in an emotional state of "I can do anything". If your breath is only half full you are hesitant. If you force air out you are in the emotional state of locking yourself up (and locking others out).

When we strike, the breath both presses our legs into the ground and sends out the arm, creating a wedge between the ground and the "opponent". Since the earth isn't going to move, the force shoots into the opponent. All of our joints are lined up with that line of force from the ground to the opponent going through the Tan-tien (preferably at a 45° angle which is most efficient).

The body is not completely tensed at the moment of impact. It tenses only enough to prevent the arm or leg from collapsing and allow the force to flow through. Less tension is needed than you might think. You absorb the partner's resistance and add it to your force, as described before. The power flows through so smoothly that you hardly feel as though you are striking. The other person feels it, though.

It is very difficult to do all this in a fraction of a second. There is no time to think about it. Yet when you organize it from the breath, it is much easier. The breath becomes the control panel to organize all these forces and mechanics. It is like the expanding car air bag, pushing you back into your seat and absorbing the force of your body into its expansion. Any preconceived ideas and assumptions which vie for control of your behavior, show up very clearly. They interfere with the breath.

As you train, you examine your assumptions and the effect they have on proper body mechanics. You also examine how improving your breathing process affects those assumptions. Imagine seeing someone thrown fifteen feet across the room with your punch or push simply because you were relaxing more and breathing properly. That would affect your assumptions, especially the one about the more tense you get the more powerful you are.

The control of body mechanics through breathing is similar to picking up a long pipe at the central balancing point rather than at the end. Breathing is the balance "point" of focusing our attention that gives us the most control and power. It is the medium through which Yin and Yang interpenetrate.

In order to explain this last sentence, I would ask you to try an exercise. It is easiest to do seated. Breathe in and allow your attention to be completely on the breath. Notice the speed and momentum with which the breath moves in. Allow your attention to flow into the body from the ground and out your back as you breathe in, and at the same pace as the breath. Your breath and attention are timed to each other.

Allow your attention to keep flowing out your back as your in-breath slows and then, as you begin to breath out, begin a new flow of attention down back to the ground through your legs WHILE THE FIRST WAVE OF ATTENTION IS STILL FLOWING OUT YOUR BACK. Your attention will be like waves in the ocean, some water flowing forward and some back at the same time. Keep doing this so that the waves of attention, to and fro, blend with each other and become continuous - a continuous flowing cycle of attention.

Breathing is the balance point between the spirit world and the physical world, between the sense of chi and the sense of sight. It allows the interpenetration of the two worlds and the two senses. It is easy to balance the two worlds from the control panel of breathing.

And when they are balanced, the spirit can fly. In this exercise, the interpenetration of the inward and upward flowing energy (the energy flowing from the ground, into the body and out the back) (Yang) and the downward, grounding energy (Yin) provides the power, the "lift" for the spirit's wings. When these two energies flow through each other, they are like a strong, steady wind that keeps the "eagle" aloft with little effort.

There are basic movements of energy through our bodies. One is Yang energy flowing upward and Yin energy flowing downward. Another set of Yin/Yang energy flows is spherical. The Yang energy moves outward from the center and the Yin energy moves into the center. These two flows interact with each other and with the movements of the body. Many Zookinesis exercises play with these interactions of energy for healing or to help you become more aware of the spirit world.

When you turn and breathe in, the body expands in the front along the diagonal, from the front of the rear hip to the opposite front of the shoulder. The rear diagonal (along the back) from the same hip to the same opposite shoulder, relaxes so that the bottom of the shoulder blade sinks closer the tailbone. When you turn and breathe out, the rear diagonal expands and the front diagonal relaxes. The tailbone always seeks the heel of the weighted foot so every part of the body is connected to the root.

Beginning students are taught to sink their attention to the earth on the out-breath and allow attention to lift to "heaven" on the in-breath. Later they will allow the flow of attention in all directions at all times. It is important to point out that you are not pushing your attention down or up because that implies a vantage point from which you push. Even the vantage points (such as attention in the head) must sink and rise so that eventually attention can move freely. To emphasize again – this is not the same as "paying attention to" something. Attention is freed so there is no longer a master/slave relationship between the thinking mind (which manipulates attention) and attention itself.

When you breathe in, your diaphragm pulls downward. So the initiation of an in-breath feels like breathing down into the ground, pressing into the root. The bottom of the belly (below the navel) expands downwards. When the maximum downward breathing pressure is reached, then the breath expands forward and the upper belly expands (above the navel). Finally, the breath then fills the upper part of the lungs. So breathing in begins at the bottom (at the root). When you breathe out, you relax the bottom of the lungs first, then middle and upper lungs.

The body must go through the full range of densities in accordance with breathing. The legs are heavy, the top light and the middle in-between. In the same sense, the first part of the clamshell breathing (into the lower belly) must be strong, the top of the breath (into the chest) very light and the upper belly in the middle should be in-between in strength.

The arms, legs and head move as a result of the breathing and the sequential expansion and relaxation of the joints. They don't move by their own muscular power. But of course, you have to hold the arms and legs in particular positions according to your postures. You use the minimum energy possible to hold the arms in their positions, just enough so that if you used just a little less, the arms would fall.

If your front expands, the back relaxes. If the right expands, the left relaxes. If the bottom energizes downwards, the top floats upwards. Each part of the body counterbalances its other side. This gives rise to the expression "power is a directed relaxation". This means that relaxing releases power, but that power does not just dissipate. The breath directs the power. If you breathe downward and forward, for example, the power roots and from that root, moves forward. If you breathe into the right side of your lungs, the energy moves right. But if you first breathe into the upper part of the lungs, the energy pulls you up out of your root.

ROTATION

The smallest changes in how we use our bodies can lead to much greater health, physical skill and longevity.

The body is affected by the breath so that it lifts with the in-breath and relaxes with the out-breath. This results in a vertical undulation of the body, yet the center (the "Tan-tien") remains at the same level.

In the form you are turning from side to side as you move. If you combine the undulation with the turning you will get a spiraling twist of the body that includes the spine, like the effect of a barbershop rotating pole. This action not only stretches each muscle and joint - it stretches it as it twists, resulting in a very flexible yet strong body.

We often mistake moving a joint around in space for moving the joint itself. For example, if we wanted to push, we might thrust our hip forward rather than rotating the joint in place while keeping the position of the joint stable. The sequential movement of the joints within the body, along with the even expansion of the breath, leads to greater force than just throwing your joint at the object you want to push.

But it is hard to feel the difference between these two actions, let alone to sequentially move the joints in the proper order to perform the task. This issue is at the heart of learning any sport or activity. The human body is designed to be very powerful in the intricacy of its movement. We tend to substitute brute physical force for the lack of fine motor coordination.

Your attention needs to be within the joint itself to move it properly. Too often we think of a joint as "over there" because our attention is in our head. Human beings can move the center of our attention within a part of the body to make it function properly. This is an essential part of Tai-chi training.

I call the low back the "control panel" because its flexibility is essential in initiating any movement. Even the sacrum, whose bones are fused, should be flexible and the coccyx bone (last bone of the spine) should be very active in your movements. But most people have frozen hips and low backs. All their attention to movement is in the upper body. While the thoracic spine is much more capable of twisting than the lumbar spine, we train to bring as much flexibility to the lumbar spine as possible.

In Tai-chi, movement begins at the center of the body and then emanates out into the rest of the torso, legs, arms and head. It is like dropping a pebble into a calm lake. Waves then ripple out in all directions. This keeps the movements centered and the body stable.

The chi-gung system, Zookinesis, is very effective for developing awareness of and flexibility of the center of the body. There are many exercises that create specific patterns of movement or vibration at the center, which you then allow to flow out through the rest of the body.

When you shift from back to front the pelvis acts as a shovel. It first circles back as you shift back, then digs in towards the ground as you begin to shift forward (breathing out). Then it lifts forward as you finish the shift (breathing in) as if you were throwing the dirt from the shovel on a pile in front of you. This rotation of the pelvis during shifting energizes the center of the body and provides grounding. It also allows the energy from the torso and legs to interact, so your efforts are more efficient. Even walking becomes easier.

An important step in developing decentralized attention is to develop the centers of rotation in the body. The body can move like a marionette. The puppeteer holds a crossed stick from which several strings attach to the parts of the marionette. The stick can be moved from left to right, tilted front to back, and tilted side to side. All the marionette's movements come from those movements of the crossed stick.

We make sure that each joint has a full range of motion appropriate for that joint. Then we practice moving two joints at a time, then three, in various patterns. The animal forms and Zookinesis exercises are based on this idea, especially tiger, snake, monkey and drunken. Grappling with someone who has developed an intricacy of body rotation is nearly impossible; it is like running on a floor covered with marbles. Striking such a person is also difficult; it is like grabbing the tail of a scurrying mouse, as described before, or like catching a fly in mid-air with chopsticks as you see in Kung-fu movies.

This flexibility and coordination also allow you to "lead" the force of a punch, which lands on your body, downward into the legs and from there into the ground. This is done by sequentially relaxing muscles from the point of impact to the legs. Thus, the incoming force simply compresses the body, coiling the "spring" even more. You can also use this received force to turn you, and send your own fist into the other person.

We imagine the body as an assortment of ball bearings (joints), which are either rotating or ready to rotate but never locked. Each joint can move independently to adjust the angles of the body according to the movements. When you "receive" force from the opponent, that force moves into the rotating joints as if you punched into a container of plastic balls. The force goes into the rotation of the balls or joints. The body then rotates, and the force returns to its source. With so many joints rotating, the force is magnified.

We can duck in one direction and circle our arm around to the other side to strike upwards to the opponent's head. With each part of the body moving with an independent quality, the opponent never knows how he will be punched or kicked.

Many Tai-chi teachers have read the "classics", which are the standard ancient writings about Tai-chi and Taoism. One of the principles is "whole body movement". By now you should realize that this means each joint and muscle moves in turn, beginning with the center, so that the body "oozes" from place to place. But some teachers interpret "whole body movement" as rigidity, in which there is no internal movement, but the body as a whole moves very smoothly through space as if you were moving a dead stick slowly and smoothly through space. That doesn't make the stick alive, though. Without actual experience, interpreting words can be tricky. Whole body movement means keeping Body-Mind alive.

A lot of times when we read ancient documents, we are not reading what the teacher himself (or herself) actually said. It may be what the student heard and wrote down. But if the student doesn't understand what he hears, he may not write it down accurately. A word or two out of place can make a big difference. When you read such a document you must take that into consideration. If you approach it with a genuine understanding, you will get more out of it than if you approach it to get the understanding in the first place.

YIN/YANG

There are many ways to thwart the sparring partner. Most fighters concentrate on the opponent's fists and feet and sometimes elbows and knees as well. But they don't concentrate on the space between the sparring partners. Proper Tai-chi training teaches you to move into the open spaces so that the opponent is jammed. You should be more interested in the spaces between you than in the strikes of the partner. Let his strikes trigger you to move into the open spaces where you can easily deliver your own strikes.

This requires that you don't keep running forward and back as with most styles of fighting. You stay in and don't allow the partner space to move or even time to relax and catch his breath.

Have you ever tried to lift a speck of dirt out of a cup of coffee with a spoon? The speck just flows around the spoon. Ducking and weaving speeds up the sparring because we do not block-punch, block-punch. Our strikes are continuous. Our attention focuses on the emptiness more than the opponent's strikes. If our attention were to move to his strikes, our attention would be in the most inferior position – right in front of the focal point of his force

An important principle in grappling is "Let Yang be Yang and Yin be Yin". This is an expression from Zookinesis training. It means that the Yang energy, which is expansive and energizing, should be allowed to fully express itself. The Yin energy, which is grounding, should be allowed to fully express itself. Imagine walking a dog on a leash. The dog pulls you forward, and you tug back on the leash to control the dog. If you let the leash go, the dog would run as fast as he could and feel very free and happy. You would be able to relax if you trust your dog's behavior. Letting go of the leash is "letting Yang be Yang". Relaxing is "letting Yin be Yin".

Don't pit Yin against Yang as when you are holding the dog back. If you do that throughout your life, one day your Yang energy will give out and your Yin energy will implode within you causing death. Rather, allow each energy its full expression and in that, seek balance.

Grappling is different than the dog on the leash situation because the grappler's force presses inward. In this case, seek balance by your Yang force filling the Yin areas of the opponent's body. This balance evens out the opponent's superior physical strength. You can press your body into areas where his feels empty. If a part of his body is condensed, it is empty of expansive energy and probably of attention as well. Allow your Yin force to be grounded by his physical force, bringing him into your foundation. This is "letting Yin be Yin". Allow your response to originate in your foundation to destabilize his alignment.

His Yang energy is now in your foundation so you can upset his whole body from there. Then it is a question of who has superior awareness. Will he use that connection to break your foundation or will you expand your foundation into his body?

411

Let him feel the pressure of the volcano in your foundation as Yang energy builds, and the endless depth and power of the magma is about to erupt. His force will be burned with only scattered cinders remaining and you will be in control. Then allow your Yang energy to be Yang. It will erupt by itself. You don't need to force it.

The mistake many grapplers make is to turn Yang energy into tension. In this case your Yang energy jumps within your own body, hardening it. Rather, allow your Yang energy only to jump within the opponent's body, leaving your body as relaxed as possible while still maintaining its structure. You will need very little physical movement.

Remember also that expanding Yang requires an in-breath into the lower part of the lungs, then sequentially up the lungs. You should not breathe out when Yang leaps out.

All of this requires a great deal of training of course. But the result is that when you are faced with everyday life you respond the way you are trained. You don't get rattled. You simply assess your own balance of energy, the other person's balance and make the most advantageous response that is usually the simplest. You let the other person fill their bodies, minds and emotions with only Yang energy, overcoming their Yin energy, while you remain balanced. And you don't wear yourself out by pitting Yin against Yang. This keeps you young and energized.

Letting the opponent's body express how strong it is, keeps him busy. We do not need to argue that point. Our job is to make him ineffective, not to battle with him.

Be a master of empty space. Matter is mostly empty space. The distance between atoms is vast. Take advantage of that by allowing your body to "occupy" the partner (energetically) and allowing his body to "occupy" you. Fill in the space, not only between you but also inside your partner. Inhabit the spaces.

Pay attention to the empty spaces, not the solid places. The emptiness is your power. Allow there to be emptiness inside of you (empty of attitude and resistance). The degree of independent movement of each part of the body determines the amount of "space" inside you.

HEALING

When you heal in Tai-chi massage, you are "looking for" all the stresses that led to the present state of the body. That state affects the way the client responds to each situation in life. It is a "packet of information" that the healer deciphers to serve as the basis of the healing.

These stresses arise from the culture in which that client was raised. So the "packet of information" has to also include an analysis of the history of the culture and its effect on its members. A study of history, sociology and anthropology is very useful in this type of healing.

Healing that culture is "real" healing for the individual and the larger culture. In each case the use of symbols or metaphors is used to guide people to a healthier state. In chi-gung for example, you might imagine the sun shining inside your Tan-tien and radiating its warmth throughout the body.

If we want to save a natural area, we might choose one animal within that area that is especially cute and cuddly, and focus on saving that animal. If we succeed then all the other animals and plants living there, which might not be as cute, will also be saved.

The metaphor serves to focus our attention. It can reach within us as if planting a little sunshine within our bodies and remind us that we are capable of feeling good. That is why I worked to bring the leopard gecko lizard into the pet industry. I felt its personality and beauty could represent all of nature and reach within our hearts.

A Tai-chi teacher uses whichever metaphors make sense to the student, keeping in mind the student's experiences and profession. Sometimes I throw out a few metaphors in a row until one clicks with the student. If the principles of Tai-chi have become embodied in you then you can use many metaphors as landmarks to guide the student along a path to the same goal.

Once the student is aware of the intricate relationship in her inner culture, the metaphor can resonate within every cell of the body, helping to heal it. Spending time in nature does the same. Awareness of the inner culture opens each cell to the influences of positive environments and images. It allows the inside and the outside to reflect each other. Opening and connecting is healing.

The evolution of animals leading to humans is a move towards less instinctual behavior and more of a requirement to learn and adapt, to use our creativity. If we instead, allow the programmed behavior patterns of our culture to take the place of instinct, we will miss the point of this trend in evolution. A certain amount of programming is needed to carry on our everyday activities conveniently but it shouldn't take the place of placing the seat of our attention, our vantage point, in creativity itself. In this way, the evolution of life will become a return to the source of creation.

We have been in a shell made of the way we have been programmed to perceive our relationship to the world around us. To be healed is to break that shell, peek out and realize that there is a larger world of which we are part. Just as a baby has to learn how to use his muscles and joints to move, we need to learn about the other "parts" of us to move within the larger world of life.

Tai-chi teaches us to dissolve the blockages to the flow of physical movement, energy and attention so we can grow in our connection to the world around us. The beginner is a point on the spiral staircase of life. The goal is to be the flow of life itself.

EPILOGUE

The word had gone out that there would be a gathering of all Tai-chi teachers who were interested, to meet on a 103-acre farm in Warwick, New York. The farm was owned by Master, Jou, Tsung-Hwa and he wanted it to serve as a center of learning for all Tai-chi teachers throughout the world.

I sat in the Zhang building that first day and looked around me. There were 35 Tai-chi teachers or so and I was amazed that so many teachers were in one place at one time. Master Jou explained that he wanted to have a festival each year to commemorate the birth of Chang, San-Feng, the legendary founder of Tai-chi-Chuan. We would invite all who were interested, throughout the world, and give workshops on the aspects of this art that we were interested in teaching.

From that day in 1984, the festival eventually grew to over 1,200 people per year. My wife and I gave our workshops each year and attended the workshops of the other teachers to get different points of view. After Master Jou's untimely death in 1998, the tradition continued at the property of one of his students, Bruce LaCarrubba, who was able to duplicate the essence of the Tai-chi Farm.

Each year, interest in Tai-chi grew throughout the country and the world. Many other Tai-chi get-togethers and organizations were organized and many approaches to this ancient art developed. After seeing and working with thousands of Tai-chi teachers and students, I

415

can report that this training attracts a real cast of creative characters. And, while their creativity results in the blossoming of Tai-chi into a thousand flowers, it is always rooted in the classical principles and writings such as the Tao-Te-Ching and the I-Ching.

My wife and I used to bring our daughter along with us to the Tai-chi Farm from the time she was a toddler, and she wandered around, playing with Master Jou's geese or walking up the trail along the river with a friend. We wanted her to experience all those characters and realize that this world is made of many different kinds of people and many viewpoints.

When she grew up, she got involved in exercise and healthy eating. To my surprise, she is also now interested in breeding reptiles. You never know what seeds you plant.

When I was a student at Cornell, I produced the radio series, "Worlds of Life" for the local radio station WTKO in Ithaca, NY. One day someone called me and thanked me for the programs. I told her I didn't know if anyone was actually listening to the programs and thanked her for letting me know at least one person was. She said that many people listen to the programs and that, even though someone doesn't know what effect his work is having, it actually helps and affects many people, and that is something I should just trust.

I present this book in that spirit – planting seeds - and I hope the resulting garden provides nourishing food.

INSTRUCTIONAL DVDs
BY BOB KLEIN
FROM ARTISTIC VIDEO

Over 70 titles
https//store.movementsofmagic.com
1-888-9TAICHI (1-888-982-4244)
(631) 744-5999

How to Learn and Teach Tai-chi

7 DVD series – almost 14 hours of training. This series is designed to be used with this book. It trains you in the 60 movement Yang short form and includes all the principles of each movement. Many camera angles are used for step-by-step instruction. The most complete training of a Tai-chi form available. Great for teachers looking for new ways to explain the principles and for students looking to deepen their training. 19.95 each or $99.65 for the set of 7 DVDs).

Information about classes with Bob Klein, either in person or online is also available at: https//store.movementsofmagic.com under "Classes and workshops with Bob Klein" section. Or call: (631) 744-5999 - bobklein@movementsofmagic.com

Tai-chi for Beginners

An introduction to Tai-chi. This DVD teaches a simple, 20 movement form, explaining the basic principles. Both front and back views are shown. Several movements are taught at a time and repeated several times so you can follow.

Tai-chi Exercises for Seniors

Several sets of exercises are taught as a preparation for learning Tai-chi forms specifically designed for seniors. A 14 movement form is also taught.

Chi-Gung for Fitness

This is the Chi-Gung (Qigong) set taught by Bob Klein at the Long Island School of Tai-chi-Chuan. It increases mobility of the joints, increases breathing capacity and the flow of internal energy (chi) and unites mind and body. It is based on animal movements and is especially useful for martial arts students. 43 minutes $19.95

Zookinesis Chair Exercises for Seniors

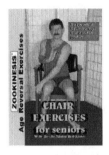

The Zookinesis system of Chi-Gung is called, "Age Reversal Exercises". They strengthen and increase mobility of the joints, improve breathing, digestion, and cognition, strengthen the immune system and a positive, uplifting feeling. The following DVDs are appropriate for seniors and are done from a seated position $19.95 each. At least 45 min ea.

1. CHAIR EXERCISES FOR SENIORS
2. MORE CHAIR EXERCISES FOR SENIORS
3. CHAIR EXERCISES FOR FLEXIBILITY
   AND STRENGTH
4. CHAIR EXERCISES FOR WEIGHT
   REDUCTION

Tai-chi Massage

This is the massage described in this book. It is a deep-seated healing that eliminates chronic tension and emotional trauma. You can follow along with the DVD as each technique is described in detail. It brings consciousness back to the body. 60 minutes $19.95

https//store.movementsofmagic.com
1-888-9TAICHI (1-888-982-4244)
(631) 744-5999

Chinese Kickboxing

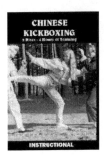

Four hours of training (2 discs) of Tai-chi-Chuan ("The Grand Ultimate Martial Art"). Includes stretching, punching, kicking, grappling, ground fighting and evasive techniques. Taught with students. Many training exercises shown and fighting in animal styles. The philosophy of the martial arts also explained. $29.95.

Push Hands

3 DVDs teaching all the principles of traditional Push Hands – a two-person exercise designed to develop, sense and use internal energy. You will learn to neutralize force directed against you and transform the "opponent's" force to uproot him. Teaches proper body alignment and body mechanics.

Push Hands – The Heart of Tai-chi Training 120 min. $24.95

Push Hands – Game of Life Vol 1 90 min. $24.95

Push Hands – Game of Life Vol 2 120 min. $24.95

Set of all 3 DVDs $54.85 (Save $20)

Information about classes with Bob Klein, either in person or online is also available at: https//store.movementsofmagic.com under "Classes and workshops with Bob Klein" section. Or call: (631) 744-5999 - bobklein@movementsofmagic.com

Made in the USA
Columbia, SC
11 November 2023

25950102R00235